DIFFERENTIAL EQUATIONS

DIFFERENTIAL EQUATIONS

BY

RALPH PALMER AGNEW

Professor of Mathematics
Cornell University

McGRAW-HILL BOOK COMPANY, Inc.

NEW YORK AND LONDON

1942

DIFFERENTIAL EQUATIONS

COPYRIGHT, 1942, BY THE
McGraw-Hill Book Company, Inc.

PRINTED IN THE UNITED STATES OF AMERICA

VII

PREFACE

This is a first course in differential equations. It is designed for students who have a reasonable working knowledge of algebra, trigonometry, and elementary calculus. Its object is to acquaint students in pure and applied mathematics with useful methods of solving problems by means of differential equations.

The first seven chapters constitute an essential foundation of a first course in differential equations; it is intended that these be studied in the order of their appearance. Beyond this, a teacher or reader or student may follow his inclinations. Chapter 8 is a requirement for those who must acquire the ability to solve linear equations rapidly. Some of the methods and terminology developed in Chapter 8 are used in Chapters 9 and 10 on mechanical and electrical problems. If Chapter 8 is omitted, it is possible to cover either or both of Chapters 9 and 10 by solving the differential equations by the less rapid methods of Chapter 6. Each of the remaining chapters assumes no knowledge of differential equations beyond that in the first seven chapters, except that Chapter 16 would doubtless be difficult for one who had not read Chapter 15. The book contains sufficient material for a full year's course. The author will feel that this book is a failure if students who take shorter courses from it do not read parts of it in addition to those assigned by the teachers.

This book provides much more lengthy, detailed, and accurate discussions of problems than are customary in elementary textbooks on calculus and differential equations. It is expected that the number of pages covered in an assignment will be much greater than the number to which students become accustomed in courses in elementary calculus. This involves a significant shift of emphasis in the students' work. Assignments no longer involve looking hastily at an "example" solved in "the book" and then spending two hours performing algebraic manipulations essentially like those in the example. On the contrary, a considerable portion of the students' time is to be spent reading and answering questions that arise in the course of the reading. Many of these questions can be answered without use of pencil, paper, and eraser; many others require all three. The author believes that this shift of emphasis should come at the beginning of a first course in differential equations. He has tried to control the number and the character of the problems so that students will not be impelled to spend an excessive amount of time wrestling with algebraic complications.

This book does not patronize the reader by assuming that a real understanding of differential equations is beyond him; for example, certain ideas commonly associated with courses in advanced calculus are required, and they are given in Chapter 2. Above all, the author has (except for occasions on which it seems desirable for comparative purposes to speak of quantities being "small" or "large") tried to be precise and accurate in his statements. He will be grateful for letters calling his attention to errors of commission or omission.

The writing of this book was undertaken when the author found himself to be in agreement with his associates at Cornell University and elsewhere that there should be a textbook in differential equations such as this one. The author takes this occasion to thank his colleagues for their continual encouragement and inspiration.

RALPH PALMER AGNEW.

CORNELL UNIVERSITY,
ITHACA, N.Y.,
September, 1942.

CONTENTS

vii

DIFFERENTIAL EQUATIONS

CHAPTER 1

INTRODUCTION TO DIFFERENTIAL EQUATIONS

1.1. Preliminary Remarks; Definitions.—Many fundamental problems in pure and applied mathematics are solved by determining how one quantity depends upon one or more other quantities. Such problems are often solved by means of differential equations.

A *differential equation* is an equation involving derivatives. Derivatives usually are (and always can be) interpreted as rates. For example, the *ordinary derivative* dy/dx is the rate of change of y with respect to x, and the *partial derivative* $\partial u/\partial x$ is the rate of change of u with respect to x when all independent variables except x are given fixed values. Derivatives of higher orders are interpreted as rates of rates, as accelerations, and so on. Hence it is proper to say that a differential equation is an equation involving rates.

The "law" which states that the time rate of change of the amount x of radium in a portion of matter is proportional to the amount x, is expressed by the differential equation

$$(1.11) \qquad \frac{dx}{dt} = kx.$$

This law is discussed in detail in Sections 3.5 and 3.55. One who specializes in applied mathematics or in such subjects as engineering, physics, chemistry, and biology learns that many physical laws are expressed by differential equations. We shall meet several illustrations later.

Some examples of differential equations are

$$(1.121) \qquad \frac{dy}{dx} = 3x^2$$

$$(1.122) \qquad x + y\frac{dy}{dx} = 0$$

$$(1.123) \qquad \frac{d^2y}{dx^2} + 4y = 0$$

$$(1.124) \qquad \frac{d^2y}{dx^2} = \frac{m}{H}\sqrt{1 + \left(\frac{dy}{dx}\right)^2}$$

1

$$(1.125) \qquad \frac{d^2y}{dx^2} + \frac{g}{l}\sin y = 0$$

$$(1.126) \qquad \frac{\partial^2 u}{\partial x^2} + \frac{\partial^2 u}{\partial y^2} = 0. \quad \text{LaPlace}$$

The *order* of a differential equation is the order of the highest derivative involved. The first and second equations above are of the first order, and the others are of the second order.

A differential equation is *linear* when it is of the first degree in the dependent variable (or variables) and the derivatives. For example, the equation

$$(1.13) \qquad 2\frac{d^2y}{dx^2} + 3\frac{dy}{dx} + 4y = \sin x$$

is linear and of the second order. The coefficients 2, 3, and 4 in (1.13) are constants. Each linear differential equation of the second order with a single independent variable x and dependent variable y can be written in the form

$$(1.14) \qquad f_1(x)\frac{d^2y}{dx^2} + f_2(x)\frac{dy}{dx} + f_3(x)y = f_4(x)$$

where $f_1(x), \cdots, f_4(x)$ are functions of x. The equations

$$(1.15) \qquad \frac{d^2y}{dx^2} = y^2, \qquad y\frac{dy}{dx} = \sin x$$

are not linear.

An *ordinary differential equation* is one containing ordinary derivatives of one or more functions with respect to a single independent variable. Each of the equations heretofore given except (1.126) is an ordinary differential equation. So also is each of the two equations

$$(1.161) \qquad a\frac{dx}{dt} + b\frac{dy}{dt} = c$$

$$(1.162) \qquad d\frac{dx}{dt} + e\frac{dy}{dt} = f.$$

A *partial differential equation* is one involving partial derivatives of one or more dependent variables with respect to one or more of the independent variables. For example, (1.126) is a partial differential equation; it is known as the *Laplace equation*. The Laplace equation in three independent variables is

$$(1.17) \qquad \frac{\partial^2 u}{\partial x^2} + \frac{\partial^2 u}{\partial y^2} + \frac{\partial^2 u}{\partial z^2} = 0.$$

A simpler partial differential equation is

$$(1.18) \qquad\qquad \frac{\partial u}{\partial x} = 0.$$

1.19. Explanation of Numbering System.—Nearly all books in pure and applied mathematics facilitate reference to chapters, sections, figures, theorems, equations, problems, etc., by numbers attached to some or all of these items.   There are in current use many different numbering systems.   The system used in this book is growing in popularity.   Each number, such as **2.37**, is to be thought of as a positive number represented in decimal form.   The number before the decimal point gives the number of the chapter.   The first digit after the decimal point (except for a few cases where the first two serve) gives the number of the section.   The remaining digits complete the identification of one of the numbered items.

Except for a few instances where page make-up necessitates slight displacement of illustrations and footnotes, the numbers form an increasing sequence from the front to the back of the book.   All numbered items have numbers in this single sequence.   The number (5.17) identifies an equation in Chapter 5, Section 1.   If one is looking at (5.17) and wishes to find Fig. 5.121, one turns toward the front of the book since 5.121 < 5.17.   Finding a numbered item in the book is much like finding a word in the dictionary; one uses the natural order of numbers instead of the alphabetical order of words.   The fact that some numbers contain more digits than others and that some numbers fail to represent numbered items causes no more difficulty than the fact that some words are longer than others and that some combinations of letters fail to make words.

1.2. Explicit, Implicit, and Formal Solutions.*—A function $y(x)$ is said to be an *explicit solution* or simply a *solution* of a differential equation involving x, y, and derivatives of y with respect to x if substitution of $y(x)$ and its derivatives reduces the differential equation to an identity in x.   The function $y(x)$ is said to be a *solution over an interval I* if the identity holds for each x in the interval I.   For example, the function

$$(1.21) \qquad\qquad y = e^{-x} + \sin x$$

is a solution of the equation

$$(1.211) \qquad\qquad \frac{d^2y}{dx^2} + y = 2e^{-x}$$

since substitution of (1.21) in (1.211) gives the identity

$$(1.212) \qquad (e^{-x} - \sin x) + (e^{-x} + \sin x) = 2e^{-x}.$$

---

* An appreciation of the ways in which the words *explicit, implicit,* and *formal* are used in the calculus and other branches of mathematics shows why these words are used here.   The equation $y = x + 1$ states *explicitly* that y is $x + 1$.   The equation $x - y - 1 = 0$ does not state explicitly that y is $x - 1$ but only *implies* that y is $x - 1$ and hence states *implicitly* that y is $x - 1$.   The word *formal* is used with the meaning "having the form but not necessarily the substance."

Likewise, if c is a positive constant, the two functions $y = (c^2 - x^2)^{\frac{1}{2}}$ and $y = -(c^2 - x^2)^{\frac{1}{2}}$ are both* solutions of the equation

$$(1.23) \qquad x + y\frac{dy}{dx} = 0$$

over the interval $-c < x < c$ since substitution yields

$$(1.24) \qquad x + [\pm(c^2 - x^2)^{\frac{1}{2}}][\mp x(c^2 - x^2)^{-\frac{1}{2}}] = 0 \qquad -c < x < c.$$

An equation $f(x, y) = 0$ is said *to furnish a solution* or, briefly, *to be an implicit solution* of a differential equation involving x, y, and derivatives of y with respect to x, if one or more functions $y(x)$ exist which (a) satisfy the equation $f(x, y(x)) = 0$ and (b) are solutions of the differential equation. It should of course be recognized that if the equation $f(x, y) = 0$ can be solved for y in terms of x the result is a function $y(x)$ such that $f(x, y(x)) = 0$. An example may serve to clarify the meaning of implicit solutions. If c is a positive constant, then the equation $x^2 + y^2 - c^2 = 0$, which we may write in the form

$$(1.25) \qquad x^2 + y^2 = c^2,$$

is an implicit solution of (1.23) since solving (1.25) for y yields two functions, namely, $(c^2 - x^2)^{\frac{1}{2}}$ and $-(c^2 - x^2)^{\frac{1}{2}}$, each of which is a solution of (1.23).

Before giving the definition of *formal solution* (something having the form but not necessarily the substance of a solution) we consider a simple example. If c is a constant and we assume that the equation

$$(1.26) \qquad x^2 + y^2 = c$$

is satisfied by a differentiable function $y = y(x)$, then we can differentiate to obtain

$$(1.27) \qquad 2x + 2y\frac{dy}{dx} = 0$$

and we conclude that (1.26) is a solution (implicit) of (1.27). If c is negative, say $c = -10$, the assumption that (1.26) determines y as a

---

* Insofar as real variables are concerned, the symbols $\sqrt{Q}$ and $Q^{\frac{1}{2}}$ are defined only when Q is a nonnegative real number, and each is the nonnegative number whose square is Q. Thus $\sqrt{0} = 0$, $\sqrt{4} = 2$, and $-\sqrt{4} = -2$. It should be known that $\sqrt{R^2} = R$ if $R \geq 0$ and that $\sqrt{R^2} = -R$ if $R \leq 0$. If R is real, $\sqrt{R^2}$ is always $|R|$. Those who enjoy sad stories should be interested in the following: It is said that an electrical-engineering student was delayed a year in obtaining an advanced degree because his experiments and theory refused to "jibe." The unfortunate victim of the delay thought that the formula

$$(1.22) \qquad \sqrt{1 - \sin^2 x} = \cos x$$

holds for all x. Actually it holds only when x lies in the first or fourth quadrant.

differentiable function of x is unjustified when one is working (as we are here) with real functions of real variables; for there does not exist a single pair of real values of x and y for which (1.26) holds.   Hence, when $c \leq 0$, (1.26) is neither an explicit nor implicit solution of (1.27); but (1.26) is a formal solution of (1.27) in accordance with the following definition.

An equation $f(x, y) = 0$ is said to be a *formal solution* of a differential equation involving x, y, and derivatives of y with respect to x if an assumption (which may or may not be in accordance with the facts) that $y(x)$ exists such that $f(x, y(x)) = 0$, and formulas obtained by implicit differentiation of $f(x, y) = 0$, lead to the conclusion that $y(x)$ is an explicit solution of the differential equation.   This terminology enables us to assert that, for each constant c, the equation $x^2 + y^2 = c$ is a formal solution of $x + y(dy/dx) = 0$ and that (insofar as real variables are concerned) the formal solution becomes an implicit solution which yields explicit solutions only when $c > 0$.

When a problem is solved by means of differential equations, a solution of the differential equation either furnishes or leads to the solution of the problem.   It is usually true that an explicit solution is sought.   The importance of implicit solutions and formal solutions becomes evident when it is seen that some of the methods of solving differential equations lead directly to formal solutions; after having obtained a formal solution, there arises the problem of determining whether or not the formal solution really is an implicit solution leading to an explicit solution of the differential equation.   Thus the implicit solutions and formal solutions may be said to be necessary evils, to be avoided when possible.   There are times when implicit solutions, and even formal solutions, are referred to as simply *solutions* of differential equations.

If a function or equation is a solution of a differential equation, then it is said to *satisfy* the differential equation.

1.3. Some Remarks on Solving Differential Equations.—It is easy to give examples of differential equations having no solutions; for example,

$$(1.31) \qquad \left| \frac{dy}{dx} \right| + |x| + |y| + 1 = 0$$

is such an equation.   The equation

$$(1.32) \qquad \left| \frac{dy}{dx} \right| + |y| = 0$$

has just one solution, namely, $y = 0$.   Nevertheless, one who takes a course in elementary differential equations and then uses differential equations in the solution of problems in pure and applied mathematics learns to expect that each differential equation he meets in the course of his work will have many solutions.   To solve a problem frequently (or usually) requires that one find the solution or solutions of a differential equation satisfying one or more supplementary conditions such as boundary conditions, initial conditions, etc.   A standard method of solving such a problem is first to find all the solutions of the differential equation and then to pick out the particular solution or solutions satisfying the supplementary conditions.

This explains why it is desirable to be able to find *all* solutions of a differential equation and why solving a differential equation means finding all solutions of the differential equation.

Many attempts to solve differential equations start with an assumption that $y(x)$ is a function which, for at least some range of values of x, satisfies the differential equation.   Then, by some method or other, it is proved that $y(x)$ must have a certain form or at least that $y(x)$ must satisfy a relation of the form $F(x, y) = 0$.   This proof does not necessarily imply that the differential equation has any solutions whatever; in particular, it does not imply that each function having this certain form must be a solution of the differential equation, and it does not imply that each differentiable function $y(x)$ for which $F(x, y(x)) = 0$ is a solution of the differential equation.

One way to solve a differential equation is to prove two things, as follows: (i) If $y(x)$ is a solution of the differential equation, then $y(x)$ must have a certain form.   (ii) If $y(x)$ has this certain form, then $y(x)$ is a solution of the differential equation.

Solution of the following problems should give the student some practice in differentiation and some preliminary ideas about solutions of differential equations.

Problems

Assuming that a, b, c, c_1, and c_2 are constants, show that each function or equation on the left is a solution of the differential equation written opposite it.

(1.33) $y = (a^2 + x^2)^{\frac{1}{2}} + c$ $\dfrac{dy}{dx} = x(a^2 + x^2)^{-\frac{1}{2}}$

(1.34) $y = c_1 \sin ax + c_2 \cos ax$ $\dfrac{d^2y}{dx^2} + a^2 y = 0$

(1.35) $y = ce^{ax}$ $\dfrac{dy}{dx} = ay$

(1.36) $y - c^2 = 2c(x - c)$ $\dfrac{1}{4}\left(\dfrac{dy}{dx}\right)^2 - x\dfrac{dy}{dx} + y = 0$

(1.37) $y = x^2$ $\dfrac{1}{4}\left(\dfrac{dy}{dx}\right)^2 - x\dfrac{dy}{dx} + y = 0$

(1.38) $u = \tan^{-1}\dfrac{y}{x}$ $\dfrac{\partial^2 u}{\partial x^2} + \dfrac{\partial^2 u}{\partial y^2} = 0$

Laplace eqn

27^{-5} ✓ **Problem 1.39**

Show that the system of differential equations

$$\frac{dy}{dx} - \frac{dz}{dx} = y; \qquad 2\frac{dy}{dx} - \frac{dz}{dx} = z$$

is satisfied by the pair of functions

$$y = c_1 \cos x + c_2 \sin x; \qquad z = (c_2 + c_1) \cos x + (c_2 - c_1) \sin x.$$

$y \;\; -1$
$z \;\; -1$
$\overline{1 \;\; -1}$
$2 \;\; -1$

27^{-5} ✓ **Problem 1.391**

Show that, when c and a are constants, the function on the left is a solution of the equation written opposite it:

$$y = \frac{e^{ax} + e^{-ax}}{2a} + c \qquad \frac{d^2y}{dx^2} = a\sqrt{1 + \left(\frac{dy}{dx}\right)^2}$$

$\frac{1}{a}\cosh ax$

Problem 1.392

For what values of constant c is there a differentiable function $y(x)$ satisfying the equation

$$x^2 + y^2 + 2x + 2y = c,$$

and hence also the equations

$$2x + 2y\frac{dy}{dx} + 2 + 2\frac{dy}{dx} = 0$$

and

$$\frac{dy}{dx} = -\frac{x+1}{y+1},$$

when x is properly restricted?   *Ans.: $c > -2$.*

complete the square

CHAPTER 2

THE DIFFERENTIAL EQUATION $y' = f(x)$

2.0. Introduction.—The simplest differential equations are those of the form

$$(2.01) \qquad \frac{dy}{dx} = f(x)$$

in which $f(x)$ is a given function of x. To simplify typography, we frequently write y' or $y'(x)$ for dy/dx and f for $f(x)$; thus, (2.01) may be written $y'(x) = f(x)$ or $y' = f(x)$ or $y' = f$.

The differential equation $y' = f(x)$ is one studied in the elementary calculus. If $y(x)$ is a solution of this differential equation, that is, if $y(x)$ is a function whose derivative with respect to x is $f(x)$, then $y(x)$ is called an *indefinite integral* of $f(x)$ and is denoted by $\int f(x)dx$ so that

$$(2.02) \qquad y = \int f(x)dx.$$

Thus (2.02) means that $y' = f(x)$. For example, each of the formulas

$$(2.03) \qquad \int x\, dx = \tfrac{1}{2}x^2 + c,$$
$$(2.04) \qquad \int \sin x\, dx = -\cos x + c,$$

in which c is a *constant of integration*, means that the derivative with respect to x of the function on the right is the integrand of the integral on the left. Thus the function $y = \tfrac{1}{2}x^2 + c$ is a solution of the equation $y' = x$, and the function $y = -\cos x + c$ is a solution of $y' = \sin x$. Likewise each formula in a table of indefinite integrals is in reality a formula for the solutions of a differential equation of the form $y' = f(x)$. A good integral table gives several hundred of these formulas. A student of differential equations should have such a table.

In order to understand and use differential equations, it is necessary to have precise information relating to the differential equation $y' = f(x)$. This chapter gives, largely without proofs, a connected account of pertinent definitions and theorems. Try to master the fundamental ideas as well as you can. Whatever you learn and whatever sophistication you gain should be very profitable to you in all of your work in pure and applied mathematics.

2.05. Limits.—A function $f(x)$ is said to have a *limit L* as x approaches a, and we write

$$(2.06) \qquad \lim_{x \to a} f(x) = L,$$

8

if to each $\epsilon > 0$ corresponds a $\delta > 0$ such that $|f(x) - L| < \epsilon$ when $x \neq a$ and $|x - a| < \delta$.

One should understand thoroughly this definition and its geometrical significance.* Let us consider the meaning of the fact that

$$(2.07) \qquad \lim_{x \to 0} (1 + x)^{1/x} = e,$$

where $e = 2.718281828459045 \cdots$. Let, when $x > -1$ and $x \neq 0$,

$$(2.08) \qquad f(x) = (1 + x)^{1/x}.$$

A part of the graph of $f(x)$ is shown in Fig. 2.09. The assertion (2.07) means that, when a positive number ϵ is first assigned, then it is possible to find a positive number δ such that $|f(x) - e| < \epsilon$, that is,

$$(2.091) \qquad e - \epsilon < f(x) < e + \epsilon,$$

for each x for which $x \neq 0$ and $-\delta < x < \delta$. Figure 2.09 shows a given positive ϵ, and a positive δ which meets the requirement.

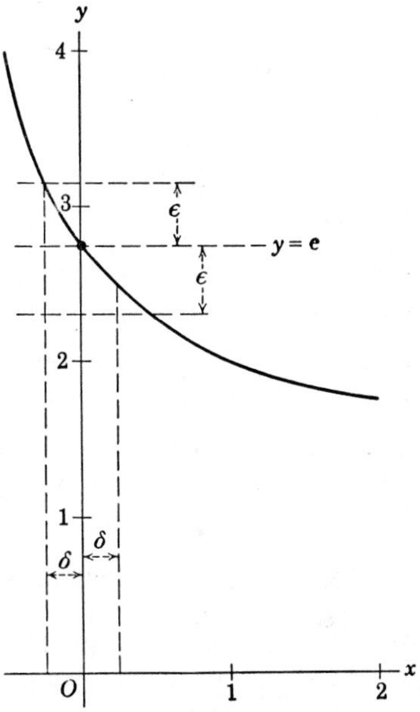

2.1. Derivatives and Continuity.— If $y(x)$ is a function of x, then

$$(2.11) \qquad \frac{dy}{dx} = \lim_{\Delta x \to 0} \frac{y(x + \Delta x) - y(x)}{\Delta x}$$

when the limit exists. This definition of derivative is used in the elementary calculus to obtain the familiar formulas for derivatives of powers, logarithms, trigonometric functions, inverse trigonometric functions, and products and quotients of differentiable functions.

A function $f(x)$ is *continuous at a point* x if

$$(2.12) \qquad \lim_{\Delta x \to 0} f(x + \Delta x) = f(x).$$

Fig. 2.09.

The functions $f_1(x) = x^2$ and $f_2(x) = \sin x$ are examples of functions continuous for all x. A function is *continuous over an interval* if it is continuous at each point of the interval. An example of a function *discontinuous* (that is, not continuous) at $x = 0$ is furnished by the

---

* It is correct to say that (2.06) means "$f(x)$ is near L when x is near a" if this vague phrase is understood to be a technical phrase meaning that to each $\epsilon > 0$ corresponds a $\delta > 0$ such that $|f(x) - L| < \epsilon$ when $x \neq a$ and $|x - a| < \delta$.

function sgn x (read "signum x") defined by the formula

$$(2.13) \qquad \begin{aligned} \operatorname{sgn} x &= 1 && x > 0 \\ &= 0 && x = 0 \\ &= -1 && x < 0. \end{aligned}$$

The graph of sgn x is shown in Fig. 2.131.   The function is continuous over the infinite interval $x > 0$; it is continuous over the infinite interval $x < 0$; but it fails to be continuous over an interval when the interval contains the point $x = 0$.

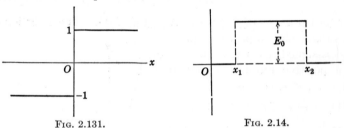

FIG. 2.131.   FIG. 2.14.

One whose training has been such as to make him skeptical of the value of the discontinuous signum function may take a few minutes to show that the graph of the function

$$y = \tfrac{1}{2}E_0[\operatorname{sgn}(x - x_1) - \operatorname{sgn}(x - x_2)]$$

has, when $0 < x_1 < x_2$, the form shown in Fig. 2.14 and to read Section 3.9 through equation (3.94).   One who still feels that the function sgn x is too simple and undignified to be worthy of notice may be impressed by the formula

$$(2.15) \qquad \operatorname{sgn} x = \frac{1}{\pi} \int_{-\infty}^{\infty} \frac{\sin xt}{t}\, dt,$$

the integral on the right being the *Dirichlet discontinuous integral* which occurs in many phases of mathematical analysis.

The function cot x is continuous for each x different from an integer multiple of π; if x is an integer multiple of π, then neither cot x nor the limit as $\Delta x \to 0$ of cot $(x + \Delta x)$ exists and hence the criterion for continuity shows that cot x is discontinuous.

Problem 2.16

The cost y in cents of mailing first-class matter with weight x measured in ounces is determined by the rule: "the cost is 3 cents per ounce or fraction thereof." Draw a graph of $y(x)$, and note the discontinuities.

It is easy to show that *if $y(x)$ is differentiable* [that is, if $y'(x)$ exists], *then $y(x)$ must be continuous.*   Indeed, if

$$(2.17) \qquad \lim_{\Delta x \to 0} \frac{y(x + \Delta x) - y(x)}{\Delta x} = y'(x),$$

then

$$\lim_{\Delta x \to 0} [y(x + \Delta x) - y(x)] = \lim_{\Delta x \to 0} \frac{y(x + \Delta x) - y(x)}{\Delta x} \Delta x = y'(x) \cdot 0 = 0$$

so that $\lim y(x + \Delta x) = y(x)$, and $y(x)$ is continuous. *(handwritten: How does this prove continuity?)*

(handwritten: $\lim_{\Delta x \to 0} f(x + \Delta x) = f(x)$?)

If every blonde whom you have seen happens to have had blue eyes, you may blithely (and incorrectly) assume that all blondes have blue eyes—until you meet a brown-eyed blonde. Likewise, if your elementary calculus dealt only with functions which are differentiable wherever they are continuous, you may blithely (and incorrectly) assume that functions are differentiable wherever they are continuous—until you meet an exception which rectifies your ideas. No mathematician can be really sophisticated until he knows that Weierstrass (1815–1897) gave an example of a continuous function which is nowhere differentiable. The example of Weierstrass is too complicated to be given here,

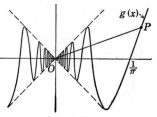

Fig. 2.181.

but we shall give a classic example of a continuous function $g(x)$ for which $g'(0)$ fails to exist. Let

(2.18) $$g(x) = 0 \qquad\qquad x = 0$$
$$= x \sin \frac{1}{x} \qquad x \neq 0.$$

(handwritten: Can you write this as a single eqn? No!)

Since $| g(x) | \leq x$ for all x, $g(x) = x$ when $x = 1/(2n\pi + \pi/2)$, and $g(x) = -x$ when $x = 1/(2n\pi - \pi/2)$, it is easy to show that $g(x)$ is continuous and the graph of $g(x)$ is as shown in Fig. 2.181. When $\Delta x \neq 0$,

(2.182) $$\frac{\Delta g}{\Delta x} \equiv \frac{g(0 + \Delta x) - g(0)}{\Delta x}$$

is the slope of the line OP. We see that $\Delta g/\Delta x$ is $+1$ for a sequence of values of Δx converging to 0 and that $\Delta g/\Delta x$ is -1 for another sequence of values of Δx converging to 0. Hence there is no number $g'(0)$ such that (2.182) converges to $g'(0)$ as $\Delta x \to 0$, and therefore $g'(0)$ does not exist. Another continuous function $h(x)$ for which $h'(0)$ fails to exist is $h(x) = | x |$.

We have seen that continuous functions need not be differentiable. A student who wishes an exercise involving continuity and differentiability may wish to show that the function $f(x)$ defined by $f(0) = 0$ and

(2.19) $$f(x) = x^2 \sin \frac{1}{x} \qquad\qquad x \neq 0$$

is differentiable for all x but that $f'(x)$ is not continuous at $x = 0$.

2.2. Applications of the Law of the Mean of the Differential Calculus.—The *law of the mean of the differential calculus* is embodied in the following theorem:

THEOREM 2.21.—*If $f(x)$ is continuous over $a \leqq x \leqq b$ and $f'(x)$ exists over $a < x < b$, then there is at least one point x_0 such that $a < x_0 < b$ and*

(2.211)
$$\frac{f(b) - f(a)}{b - a} = f'(x_0).$$

We shall not give a proof of this theorem here. The geometric interpretation of (2.211) is shown in Fig. 2.212: the tangent to the graph of $y = f(x)$ at the point x_0 is parallel to the chord joining the points $(a, f(a))$ and $(b, f(b))$. If the hypotheses of Theorem 2.21 hold and $f(a) = f(b) = 0$, the formula (2.211) becomes $f'(x_0) = 0$. This gives Rolle's theorem which we state below.

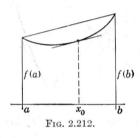

FIG. 2.212.

ROLLE'S THEOREM 2.22.—*If $f(x)$ is continuous over $a \leqq x \leqq b$, if $f(a) = f(b) = 0$, and if $f'(x)$ exists over $a < x < b$, then there is at least one point x_0 such that $a < x_0 < b$ and $f'(x_0) = 0$.*

One of the reasons why Theorem 2.21 is important is that it can be used to give a simple proof of the following theorem:

THEOREM 2.23.—*If $f'(x) = 0$ over $a \leqq x \leqq b$, then $f(x)$ is constant over $a \leqq x \leqq b$.*

Assuming Theorem 2.21, we prove Theorem 2.23. Since $f'(x) = 0$ over $a \leqq x \leqq b$, it follows that $f'(x)$ and $f(x)$ are continuous over $a \leqq x \leqq b$. Let x be fixed such that $a < x \leqq b$. By Theorem 2.21 there must exist a point x_0 such that $a < x_0 < x$ and

(2.231)
$$\frac{f(x) - f(a)}{x - a} = f'(x_0).$$

But $f'(x_0) = 0$. Therefore $f(x) = f(a)$. Thus $f(x) = f(a)$ when $a < x \leqq b$, and Theorem 2.23 follows.

The same proof gives the following slightly stronger theorem which we shall need later:

THEOREM 2.24.—*If $f(x)$ is continuous over $a \leqq x \leqq b$ and $f'(x) = 0$ over $a < x < b$, then $f(x)$ is constant over $a \leqq x \leqq b$.*

We can now make an application of Theorem 2.23 to obtain the following theorem pertaining to the differential equation $y' = f(x)$:

THEOREM 2.25.—*If $y_1(x)$ is a solution of $y' = f(x)$ over $a \leqq x \leqq b$, then each function $y(x)$ which is a solution of $y' = f(x)$ over $a \leqq x \leqq b$*

must have the form

(2.251) $y = y_1(x) + c$ $a \leq x \leq b$

where c is a constant.

If $y_1(x)$ and $y(x)$ are two functions such that $y_1'(x) = f(x)$ and $y'(x) = f(x)$ over $a \leq x \leq b$ and we put $g(x) = y(x) - y_1(x)$, then $g'(x) = y'(x) - y_1'(x) = f(x) - f(x) = 0$ so that, by Theorem 2.23, $g(x)$ must be a constant c and hence (2.251) holds. This proves Theorem 2.25.

The following problems illustrate a few of the many applications of these theorems. The results are important, but our main present interest lies in the method of obtaining the results.

Problem 2.251

Show that, if y is a function of x for which

$$\frac{d}{dx} e^{ax} y = 0,$$

then there is a constant c such that $y = ce^{-ax}$.

Problem 2.252

Show that, if

$$x \frac{dy}{dx} + y = 2x,$$

then there is a constant c for which $xy = x^2 + c$.

Problem 2.253

If

$$\frac{dy}{dx} + y = e^{-x} \sin x,$$

show that

$$\frac{d}{dx} e^x y = \sin x$$

and hence that $y = (c - \cos x)e^{-x}$. What is the value of c if $y = 0$ when $x = 0$?

Problem 2.254

Prove that if $u(x, y)$ is a function of x and y for which $\partial u / \partial x = 0$ then there is a function $\phi(y)$ such that $u(x, y) = \phi(y)$. Prove that if $v(x, y)$ is a function of x and y for which $\partial v / \partial x = y$, then there is a function $\theta(y)$ such that $v = xy + \theta(y)$. *Hint:* For each fixed y, the derivative with respect to x of $v - xy$ is 0; hence, for each fixed y, $v - xy$ must have a constant value.

Problem 2.255

It can be shown that if $u(x, t)$ is a function which has continuous partial derivatives of second order and satisfies the *wave equation*

$$a^2 \frac{\partial^2 u}{\partial x^2} = \frac{\partial^2 u}{\partial t^2}$$

in which a is a positive constant, and if two new variables ξ and η are defined by the formulas $\xi = x + at$ and $\eta = x - at$, then

$$\frac{\partial^2 u}{\partial \eta \, \partial \xi} = 0.$$

Use this fact to show existence of functions f and g such that $u = f(\xi) + g(\eta)$ and accordingly

$$u = f(x + at) + g(x - at).$$

Remark: This result has a vivid meaning to mathematical physicists.

Problem 2.256

Let $u(x, y)$ be a function of x and y for which

(2.257)
$$x \frac{\partial u}{\partial x} + y \frac{\partial u}{\partial y} = 0.$$

By use of the formula

$$\frac{d}{dt} F(\alpha, \beta) = \frac{\partial F}{\partial \alpha} \frac{d\alpha}{dt} + \frac{\partial F}{\partial \beta} \frac{d\beta}{dt},$$

show that if x and y are fixed and $F(t)$ is defined by the formula $F(t) = u(tx, ty)$ then $F(t)$ is independent of t. By giving t the two values $t = 1$ and $t = 1/x$, show that when $x \neq 0$

$$u(x, y) = u\left(1, \frac{y}{x}\right).$$

[This shows that each solution of the differential equation (2.257) must be a function of y/x, say $\phi(y/x)$. Conversely, if ϕ is differentiable, then differentiation shows that $\phi(y/x)$ satisfies (2.257) when $x \neq 0$.]

2.26. An Example.—It should be observed that Theorem 2.25 does not assert that the equation $y' = f(x)$ has any solutions. Whether the equation $y' = f(x)$ has any solutions depends upon $f(x)$. The equation $y' = 3x^2$ does have solutions; in fact, $y = x^3 + c$ is a solution for each constant c.

We shall now find out whether or not the differential equation

(2.27)
$$\frac{dy}{dx} = \operatorname{sgn} x$$

has any solutions. If $y(x)$ satisfies (2.27) when $x > 0$, then $y'(x) = 1$ and therefore (why?) c_1 exists such that $y = x + c_1$ when $x > 0$. If $y(x)$ satisfies (2.27) when $x < 0$, then $y'(x) = -1$ and therefore c_2 exists such that $y = -x + c_2$ when $x < 0$. Figure 2.281 exhibits the graph of a function $y(x)$ which satisfies the equation $y' = \operatorname{sgn} x$ for $x \neq 0$. If $y(x)$ satisfies $y' = \operatorname{sgn} x$ for all x, then $y(x)$ must be continuous; therefore c_1 and c_2 must be equal, and $y(x)$ must have the form

$$y = |x| + c$$

where c is the common value of c_1 and c_2. The graph of $y = |x| + c$ is shown in Fig. 2.282. Since $y'(0)$ does not exist, it is not true that $y'(0) = \operatorname{sgn} 0$; accordingly, we must conclude that $y(x)$ does not satisfy $y' = \operatorname{sgn} x$ for all x. We have shown (a) that, if $y(x)$ satisfies $y' = \operatorname{sgn} x$ for all x, then $y(x) = |x| + c$ where c is a constant and (b) that the function $|x| + c$ fails to satisfy $y' = \text{sgn } x$ for all x. We deduce from (a) and (b) that there is no function $y(x)$ satisfying for all x the differential equation $y' = \text{sgn } x$. The best we can do is find a function which is continuous over $-\infty < x < \infty$ and satisfies $y'(x) = \text{sgn } x$ when $x \neq 0$.

This example shows that, if $f(x)$ is not continuous, then there may fail to be a function $y(x)$ such that $y'(x) = f(x)$. We shall show by means of the Riemann (definite) integral that, if $f(x)$ is continuous, then a function $y(x)$ must exist such

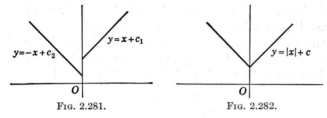

FIG. 2.281.   FIG. 2.282.

that $y'(x) = f(x)$. We shall then know, among other things, that there is a function whose derivative is $\sqrt{1 + x^2}\, e^{-x}$. One answer will turn out to be

$$\int_0^x \sqrt{1 + t^2}\, e^{-t}\, dt.$$

2.3. Riemann Integrals.—We proceed to define the Riemann integral of a function $f(x)$. This integral, which as we shall see is defined as a limit of certain sums, is sometimes called a definite integral; but many other kinds of integrals are also definite integrals, and the term *Riemann integral* is preferable. Throughout this section, all integrals are Riemann integrals.

Let $f(x)$ be a function defined over an interval $a \leq x \leq b$, and let x be fixed such that $a < x \leq b$. Let n be a positive integer. Let the interval from a to x be subdivided into n subintervals by points $x_1, x_2, \cdots, x_{n-1}$ so that

(2.301) $a = x_0 < x_1 < x_2 < x_3 < \cdots < x_{n-1} < x_n = x.$

For each $k = 1, 2, \cdots, n$, the length of the kth subinterval is $x_k - x_{k-1}$. Let t_k be a point such that $x_{k-1} \leq t_k \leq x_k$. The number

(2.302) $$\sum_{k=1}^{n} f(t_k)(x_k - x_{k-1})$$

is called a *Riemann sum* formed for the division (2.301) of the interval from a to x. If

(2.303) $$\lim \sum_{k=1}^{n} f(t_k)(x_k - x_{k-1})$$

exists, the limit being taken as the number n of subintervals of the interval from a to x becomes infinite in such a way that the greatest of the lengths of the subintervals approaches 0; then the limit is called the *Riemann integral* of $f(x)$ over the interval (a, x) and we write*

$$(2.31) \qquad \int_a^x f(t)dt = \lim \sum_{k=1}^{n} f(t_k)(x_k - x_{k-1}).$$

If the limit does not exist, one says that the function is not integrable (that is, not Riemann integrable) over the interval.

It should be completely and thoroughly understood that the left member of (2.31) is merely a symbol to represent the number which is the limit in the right member of (2.31). The symbol

$$(2.311) \qquad \int_a^x f(x)dx$$

is commonly used in elementary-calculus books; but in more advanced work it is customary to choose a "dummy" variable of integration different from the letters used to represent the end points of the interval of integration. The left member of (2.31) would mean the same thing if t were replaced by u or y or α or ϕ or any other letter. Only $a, x, f,$ and d are to be avoided.

The definition of the Riemann integral is completed by defining

$$(2.312) \qquad \int_a^x f(t)dt$$

to be 0 when $x = a$ and to be

$$(2.313) \qquad -\int_x^a f(t)dt$$

when $x < a$ and the latter integral exists.

All information obtained about Riemann integrals must be derived from their definitions as limits of Riemann sums. A careful consideration of the definitions is required to prove that, if $f(x)$ is integrable over an interval with end points at a and b, where a may be either less or greater than b, and if c lies between a and b, then all three integrals

---

* The precise meaning of (2.31) is the following: To each $\epsilon > 0$ corresponds a $\delta > 0$ such that

$$\left| \int_a^x f(t)\, dt - \sum_{k=1}^{n} f(t_k)(x_k - x_{k-1}) \right| < \epsilon$$

for each division $a = x_0 < x_1 < \cdots < x_n = x$ of the interval (a, x) for which

$$| x_k - x_{k-1} | < \delta \qquad\qquad k = 1, 2, \cdots, n$$

and each choice of the points $t_1, \cdots, t_n$ for which $x_{k-1} \leqq t_k \leqq x_k$ when $k = 1, 2, \cdots, n$. A geometric interpretation of Riemann sums and integrals is given in Section 2.7.

$$(2.314) \qquad \int_a^b f(t)dt = \int_a^c f(t)dt + \int_c^b f(t)dt$$

exist and the equality holds. One of the simplest and most useful properties of Riemann integrals is embodied in the following theorem which is known as the *mean-value theorem of the integral calculus:*

THEOREM 2.32.—*If $f(x)$ is integrable over an interval with end points a and b, where a may be either less or greater than b, and if m and M are constants such that*

$$(2.321) \qquad\qquad m \leqq f(x) \leqq M$$

over the interval, then

$$(2.322) \qquad\qquad m \leqq \frac{1}{b-a} \int_a^b f(t)dt \leqq M.$$

To prove this we consider first the case in which $a < b$. With the notation used in defining integrals, we have

$$(2.323) \qquad\qquad m \leqq f(t_k) \leqq M \qquad\qquad k = 1, 2, \cdots, n$$

so that

$$(2.324) \qquad m(x_k - x_{k-1}) \leqq f(t_k)(x_k - x_{k-1}) \leqq M(x_k - x_{k-1})$$

and addition gives

$$(2.325) \qquad m(b-a) \leqq \sum_{k=1}^n f(t_k)(x_k - x_{k-1}) \leqq M(b-a).$$

The first and last members of (2.325) are constants independent of n. Letting $n \to \infty$ in such a way that the greatest of the numbers $x_k - x_{k-1}$ approaches 0, we obtain

$$(2.326) \qquad\qquad m(b-a) \leqq \int_a^b f(t)dt \leqq M(b-a)$$

since the middle term of (2.325) must converge to the middle term of (2.326). Dividing (2.326) by $(b-a)$ gives (2.322) for the case in which $a < b$. If $b < a$, we can write the inequality obtained by interchanging a and b in (2.322) and then interchange a and b to obtain (2.322). This proves Theorem 2.32.

An important theorem (which most elementary-calculus books do not prove and which we shall not prove here) is the following:

THEOREM 2.33.—*If $f(x)$ is continuous over the interval $a \leqq x \leqq b$, then*

$$(2.331) \qquad\qquad \int_a^x f(t)dt$$

exists when $a \leqq x \leqq b$.

A function is said to be *bounded* over an interval if there is a constant B such that $|f(x)| \leq B$ for each point x of the interval. The following theorem, which is stronger than Theorem 2.33, is often useful:

THEOREM 2.34.—*If $f(x)$ is bounded and is continuous except at a finite number of points in the interval $a \leq x \leq b$, then*

$$(2.341) \qquad\qquad \int_a^x f(t)dt$$

exists when $a \leq x \leq b$.

Modern students of mathematical analysis know that (2.341) exists for a bounded function $f(x)$ if and only if the points of the interval $a \leq x \leq b$ at which $f(x)$ is not continuous form a set having Lebesgue measure 0; but proof, discussion, and use of this more profound result lie beyond a first course in differential equations.

The answer to the question whether the equation $y' = f(x)$ must have a solution when $f(x)$ is continuous is given by the following theorem, which is known as the FUNDAMENTAL THEOREM OF THE CALCULUS and which furnishes a connection between the processes of integration and differentiation:

THEOREM 2.35.—*If $f(x)$ is continuous over the interval $a \leq x \leq b$ and*

$$(2.351) \qquad\qquad F(x) = \int_a^x f(t)dt \qquad\qquad a \leq x \leq b,$$

then

$$(2.352) \qquad\qquad F'(x) = f(x) \qquad\qquad a \leq x \leq b.$$

The following theorem, which is stronger than Theorem 2.35, is often useful:

THEOREM 2.36.—*If $f(x)$ is bounded and is continuous except at a finite number of points in the interval from a to b and*

$$(2.361) \qquad\qquad F(x) = \int_a^x f(t)dt,$$

then $F(x)$ is continuous over $a \leq x \leq b$ and $F'(x) = f(x)$ for each x for which $f(x)$ is continuous.

We prove Theorem 2.36 and hence also at the same time the weaker Theorem 2.35. Our hypothesis and Theorem 2.34 imply that the integral in (2.361) exists when $a \leq x \leq b$. Let B be a constant such that

$$(2.362) \qquad\qquad -B \leq f(x) \leq B \qquad\qquad a \leq x \leq b.$$

Using (2.361) and (2.314), we obtain

$$(2.363) \quad F(x + \Delta x) - F(x) = \int_a^{x+\Delta x} f(t)dt - \int_a^x f(t)dt = \int_x^{x+\Delta x} f(t)dt,$$

and dividing by Δx gives

$$(2.364) \qquad \frac{F(x + \Delta x) - F(x)}{\Delta x} = \frac{1}{\Delta x} \int_x^{x+\Delta x} f(t)dt.$$

Using (2.362) and the law of the mean (Theorem 2.32), we obtain

$$(2.365) \qquad -B \leqq \frac{F(x + \Delta x) - F(x)}{\Delta x} \leqq B.$$

Multiplying (2.365) by Δx and letting $\Delta x \to 0$, we see that

$$(2.366) \qquad \lim_{\Delta x \to 0} F(x + \Delta x) = F(x).$$

This proves continuity of $F(x)$.   Now let x be a point at which $f(x)$ is continuous; it remains for us to show that $F'(x) = f(x)$.   Let $\epsilon > 0$, and choose $\delta > 0$ such that

$$(2.367) \qquad f(x) - \epsilon < f(t) < f(x) + \epsilon \qquad |t - x| < \delta.$$

Then, when $|\Delta x| < \delta$, we can use the law of the mean (Theorem 2.32) to obtain

$$(2.368) \qquad f(x) - \epsilon < \frac{1}{\Delta x} \int_x^{x+\Delta x} f(t)dt < f(x) + \epsilon \qquad 0 < |\Delta x| < \delta.$$

Therefore, because of (2.364),

$$(2.369) \qquad -\epsilon < \frac{F(x + \Delta x) - F(x)}{\Delta x} - f(x) < \epsilon \qquad 0 < |\Delta x| < \delta.$$

This means, by definition of limit, that

$$\lim_{\Delta x \to 0} \frac{F(x + \Delta x) - F(x)}{\Delta x} = f(x)$$

and hence, by definition of derivative, that $F'(x) = f(x)$.   This completes the proofs of Theorems 2.35 and 2.36.

Combining Theorems 2.25 and 2.35 and using the obvious fact that the derivative of a constant is 0, we obtain the following fundamental theorem:

THEOREM 2.37.—*If $f(x)$ is continuous over an interval I containing a point a, then each solution of the differential equation*

$$(2.371) \qquad \frac{dy}{dx} = f(x)$$

over the interval I must have the form

$$(2.372) \qquad y = \int_a^x f(t)dt + c$$

where c is a constant; moreover, (2.372) is a solution of (2.371) over I for each constant c.

From the last theorem we obtain immediately the familiar formula used for the evaluation of integrals of continuous functions $f(x)$. If $\phi(x)$ is any function (obtained from whatever source) whose derivative is $f(x)$, then c exists such that

$$(2.373) \qquad \phi(x) = \int_a^x f(t)dt + c.$$

Setting $x = a$, we find that $c = \phi(a)$. Hence, using the familiar notation

$$(2.374) \qquad \phi(t)\Big]_a^x = \phi(x) - \phi(a),$$

we obtain the familiar formula

$$(2.375) \qquad \int_a^x f(t)dt = \phi(t)\Big]_a^x = \phi(x) - \phi(a)$$

which is often used to evaluate integrals.

In many problems (such as the electric-circuit problem to be discussed in Section 3.9) one needs not only Theorem 2.36 but also the following converse theorem:

THEOREM 2.38.—*If $f(x)$ is bounded over an interval $a \leqq x \leqq b$ and is continuous except at a finite number of points in the interval, then each function $y(x)$ which is continuous over $a \leqq x \leqq b$ and such that*

$$(2.381) \qquad \frac{dy}{dx} = f(x)$$

for each x for which $f(x)$ is continuous must have the form

$$(2.382) \qquad y(x) = \int_a^x f(t)dt + c \qquad\qquad a \leqq x \leqq b$$

where c is a constant.

Proof of Theorem 2.38 is not difficult. Let the points of discontinuity $x_1, x_2, \cdots, x_n$ be named so that $x_1 < x_2 < x_3 < \cdots < x_n$. By Theorem 2.36 the function $y_1(x)$ defined by

$$y_1(x) = \int_a^x f(t)dt$$

is one continuous function such that $y_1'(x) = f(x)$ except at the points $x_1, x_2, x_3, \cdots, x_n$. If $y(x)$ is another such function and we set $Y(x) = y(x) - y_1(x)$, we see that $Y(x)$ is continuous and that $Y'(x) = 0$ except perhaps at the points $x_1, x_2, \cdots, x_n$. It follows from Theorem 2.24 that $Y(x)$ must be a constant c over $a \leqq x \leqq x_1$, a constant c_1 over $x_1 \leqq x \leqq x_2$, a constant c_2 over $x_2 \leqq x \leqq x_3$, and so on. The conditions $Y(x_1) = c$ and $Y(x_1) = c_1$ imply that $c = c_1$; likewise

$c = c_1 = c_2 = \cdots$, and hence $Y(x)$ is the constant c over the entire interval $a \leqq x \leqq b$. Thus $y(x) - y_1(x) = c$ over $a \leqq x \leqq b$, and this gives our result (2.382).

Problem 2.391

Explain carefully what the left member of the equality

$$\int_4^5 x^2 \, dx = \frac{1}{3} x^3 \Big]_4^5 = \frac{61}{3}$$

is, and tell why the equality holds.

Problem 2.392

Prove that if a and x are both positive or both negative, then

$$\int_a^x \frac{1}{t} \, dt = \log |t| \Big]_a^x = \log |x| - \log |a|.$$

You may use the fact that if $f(x)$ is differentiable and $f(x) > 0$, then the derivative with respect to x of $\log f(x)$ is $f'(x)/f(x)$.

Problem 2.393

Let $f(x) = 1$ when the greatest integer less than or equal to x is even (*i.e.*, 0, -2, 2, -4, 4, $\cdots$), and let $f(x) = -1$ when the greatest integer less than or equal to x is odd (*i.e.*, -1, 1, -3, 3, $\cdots$). The function $f(x)$ may be described as the function with period 2 which is 1 when $0 \leqq x < 1$ and is -1 when $1 \leqq x < 2$. Draw graphs of $f(x)$ and

$$y(x) = \int_0^x f(t)\,dt.$$

Show that $y(x)$ is continuous and that $y'(x) = f(x)$ except when x is an integer.

Problem 2.394

A particle of unit mass is placed at rest at the origin of a horizontal x axis at time $t = 0$. During the first half of each minute it is pushed toward the right by a constant unit force, and during the second half of each minute it is pushed toward the left by a constant unit force. Where is the particle at the end of 10 minutes? [For the benefit of anyone whose knowledge of mechanics is fragmentary or untrustworthy, we remark that, if $x(t)$ is the displacement of a particle of mass m moving under the action of a horizontal force $f(t)$ which is positive or negative according as the force pushes toward the right or left, then $x(t)$ is continuous and has a continuous derivative $x'(t)$. Moreover, by a fundamental law of Newton, $x''(t) = d^2x/dt^2$ exists for each value of t for which $f(t)$ is continuous and $f(t) = mx''(t)$.] Draw graphs of $x(t)$, $x'(t)$, and $x''(t)$.

2.4. Cauchy Integrals.

A function $f(x)$ can have a Riemann integral over an interval $a \leqq x \leqq b$ only when the interval is finite and the function $f(x)$ is bounded over $a \leqq x \leqq b$. If $f(x)$ is defined over $a \leqq x \leqq b$ except perhaps at a single point c where $a \leqq c \leqq b$ and if for each h such that $h > 0$ and $c - h > a$ the Riemann integral

$$\int_a^{c-h} f(t)\,dt$$

exists, we define

$$(2.41) \qquad \int_a^c f(t)dt = \lim_{h \to 0+} \int_a^{c-h} f(t)dt$$

when the limit exists.　Similarly we define

$$(2.42) \qquad \int_c^b f(t)dt = \lim_{h \to 0+} \int_{c+h}^b f(t)dt$$

when the limit exists.　If the limits in (2.41) and (2.42) both exist, we define

$$(2.43) \qquad \int_a^b f(t)dt = \lim_{h \to 0+} \int_a^{c-h} f(t)dt + \lim_{h \to 0+} \int_{c+h}^b f(t)dt.$$

We also define

$$(2.44) \qquad \int_a^\infty f(t)dt = \lim_{h \to \infty} \int_a^h f(t)dt$$

$$(2.45) \qquad \int_{-\infty}^a f(t)dt = \lim_{h \to -\infty} \int_h^a f(t)dt$$

$$(2.46) \qquad \int_{-\infty}^\infty f(t)dt = \lim_{a \to -\infty} \int_a^\infty f(t)dt,$$

in case the limits exist.　The integrals in the left members of (2.41) to (2.46) are called *Cauchy integrals* or *improper integrals*.　The author prefers the first alternative since he sees no reason why defamatory terminology should be applied to useful integrals.　The term *infinite integral* is sometimes used, but many persons object violently to this term.

A more abstruse integral, known as the *Cauchy principal-value integral*, is defined by

$$(2.47) \qquad \int_a^b f(t)dt = \lim_{h \to 0+} \left[\int_a^{c-h} f(t)dt + \int_{c+h}^b f(t)dt \right]$$

when the integrals on the right exist as Riemann or Cauchy integrals and the limit on the right exists.　The important point to notice here is that the integral in (2.47) can exist when neither of the two separate limits in the right member of (2.43) exists.　For an example, see Problem 2.483.

Problem 2.481

Show that

$$\int_0^\infty e^{-x}\, dx = 1; \qquad \int_0^1 \log x\, dx = -1.$$

Problem 2.482

Determine, for each of the two integrals

$$\int_1^\infty t^p\, dt, \qquad \int_0^1 t^p\, dt,$$

the values of the exponent p for which the integrals exist.   *Ans.:* $p < -1; p > -1$.

Problem 2.483

Draw graphs of $f(x) = 1/x$ and

$$(2.484) \qquad\qquad y(x) = \int_{-2}^x \frac{1}{t}\, dt$$

for those values of x between -2 and 2 for which the functions are defined.   Pay careful attention to the kind or kinds of integral you use.   Is $y'(x) = f(x)$?

2.5. Indefinite Integrals.—The symbol

$$(2.51) \qquad\qquad \int f(x)dx$$

is used to denote a function of x whose derivative is $f(x)$; the function is called an *indefinite integral* of $f(x)$.   For example, x^3 and $x^3 + 1{,}776$ are both indefinite integrals of $3x^2$, and each indefinite integral of $3x^2$ has the form $x^3 + c$ where c is a constant.

If $f(x)$ is continuous, then for each constant a the function

$$(2.52) \qquad\qquad \int_a^x f(t)dt$$

is *an* indefinite integral of $f(x)$.   It is not necessarily true that each indefinite integral of $f(x)$ can be represented in the form (2.52); for if $f(x) = \cos x$ so that

$$(2.53) \qquad\qquad \int_a^x \cos t\, dt = \sin t\Big]_a^x = \sin x - \sin a,$$

then it is impossible to choose a such that (2.53) is the indefinite integral $(\sin x - 10)$ of $\cos x$.   However, each indefinite integral of $f(x)$ can be represented in the form

$$\int_a^x f(t)dt + c.$$

2.6. Elementary Functions; Integration.—The so-called *elementary functions* include powers, roots, exponentials, logarithms, trigonometric and inverse trigonometric functions, and finite combinations of these obtained by addition, subtraction, multiplication, and division.   For example, x^3, e^x, $(1 + x^2)^{\frac{1}{2}}$, $\log \sin x$, and

$$(2.601) \qquad\qquad (1 + \log x)x^4 e^{-x^2} \cos \frac{x^2 - 1}{x^2 + 1}$$

are elementary functions of x.

A considerable part of a course in elementary calculus is devoted to the following problem which is there called the *problem of integration:* Given an elementary function $f(x)$, find an elementary function $y(x)$ such that $y' = f(x)$ or

(2.61) $\int f(x)dx = y(x)$.

The techniques for finding $y(x)$ include, among others, integration by parts, change of variable, separation of quotients into partial fractions, remembering results of differentiation, guessing, and use of integral tables.

If, $f(x)$ being given, say $f(x) = x \sin x$, a student is unable to find an elementary function $y(x)$ for which (2.61) holds, he says, "I cannot integrate $f(x)$." Only this hypothetical student of the calculus can say whether a blind faith in his calculus teacher led him to believe his "teacher could integrate everything." Just as a lass may walk through the grass and, seeing no snakes, believe that there are no snakes, so also a student may pass through elementary calculus and, seeing only elementary functions having elementary functions for integrals, believe that each elementary function necessarily has an elementary function for an integral. Assuming that students who would be unduly shocked by discovery of presence of snakes have not ventured into a study of differential equations, we mention three examples of functions which are not elementary functions:

(2.611) $$\int_0^x \sqrt{1 - k^2 \sin^2 t}\, dt$$

(2.612) $$\int_0^x \frac{\sin t}{t}\, dt$$

(2.613) $$\frac{2}{\sqrt{\pi}} \int_0^x e^{-t^2}\, dt.$$

These integrals are important because of their physical and other applications. Values of all three functions have been tabulated, the tables being used just as tables of logarithms and trigonometric functions are used.*

Even when $f(x)$ is a given elementary function and x is restricted to an interval $a \leqq x \leqq b$ over which $f(x)$ is continuous, it is often true that one simply does not know whether the function $y(x)$ defined by

(2.62) $$y(x) = \int_a^x f(t)dt$$

* Tables of these and many other nonelementary functions are given in a book entitled *Funktionentafeln* and *Tables of Functions* by E. Jahnke and F. Emde. This book, published by B. G. Teubner in several editions, gives descriptions of the tables in both German and English and also gives references to other sources of information.

is an elementary function.   If one can "integrate $f(x)$" by finding an elementary function $F(x)$ such that $F'(x) = f(x)$ or $F(x) = \int f(x)dx$, then of course $y(x) = F(x) - F(a)$ and accordingly $y(x)$ is an elementary function.   However, a mere failure to find such an elementary function $F(x)$ does not of itself imply that such a function $F(x)$ cannot be found or that $y(x)$ is not an elementary function.   As one may suspect, the problem of showing that functions are not elementary is a difficult one; in fact, little is known about the matter.   There is an obvious advantage in knowing that the functions in (2.611), (2.612), and (2.613) are not elementary: one does not waste time in trying to express the integrals as elementary functions.

We are now in a position to emphasize the result of Theorems 2.36 and 2.38.   If $f(x)$, whether an elementary function or not, is bounded over an interval $a \leq x \leq b$ containing a point x_0 and if $f(x)$ is continuous except at a finite number of points of the interval, then for each constant c the function

$$(2.621) \qquad\qquad y(x) = \int_{x_0}^{x} f(t)dt + c \qquad\qquad a \leq x \leq b$$

is, whether an elementary function of x or not, a continuous function of x such that $y'(x) = f(x)$ wherever $f(x)$ is continuous; and, moreover, different values of the constant c give all the functions $y(x)$ with the properties.   If one is so fortunate as to find, in an integral table or otherwise, an elementary function $F(x)$ equal to $\int f(x)dx$, then [see (2.375)] the formula

$$(2.63) \qquad\qquad y(x) = F(x) - F(a) + c$$

gives $y(x)$ as an elementary function.   If one is not so fortunate, one can always use the methods of the following sections to find approximations to $y(x)$.

Problem 2.64

Prove that

$$(2.641) \qquad\qquad |x| = \int_{0}^{x} \operatorname{sgn} t \, dt.$$

[The signum function was defined in (2.13)].   One who feels that (2.641) is a foolish formula should be impressed by knowledge that (2.641) and the Dirichlet formula (2.15) can be used to show that

$$(2.642) \qquad\qquad |x| = \frac{1}{\pi} \int_{-\infty}^{\infty} \frac{1 - \cos xt}{t^2} \, dt.$$

Problem 2.65

Using the rule for differentiating a function of a function of x, show that if

$$(2.651) \qquad\qquad y = 2 \int_{0}^{\sqrt{x}} e^{-t^2} \, dt + c \qquad\qquad x > 0$$

then

$$(2.652) \qquad \frac{dy}{dx} = \frac{e^{-x}}{\sqrt{x}} \qquad x > 0.$$

Can you show that, if (2.652) holds, then (2.651) must hold?

Problem 2.66

A mathematician spent several weeks trying to find solutions of the differential equation

$$(2.661) \qquad x^2 y'' + (3x - x^2)y' + (1 - x - e^{2x})y = 0$$

and was elated when he found that the function

$$(2.662) \qquad y(x) = x^{-1} e^{\phi(x)},$$

where

$$(2.663) \qquad \phi(x) = \int_{-\infty}^{x} u^{-1} e^u \, du,$$

is a solution of (2.661). Considering values of x for which $x \neq 0$, show that the function $y(x)$ defined by (2.662) and (2.663) really is a solution of (2.661).

The differential equation (2.661) arose in connection with research in analytic number theory. The function $\phi(x)$, defined for $x \neq 0$ by the Cauchy principal-value integral in (2.663), is an important nonelementary function known as the *exponential-integral function* and denoted by Eix. Tables and references to literature bearing on this function may be found in the Jahnke-Emde tables cited above. The equation (2.661) will be solved later, in Section 5.86.

Problem 2.67

Show that if A, B, and a are constants, the function $u(x, t)$ defined for $t > 0$ by

$$u = A + B \int_0^{x/\sqrt{t}} e^{-\frac{1}{4}a^2 s^2} \, ds$$

is a solution of the *heat equation*

$$\frac{\partial^2 u}{\partial x^2} = a^2 \frac{\partial u}{\partial t}.$$

[In applications of this result, t is time, x is a coordinate, and u is temperature.]

2.7. Integrals and Areas.—The following discussion applies to a function $f(x)$ which is positive and continuous over an interval $a \leqq x \leqq b$. Let x be fixed such that $a < x \leqq b$, and let

$$a = x_0 < x_1 < x_2 < \cdots < x_n = x$$

be a division of the interval from a to x as in (2.301). If

$$x_{k-1} \leqq t_k \leqq x_k,$$

then the product $f(t_k)(x_k - x_{k-1})$ is the area of a rectangle of height $f(t_k)$ standing on the interval from x_{k-1} to x_k on the x axis. Hence, the Riemann sum

$$(2.71) \qquad \sum_{k=1}^{n} f(t_k)(x_k - x_{k-1})$$

is the sum of the areas of such rectangles (see Fig. 2.711).

Everyone should have at least a vague feeling that, if n is large and the greatest of the numbers $x_k - x_{k-1}$ is small, then the Riemann sum (*i.e.*, the sum of the areas of the rectangles) should be nearly equal to the area of the portion of the plane which lies above the x axis, under the curve whose equation is $y = f(x)$, and between the lines with abscissas a and x.   It is in accordance with this feeling that the

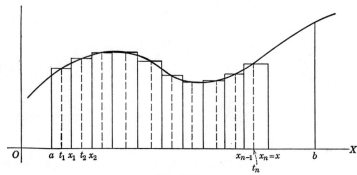

FIG. 2.711.

area of the region in question is defined* to be the limit of the Riemann sums (*i.e.*, the limit of the sum of areas of rectangles).   The area in question depends on x and may be denoted by $A(x)$.   Since $A(x)$ and the definite integral are both (by definition) equal to the limit of Riemann sums, we have

$$(2.72) \qquad A(x) = \int_a^x f(t)dt$$

In case the graph of $f(x)$ lies below the x axis, the integral in (2.72) is not the area of the region bounded by the curve, the x axis, and the two lines with abscissas a and x; the integral is the negative of that area.   In case the graph of $f(x)$ is sometimes above and sometimes below the x axis, the integral is a sum of areas and the negatives of areas.

In elementary calculus, the connection between integrals and areas is often represented as being important because it enables one to find areas by evaluating integrals.   Apart from the solution of problems in calculus books (a worthy pursuit), one seldom finds areas by

---

* The student may recall that, even in elementary plane geometry, the area of a circle is *defined* to be the limit of areas of polygons.

evaluating integrals.   The real importance of the connection between integrals and areas lies in the fact that it enables one to obtain approximate values of integrals by estimating areas.

2.73. Graphical Solutions.—The connection between integrals and areas furnishes a practical method of constructing graphs of solutions of $y' = f(x)$ when $f(x)$ is given.   Let the graph of $f(x)$ be drawn on closely ruled graph paper (see Fig. 2.75), and let a convenient value of a be selected.   Then for each of several judiciously spaced values of x it is possible (simply by counting the squares, and estimating the

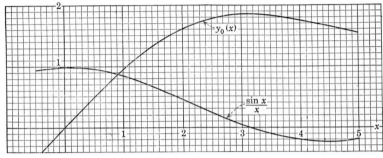

FIG. 2.75.

partial squares, inside the proper regions) to estimate areas and hence to estimate

$$(2.74) \qquad\qquad y_a(x) \equiv \int_a^x f(t)dt.$$

Plotting against x the estimated values of $y_a(x)$ furnishes points through which we may draw an approximation to the graph of $y_a(x)$. An approximation to the graph of any other solution $y(x)$ of $y' = f(x)$ is obtained by adding an appropriate constant to the ordinates of the graph already found.

In Fig. 2.75 we illustrate this construction for the case in which $a = 0$, $f(0) = 1$, and $f(x) = (\sin x)/x$ when $x \neq 0$.   Values of $(\sin x)/x$ used in construction of the graph may be found by use of a table of sines and by division.   However, it is simpler to use tables giving values of $(\sin x)/x$; such a table may be found in the Jahnke-Emde work cited in Section 2.6.   In fact this book contains a table of values of

$$y_0(x) = \int_0^x \frac{\sin t}{t}\, dt.$$

The *graphical*, or *square-counting*, method of solving $y' = f(x)$ can sometimes be applied even when one does not have a formula for the function $f(x)$.   If one can determine by measurements (which

may be based on physical, chemical, biological, or other experiments)
the values of $f(x)$ for enough values of x to permit construction of the
graph (or an approximation to the graph) of $f(x)$, then the graphical
method yields an approximate solution of $y' = f(x)$ which may be
sufficiently accurate for practical purposes.

Problem 2.76

Draw carefully on graph paper a graph of the function

$$(2.761) \qquad f(x) = \frac{1}{1 + x^4}$$

for $0 \leq x \leq 3$, and use the method of this section to obtain an approximation to the
graph of

$$(2.762) \qquad y(x) = \int_0^x f(t)dt$$

for $0 \leq x \leq 3$.

2.77. Other Methods of Evaluating Integrals.—There are "integrating machines" (planimeters and integraphs) by means of which
areas of regions can be found by pushing a point tracer of the apparatus
around the boundaries of the regions. Some graph paper is carefully
made with uniform known weight per unit area so that areas of regions
may be found by cutting them out and weighing them.

An obvious way to obtain an approximate value of

$$(2.771) \qquad \int_a^x f(t)dt,$$

when the integral exists as a Riemann integral, is to compute the
Riemann sum

$$(2.772) \qquad S_n = \sum_{k=1}^{n} f(a + k\,\Delta t)\Delta t$$

where $\Delta t = (x - a)/n$, for a large value of n. (Why?) A better
method of approximating the integral is to compute

$$(2.78) \quad T_n = [\tfrac{1}{2}f(a) + f(a + \Delta t) + f(a + 2\,\Delta t) + \cdots$$
$$+ f(a + \overline{n - 1}\,\Delta t) + \tfrac{1}{2}f(a + n\,\Delta t)]\Delta t$$

where $\Delta t = (x - a)/n$. The sum T_n is the sum of areas (or negatives
of areas) of trapezoids; with this hint a student should be able to see
why this *trapezoidal formula* (2.78) is appropriate.

A still better method is to compute U_n by *Simpson's formula,*

$$(2.79) \quad U_n = \tfrac{1}{3}[f(a) + 4f(a + \Delta t) + 2f(a + 2\,\Delta t) + 4f(a + 3\,\Delta t)$$
$$+ 2f(a + 4\,\Delta t) + \cdots + 4f(a + \overline{n - 1}\,\Delta t) + f(a + n\,\Delta t)]\Delta t$$

where n is even and $\Delta t = (x - a)/n$. The right member is the sum of areas (or negatives of areas) partially bounded by parabolas; details may be found in many calculus books. For equal values of n, U_n is ordinarily a much closer approximation to the integral than S_n or T_n. Simpson's formula is often used. Its excellence is illustrated by obtaining the numerical value of

$$(2.791) \qquad \int_0^1 \frac{1}{1 + t^2}\, dt = \tan^{-1} t \ \Big]_0^1 = \frac{\pi}{4}.$$

Taking $n = 4$, we find

$$(2.792) \quad U_4 = \tfrac{1}{12}[f(0) + 4f(\tfrac{1}{4}) + 2f(\tfrac{1}{2}) + 4f(\tfrac{3}{4}) + f(1)]$$
$$= \tfrac{1}{12}[1 + \tfrac{64}{17} + \tfrac{8}{5} + \tfrac{64}{25} + \tfrac{1}{2}] = .785392157.$$

Using this value of U_4 as an approximation for the integral and hence for $\pi/4$, we obtain the approximate value

$$(2.793) \qquad\qquad \pi \sim 3.141568628.$$

The value of π, correct to 15 decimal places, is

$$(2.794) \qquad\qquad \pi = 3.141592653589793.$$

Thus very little effort was needed to obtain π correct to five digits, and few computations in applied mathematics require as much accuracy as this.

Problem 2.795

Use the formula

$$\int_0^{\frac{1}{2}} \frac{1}{1 + t^2}\, dt = \tan^{-1} t \ \Big]_0^{\frac{1}{2}} = \tan^{-1} \cdot\frac{1}{2}$$

and Simpson's formula to compute $\tan^{-1} \tfrac{1}{2}$. (The value of $\tan^{-1} \tfrac{1}{2}$ is about .4636476 radian.)

2.8. A Snowplow Problem.—In this section we propose and solve a problem which illustrates a way in which differential equations are used. It is not a "pure" mathematical problem, *i.e.*, one that provides all the hypotheses required for determination of an answer. Rather, it is of a type most frequently encountered by applied mathematicians: to solve it, one is forced to make what may be called a *physical assumption*. To anyone who may object to making assumptions, we can say that much of the progress in science is due to men who have the courage to make assumptions, the good sense to make reasonable assumptions, and the ability to draw correct conclusions from the assumptions. It will appear later in this book that many problems may be solved by means of differential equations which are consequences of physical assumptions. Our present problem is as follows:

One day it started snowing at a heavy and steady rate. A snow-plow started out at noon, going 2 miles the first hour and 1 mile the second hour. What time did it start snowing?

Our first task is to try to recover from the shock of being asked to solve such a problem, by attempting to analyze the problem. In the first place, the data of the problem are in agreement with the idea that the plow will move slower as the snow gets deeper. This idea is, however, not sufficiently precise to enable us to solve the problem; we must make some assumption involving the rate at which the plow clears snow from the road. Without pretending to determine whether different assumptions may be equally good or perhaps better, we assume that the plow clears snow at a constant rate of k cubic miles per hour. Let t be time measured in hours from noon, let x denote the depth in miles of the snow at time t, and let y denote the distance the plow has moved at time t. Then dy/dt is the velocity of the plow, and our assumption gives

$$(2.81) \qquad wx\frac{dy}{dt} = k$$

where w is the width of the plow. To find how x depends on t, let t_0 be the number of hours before noon when it started snowing, and let s be the constant rate (in miles per hour) at which the depth of the snow increases; then, when $t > -t_0$,

$$(2.82) \qquad x = s(t + t_0)$$

and we obtain the differential equation

$$(2.83) \qquad \frac{dy}{dt} = \frac{k}{ws}\frac{1}{t + t_0}.$$

This differential equation has the form $dy/dt = f(t)$, and we see that

$$(2.84) \qquad y = \frac{k}{ws}[\log (t + t_0) + c]$$

where c is a constant. It may be suspected (or expected) that knowledge of enough pairs of values of y and t will enable us to determine t_0 and thus obtain a solution of our problem. Since $y = 0$ when $t = 0$, we find from (2.84) that $c = -\log t_0$ and hence

$$(2.85) \qquad y = \frac{k}{ws}\log\left(1 + \frac{t}{t_0}\right).$$

Next we use the fact that $y = 2$ when $t = 1$ and $y = 3$ when $t = 2$ to obtain

$$(2.86) \qquad \left(1 + \frac{2}{t_0}\right)^2 = \left(1 + \frac{1}{t_0}\right)^3.$$

Expanding the powers and simplifying give the equation

$$t_0^2 + t_0 - 1 = 0.$$

Since $t_0 > 0$, we obtain $t_0 = (-1 + \sqrt{5})/2 = .618$ hours = 37+ minutes. Hence, it started snowing about 11:23 A.M.

2.9. A Mothball Problem.—Suppose it has been observed that a mothball of radius $\frac{1}{2}$ inch evaporates to leave a ball of radius $\frac{1}{4}$ inch at the end of 6 months. Express the radius of the ball as a function of the time.

This problem, like the preceding, is not a pure mathematical problem; to solve the problem, one is forced to make a physical assumption. Since evaporation occurs at the surface of the ball, it is reasonable to assume that the time rate at which the volume V decreases is proportional to the area S of surface exposed at time t; that is,

$$(2.91) \qquad \frac{dV}{dt} = -kS$$

where k is some positive constant. Denoting the radius of the ball at time t by r, we can use the formulas $V = \frac{4}{3}\pi r^3$ and $S = 4\pi r^2$ to obtain, when $r > 0$,

$$(2.92) \qquad \frac{dr}{dt} = -k.$$

(Could this equation have been surmised in the first place without arguments involving volume and area?) From (2.92) we obtain

$$(2.93) \qquad r = c - kt$$

where c is a constant of integration. Taking the radius to be $\frac{1}{2}$ when $t = 0$ shows that $c = \frac{1}{2}$; hence, $r = \frac{1}{2} - kt$. Setting $r = \frac{1}{4}$ and $t = 6$ (time being measured in months) shows that $k = \frac{1}{24}$; hence we obtain

$$(2.94) \qquad r = \frac{1}{2} - \frac{t}{24}$$

as the answer to our problem. The reader should draw a graph of $r = r(t)$ and discover precisely how the radius changes as t increases. Is $r = -\frac{1}{2}$ when $t = 24$? Is $r = 1$ when $t = -12$?

Problem 2.95

A cylindrical tank 4 feet high stands on its circular base of radius 3 feet. At noon, when the tank was full of water, a plug was removed from a circular orifice of radius $\frac{1}{2}$ inch in the bottom of the tank and the tank was thereby drained. Find the times at which the tank was one-half full, one-quarter full, and empty.

Physical considerations: If an object falls a distance h feet, its velocity is, when friction is negligible, roughly $\sqrt{2gh}$ feet per second, where $g = 32$. Hence, it seems reasonable that water escaping from an orifice in a tank should have velocity about $\sqrt{2gh}$ when h is the head. (The head is the depth of the orifice, measured from the top surface of the water.)   Hence, one could guess that, if there were no friction and no contraction of the stream near the orifice, water under head h would flow through an orifice of area A square feet at the rate $A \sqrt{2gh}$ cubic feet per second.   Experiments show that friction and contraction reduce the flow to about $0.6A \sqrt{2gh}$ cubic feet per second.

Outline of solution: Let units be feet and seconds, with $t = 0$ at noon.   If $h(t)$ is the head and $V(t)$ is the volume at time t, then $9\pi h = V$; so

$$9\pi \frac{dh}{dt} = \frac{dV}{dt} = -0.6\pi \left(\frac{0.5}{12}\right)^2 \sqrt{64h} = \frac{-\pi}{120} \sqrt{h}.$$

Division by 9π and by $2 \sqrt{h}$ gives

$$\frac{d}{dt} h^{\frac{1}{2}} = \frac{1}{2} h^{-\frac{1}{2}} \frac{dh}{dt} = -\frac{1}{2,160}$$

so $\sqrt{h} = c - t/2,160$.   Since $h = 4$ when $t = 0$, we see that $c = 2$ and, hence, that $t = 2,160(2 - \sqrt{h})$.   The tank was one-half full when $t = 1,265$ (about 12:21 P.M.), one-quarter full when $t = 2,160$ (12:36 P.M.), and empty when $t = 4,320$ (1:12 P.M.).

2.96. An Examination Question.—We close this chapter by consideration of questions of a type sometimes used by examiners to determine whether or not students have a sound knowledge of fundamental principles of the calculus.   Let a be a constant, say 0 or $\frac{1}{2}$ or 42; is there a continuous function $\phi(x)$ such that

(2.961) $$x^2 = \int_a^x \phi(t)dt$$

for all values of x?   To answer this question, a student should first assume that $\phi(x)$ is a continuous function satisfying (2.961).   The student should then realize that differentiation will eliminate the integral to give

$$2x = \phi(x).$$

This shows that, if $\phi(x)$ is continuous and satisfies (2.961), *then* $\phi(x) = 2x$; but it does *not* prove that (2.961) is satisfied when $\phi(x) = 2x$.   To determine whether (2.961) is satisfied when $\phi(x) = 2x$, it should be observed that when $\phi(x) = 2x$ the right side of (2.961) becomes

$$\int_a^x 2t\,dt = t^2 \Big]_a^x = x^2 - a^2$$

and that this is x^2 if and only if $a = 0$.   Thus it is shown that (2.961) has no continuous solutions unless $a = 0$ and that, if $a = 0$, then $\phi(x) = 2x$ is a solution and is the only continuous solution.

Problem 2.962

Prove that, if $\phi(x)$ is a continuous function for which

(2.963) $$e^x = 2 + \int_a^x \phi(t)dt,$$

then $\phi(x) = e^x$; and then show that e^x is a solution of (2.963) if and only if $a = \log 2$. [One who finds this problem too simple may consider the equation obtained by substituting x^2 for the upper limit on the integral is (2.963).]

CHAPTER 3

LINEAR EQUATIONS OF FIRST ORDER

3.0. Introduction.—In this chapter we solve successively the linear differential equations of the forms

$$y' = ky, \qquad y' = ky + a \qquad y' + py = q$$

in which k and a are constants and p and q are functions of x. Then we discuss several problems designed to illustrate various methods by which differential equations are derived (or perhaps conjured up) and used.

3.01. Solution of $y' = ky$.—If k is a constant, if $y(x)$ is a solution of the equation

$$(3.02) \qquad \frac{dy}{dx} = ky,$$

and if we know that $y(x) > 0$ for all x, then we can write

$$(3.021) \qquad \frac{1}{y}\frac{dy}{dx} = k$$

or

$$(3.022) \qquad \frac{d}{dx}\log y = k$$

so that $\log y = kx + c$ and $y = e^{kx+c} = e^{kx}e^{c}$; if we put $A = e^{c}$, then

$$(3.023) \qquad y = Ae^{kx}.$$

Similarly, if $y(x)$ is a solution of (3.02) and we know that $y(x) < 0$ for all x, we can write

$$(3.024) \qquad \frac{1}{-y}\frac{d(-y)}{dx} = k$$

or

$$(3.025) \qquad \frac{d}{dx}\log(-y) = k$$

so that $\log(-y) = kx + c$, $-y = e^{kx+c} = Ae^{kx}$, and

$$(3.026) \qquad y = -Ae^{kx}.$$

We have seen that if $y(x)$ is a solution of (3.02) which never vanishes then

$$(3.027) \qquad y = Be^{kx}$$

34

where B is a constant; and substitution shows that (3.027) is a solution of (3.02) for each constant B.

If $y(x)$ is known to be a solution of $y' = ky$ and we do not know that $y(x) \neq 0$ for all x, then the preceding method of determining $y(x)$ cannot be used. To divide by $y(x)$ would violate the *Fundamental Commandment of Mathematics* which prohibits division by zero.*

We now assume merely that $y(x)$ is a solution of (3.02) and determine the form of $y(x)$ by an impeccable process which does not involve division by $y(x)$. From (3.02) we obtain, on multiplication by e^{-kx} (this looks like a trick, but it is a good trick which we shall use repeatedly; one way in which this trick could be discovered is given in Section 13.7)

$$(3.03) \qquad e^{-kx}\left(\frac{dy}{dx} - ky\right) = 0.$$

But (3.03) may be written

$$(3.031) \qquad \frac{d}{dx}\, e^{-kx}y = 0.$$

Thus c exists such that $e^{-kx}y = c$, and hence

$$(3.04) \qquad y = ce^{kx}.$$

Therefore each solution of (3.02) must have the form (3.04); and it is easy to see that, if c is a constant (positive, negative, or 0) then $y = ce^{kx}$ is a solution of (3.02). Since e^{kx} never vanishes, it follows that each solution of $y' = ky$ is either always zero (if $c = 0$) or never zero (if $c \neq 0$).

3.05. Solution of $y' = ky + a$.—The method of solving the equation $y' = ky$ can be applied to solve the equation

$$(3.06) \qquad \frac{dy}{dx} = ky + a$$

when k and a are constants and $k \neq 0$. The trick is to transpose the term ky and multiply by e^{-kx} to write (3.06) in the form

$$(3.061) \qquad e^{-kx}\left(\frac{dy}{dx} - ky\right) = ae^{-kx}$$

---

* It is not unreasonable to suppose that the reader learned while studying arithmetic or some more advanced subject that one writes $x = b/a$ when and only when there is exactly one number x such that $ax = b$. If $a \neq 0$, the equation $ax = b$ has exactly one solution, and this is b/a. If $a = 0$ and $b \neq 0$, there is *no* number x such that $ax = b$; so b/a is meaningless. If $a = b = 0$, then *every* number x satisfies the equation; so, again, b/a is meaningless. If $a \neq 0$, the equation $ax = ay$ implies $x = y$; but the equation $0 \cdot 2 = 0 \cdot 3$ does *not* imply $2 = 3$.

and then

(3.062)
$$\frac{d}{dx}\, e^{-kx}y = ae^{-kx}.$$

Thus we see that (3.062) and hence (3.06) hold if and only if

$$e^{-kx}y = A - \frac{a}{k}\, e^{-kx}$$

or

(3.07)
$$y = Ae^{kx} - \frac{a}{k}.$$

Thus the functions obtained by giving different values to the constant A in (3.07) are solutions (and are the only solutions) of (3.06).

Problem 3.08

Show that, if $y(x)$ is a solution of (3.06) for which $ky(x) + a > 0$, then

(3.081)
$$\frac{d}{dx} \log (ky + a) = \frac{1}{ky + a}\, k\, \frac{dy}{dx} = k,$$

and derive (3.07) from (3.081).

Problem 3.09

Solve (3.06) for the case in which $k = 0$, and notice that the solutions look quite different from (3.07). One who has a little time and skill at his disposal should enjoy proving and interpreting the following: If, for each fixed k, $y(k, x)$ is the solution of (3.06) which is equal to 1 when x is 0, then

$$\lim_{k \to 0} y(k, x) = y(0, x).$$

3.1. Solution of Linear Equations of First Order.—By a *linear* differential equation of the first order is meant an equation of the form

(3.11)
$$\alpha(x)\, \frac{dy}{dx} + \beta(x)y = \gamma(x)$$

where $\alpha(x)$, $\beta(x)$, and $\gamma(x)$ are given functions of x. Assuming that $\alpha(x) \neq 0$ [values of x for which $\alpha(x) = 0$ are called *singular points* of the differential equation and are often troublesome; see Section 6.9], we can divide by $\alpha(x)$ to throw (3.11) into the form

(3.12)
$$\frac{dy}{dx} + p(x)y = q(x).$$

We consider the case in which $p(x)$ and $q(x)$ are continuous functions of x. The very important equation (3.12) can be solved by a method which should be both thoroughly understood and remembered; the method is very much like the method used to solve (3.02) and (3.06).

Letting $P(x)$ denote a function whose derivative is $p(x)$, for example,

$$(3.13) \qquad\qquad P(x) = \int_{x_0}^{x} p(t)dt,$$

we see that (3.12) holds if and only if

$$\frac{d}{dx}\, e^{P(x)}y = e^{P(x)}\left[\frac{dy}{dx} + p(x)y\right] = e^{P(x)}q(x)$$

and hence if and only if

$$(3.14) \qquad\qquad e^{P(x)}y = A + Q(x)$$

where A is a constant and $Q(x)$ is a function whose derivative is $e^{P(x)}q(x)$, say

$$(3.15) \qquad\qquad Q(x) = \int_{x_0}^{x} e^{P(t)}q(t)dt.$$

Thus we see that (3.12) holds if and only if

$$(3.16) \qquad\qquad y = Ae^{-P(x)} + Q(x)e^{-P(x)}$$

where A is a constant, and we have completely solved (3.12).

The essential point to remember is that, *when the equation*

$$(3.17) \qquad\qquad \frac{dy}{dx} + p(x)y = q(x)$$

is multiplied by the factor $e^{P(x)}$, *it becomes*

$$(3.171) \qquad\qquad \frac{d}{dx}\, e^{P(x)}y = e^{P(x)}q(x)$$

and that use of fundamental ideas then gives $y(x)$. The factor $e^{P(x)}$ is called an *integrating factor* of the differential equation (3.17).

When the formula (3.16) for the solution of (3.12) is written out in full without simplifying notation and with proper use of different dummy variables of integration, it becomes

$$(3.18) \qquad y(x) = Ae^{-\int_{x_0}^{x} p(t)dt} + \left(e^{-\int_{x_0}^{x} p(s)ds}\right)\int_{x_0}^{x} e^{\int_{x_0}^{t} p(u)du}q(t)dt.$$

By setting $q(t) = 0$ in (3.18), we see that the first term in the right member is the solution of the equation $y' + py = 0$ for which $y(x_0) = A$. By setting $A = 0$ in (3.18), we see that the last term is the solution of the equation $y' + py = q$ for which $y(x_0) = 0$. By analogy with problems involving mechanical and electrical systems [in which x represents time, y represents a "disturbance from an equilibrium position," $p(x)$ is a "governing function," and $q(x)$ represents a "disturbing function"], picturesque language is sometimes used to describe the terms in the right member of (3.18). The first term constitutes the "disturbance due to the state at time x_0" or "to the action of the disturbing function before time x_0."

The second term represents the disturbance "due to the action of the disturbing function after time x_0." The fact that the second term involves values of $q(t)$ only in the interval $x_0 \leq t \leq x$ means that the disturbance at time x is independent of the character of the disturbing function $q(t)$ when $t > x$.

Problems

Solve the following equations by use of integrating factors:

✓ (3.181) $\dfrac{dy}{dx} + xy = 0$ $X=0$?   *Ans.:* $y = ce^{-x^2/2}$

✓ (3.182) $\dfrac{dy}{dx} - \dfrac{1}{x}y = x$ $X \neq 0$ *Ans.:* $y = x^2 + cx$

✓ (3.183) $\dfrac{dy}{dx} + (\tan x)y = 0$ $x = \pm \frac{\pi}{2}$?   *Ans.:* $y = c \cos x$

(3.184) $\dfrac{dy}{dx} - ky = e^{-kx}$ *Ans.:* $y = -\dfrac{1}{2k} e^{-kx} + ce^{kx}$

✓ (3.185) $\dfrac{dy}{dx} + (\sin x)y = kx$ *Ans.:* $y = Ae^{\cos x} + ke^{\cos x} \displaystyle\int_0^x te^{-\cos t}\, dt$

(3.186) $\dfrac{dy}{dx} + \dfrac{2x}{x^2 + 1}y = x$ *Ans.:* $y = \dfrac{x^4 + 2x^2 + c}{4(x^2 + 1)}$

Problem 3.187

Show that, if m is a constant and $q(x)$ is continuous, the solution of the equation

$$\frac{dy}{dx} + my = q(x)$$

for which $y(x_0) = A$ can be written in the form

$$y(x) = Ae^{-m(x-x_0)} + \int_{x_0}^x e^{-m(x-t)}q(t)dt.$$

If $m = 2$, $x_0 = 0$, and $A = 100$, give the range of values of x for which $q(x)$ must be known before $y(10)$ can be computed.

Problem 3.188

Find all continuous functions $y(x)$ for which

$$y(x) = 1 + \int_0^x y(t)dt.$$

Hint: Use the ideas of Section 2.96.   *Ans.:* $y = e^x$.

3.19. Remarks.—If y' is interpreted as the rate of change of y with respect to x, the equation

(3.191) $$\frac{dy}{dx} = ky$$

can be read either "The rate of change of y with respect to x is proportional to y" or "The rate of change of y with respect to x is a constant times y." Of course, the two readings mean the same thing. (It may perhaps be true that the first reading is sometimes preferred because it is less likely than the second to cause some unpleasant person to ask what the constant is.)

In the remainder of this chapter we consider several problems solvable by means of the differential equation $y' = ky$ and more general linear equations. A student who wants to learn where differential equations come from and how they are used should pay careful attention to the problems. To solve a great many problems rapidly and thoughtlessly is a waste of time.

If in connection with some of these problems a student begins to feel that solving problems in applied mathematics involves so many approximations that the whole business is utter nonsense, he is to be congratulated. He is perhaps approaching a point where he may begin to learn something about the manner in which mathematics is used in the sciences.

3.2. Problems in Temperature.—A steel ball is heated to temperature 100° and placed at time $t = 0$ in a medium which is maintained at temperature 40°. Heat flows so rapidly within the ball that at each time the temperature is essentially the same at all points of the ball. At the end of 2 minutes, the temperature of the ball is reduced to 80°. We shall find the time at which the temperature of the ball will be 43°.

It is common knowledge that the ball will lose heat most rapidly and that the temperature u of the ball will fall most rapidly when the temperature difference $u - 40$ is greatest. One may guess (and experiments will show) that the rate of change of u with respect to t is proportional to $u - 40$; thus there is a constant k such that

$$(3.21) \qquad \frac{du}{dt} = -k(u - 40).$$

This is an application of *Newton's law of cooling.* The negative sign in (3.21) is inserted so that k will turn out to be positive; if $-k$ were replaced by k in (3.21), then k would be negative. If one is willing to *assume* that u always remains, for $t \geqq 0$, greater than 40, then we we may divide (3.21) by $u - 40$ to obtain

$$\frac{d}{dt} \log (u - 40) = -k$$

so that $\log (u - 40) = -kt + c$ and

$$(3.22) \qquad u = 40 + Ae^{-kt}.$$

If one wishes to *prove* rather than *assume* that $u > 40$, he can multiply (3.21) by e^{kt} to obtain

$$\frac{d}{dt} e^{kt}(u - 40) = 0$$

and then (3.22).   The fact that $u = 100$ when $t = 0$ implies that $A = 60$; hence,

(3.221) $$u = 40 + 60e^{-kt}.$$

The fact that $u = 80$ when $t = 2$ implies that $e^{-2k} = \frac{2}{3}$, $e^{2k} = 1.5$, and hence

(3.222) $$k = \tfrac{1}{2}\log 1.5 = .2027.$$

If one has no table of natural logarithms, he may write

$$2k \log_{10} e = \log_{10} 1.5$$

and then use a table of logarithms with base 10 to obtain k.   Thus,

(3.23) $$u = 40 + 60e^{-.2027t}.$$

This formula enables us to find u for each given $t > 0$ and to find t for each $u > 40$.   If $u = 43$, then (3.23) gives $e^{.2027t} = 20$; using a table of natural logarithms, we find

(3.24) $$t = \frac{1}{.2027} \log 20 = \frac{2.9957}{.2027} = 14.8;$$

the equation $.2027t \log_{10} e = \log_{10} 20$ and a table of logarithms with base 10 can be used to find t.   Thus 14.8 minutes is the time required for the ball to reach a temperature of $43°$.

It is possible to base the derivation of the differential equation (3.21) on experiments less complicated than that of measuring a rate of change of temperature. It may be verified by experiment that if the ball and the surrounding medium are maintained at temperatures u and u_0, respectively, then the number ΔH of calories of heat which flow from the ball to the medium in Δt minutes is proportional to $u - u_0$ and to Δt so that

(3.25) $$\Delta H = k_1(u - u_0)\Delta t$$

where k_1 is a constant depending on the physical properties of the ball and the medium but k_1 is independent of $u - u_0$ and Δt.   Let us now assume that the temperature u of the ball is initially greater than u_0, that no heat is added to the ball, and that the temperature of the ball decreases continuously as time passes. Let $H = H(t)$ denote the number of calories of heat lost by the ball in the first t minutes after $t = 0$.   Then, when $t_1 < t_2$, $u_1 = u(t_1)$, $u_2 = u(t_2)$, we have $u_2 < u_1$. Hence the number ΔH of calories of heat passing from the ball to the medium in the time interval from t_1 to t_2 satisfies the inequality

(3.251) $$k_1(u_2 - u_0)(t_2 - t_1) < \Delta H < k_1(u_1 - u_0)(t_2 - t_1).$$

Since the temperature u changes steadily as t increases from t_1 to t_2, we can choose a time t' between t_1 and t_2 such that

(3.252) $$\Delta H = k_1[u(t') - u_0](t_2 - t_1).$$

Setting $\Delta t = t_2 - t_1$ and dividing by Δt give

(3.253)
$$\frac{\Delta H}{\Delta t} = k_1[u(t') - u_0].$$

If we give t_1 a fixed value t and let $t_2 \to t_1$ (or give t_2 the fixed value t and let $t_1 \to t_2$), then t', which lies between t_1 and t_2, must approach t and, since $u(t)$ was assumed continuous, $u(t')$ must approach $u(t)$. Thus the right side of (3.253) has a limit as $\Delta t \to 0$; hence also the left and by definition of derivative

(3.254)
$$\frac{dH}{dt} = k_1(u - u_0)$$

where u on the right stands for $u(t)$. We have still to make the connection between calories of heat lost by the ball and temperature of the ball. It is a physical fact that (at least for ordinary temperatures) temperature scales are so adjusted that the decrease in temperature of an object is proportional to the number of calories of heat lost by the object; that is,

$$u(t) - u(t_1) = -k_2[H(t) - H(t_1)]$$

where $k_2 > 0$. Thus $du/dt = -k_2 dH/dt$ so that setting $k = k_1 k_2$ and using (3.254) give

(3.255)
$$\frac{du}{dt} = -k(u - u_0).$$

Problem 3.26

A chemist wants a jug of chemical cooled to 80°. Ten minutes ago he set the jug, with the temperature of the chemical 120°, in a vat of water at temperature 40°. Since that time he has been busy stirring both the chemical and the water and observing that the only appreciable transfer of heat is from the chemical to the water. The temperature of the chemical is now 100°, and that of the water is 55°. How long must he continue to stir? *Ans.:* When time $t = 0$ represents the instant 10 minutes after stirring started and $u = u(t)$ is the temperature of the chemical at time t, $u = \frac{520}{7} + Ae^{-k_1 t}$. Determination of constants gives $u = \frac{1}{7}[520 + 180e^{-.0575t}]$, and $u = 80$ when $t = 26.1$ minutes. The total time of the stirring is 36.1 minutes.

Problem 3.27

How long would it take to cool the chemical in Problem 3.26 from 120° to 80° if the water is maintained at temperature 40°? Explain why your answer is wrong if you get more than 36.2 minutes.

3.3. A Window Problem.—A certain type of glass is such that a slab 1 inch thick absorbs one-quarter of the light which starts to pass through it. How thin must a pane be made to absorb only 1 per cent of the light?

Let t be a variable representing thicknesses of panes of glass, and let $x = x(t)$ denote the fractional part of entering light which passes through a pane of thickness t. Then obviously x decreases as t increases. Since a pane of thickness 0 means no pane at all and accordingly no absorption of light, we have $x(0) = 1$; and, by the statement of the problem, $x(1) = \frac{3}{4}$. We are required to determine t such that $x(t) = .99$.

Let $t \geqq 0$ be fixed; let $\Delta t > 0$; and consider two panes, the first of thickness t and the second, of thickness $t + \Delta t$, obtained by adding a layer of thickness Δt to the right side of the first. Of L units of light entering the first pane at the left, xL units emerge from the first pane to enter the layer, and $(x + \Delta x)L$ units emerge from the layer. The homogeneity of the glass used indicates that there is a constant k (depending only on the type of glass used and the kind of light considered) such that, if xL units of light enter a "thin" pane of thickness Δt, then the amount $(-\Delta x)L$ of light absorbed by the thin pane will be roughly $kxL \, \Delta t$; using the symbol $\sim$ to mean "is roughly equal to," we may express this idea by writing

$$(3.31) \qquad\qquad -\Delta xL \sim kxL \, \Delta t.$$

This idea may be expressed otherwise by saying that the amount of light absorbed by a "thin" pane is roughly proportional to the amount entering and to the thickness of the pane. The idea is an extension to other factors of the idea that, if one doubles (or halves) the amount of entering light, then one will also double (or halve) the amount of absorbed light; and that, if one doubles (or halves) the thickness of a thin pane, one will roughly double (or halve) the amount of light absorbed. The reason why one must say "roughly double" instead of "double" lies in the fact that, if light passes through two thin panes each of thickness Δt, then the first pane which the light reaches will absorb slightly more than the second because the amount of light which enters the first pane is slightly greater than the amount which enters the second pane.

If we write (3.31) in the form

$$(3.32) \qquad\qquad \frac{\Delta x}{\Delta t} \sim -kx$$

and make the natural assumption that the error in the approximation decreases and approaches 0 as the thickness Δt approaches zero, then we can let Δt approach 0 to obtain (by definition of derivative)

$$(3.33) \qquad\qquad \frac{dx}{dt} = -kx.$$

Solving (3.33) gives $x = Ae^{-kt}$. Since $x(0) = 1$, we can put $t = 0$ and $x = 1$ to find that $A = 1$ and $x = e^{-kt}$. Since $x(1) = \frac{3}{4}$, we can set $x = \frac{3}{4}$ and $t = 1$ to obtain

$$k = -\log \tfrac{3}{4} = .288;$$

or if no table of logarithms with base e is available, we can solve the equation $\log_{10} \frac{3}{4} = -k \log_{10} e$ to find k.   Hence,

(3.34) $x = e^{-.288t}$.

Setting $x = .99$ and solving for t by one or the other of the equations

$$-.288t = \log .99 = -.010, \qquad -.288t \log_{10} e = \log_{10} .99$$

gives $t = .035$ inch as the thickness of a pane which allows 99 per cent of the light to pass through and therefore absorbs 1 per cent.

Problem 3.35

That water absorbs light is attested by the fact that it is dark in the ocean depths.   If 10 feet of water absorb 40 per cent of the light which strikes the surface, at what depth would the light at noonday be the same as bright moonlight which is 1/300,000 that of noonday sunlight?   *Ans.:* About 247 feet.

3.4. Atmospheric Pressures.—It is well known that atmospheric pressure as measured by a barometer at a given place on the earth is not constant but is a function of the time; the barometer, invented in 1643, has long been used in weather forecasting.   It is also well known that atmospheric pressure p decreases as distance h above sea level increases.   We propose to disregard pressure changes which depend on the time and, assuming the earth to be surrounded by a motionless gas to which we may apply fundamental gas laws, to try to determine how p depends on h.

We begin by assuming that $p(h)$ is a continuous function which decreases as h increases.   Let a rectangular parallelepiped be constructed whose lower base is 1 unit square and h_1 units above sea level and whose upper base is h_2 units above sea level.   (The reader should draw a figure and amplify it as the discussion proceeds.)   Then $p(h_1)$ is the magnitude of the upward force which would be exerted on the lower base if it were a part of the surface of a tank from which all air has been pumped, and $p(h_2)$ is the magnitude of the smaller downward force similarly determined for the upper base.   Let $\Delta h = h_2 - h_1$ and $\Delta p = p(h_2) - p(h_1)$.   Since the air in the parallelepiped moves neither up nor down, the pressure difference $-\Delta p$ must be equal to the weight Δw of the air within the parallelepiped.

To put ourselves in a position to estimate Δw, let us think about the weight of the air in a tank.   If air is pumped from the tank, then the pressure decreases and the weight of the air in the tank decreases; if air is pumped into the tank, both pressure and weight increase.   If the tank is sealed and heated or cooled, then pressure is increased or decreased but the weight of the air in the tank does not change.   These considerations indicate that pressure, temperature, and weight are interrelated and that we may be able to use the *fundamental gas law*, one form of which is the following: If N molecules of a gas at pressure p and absolute temperature T are confined in a volume v, then

$$(3.41) \qquad N = \frac{k_1 pv}{T}$$

where k_1 is an absolute constant depending only on the units used. Since the mass, which we denote by Δm, of the gas is proportional to the number of molecules, we obtain

$$(3.42) \qquad \Delta m = \frac{k_2 pv}{T}.$$

Our first observation, when we come to apply (3.42) to obtain the mass of the air in the rectangular parallelepiped, is that neither (3.42) nor the fundamental formula (3.41) from which it is obtained takes into account the very fact which gives rise to our problem, namely, the fact that pressure is different at different distances h above sea level. Likewise, formulas (3.41) and (3.42) do not take into account the fact that the temperature T may be different at different points. (Dependence of T on h will be discussed later.) Let us meet these difficulties by making the assumption that (3.42) will hold if p and T are taken, respectively, to be the pressure and temperature at two properly chosen points of the rectangular parallelepiped. The volume v is easily obtained, for the base has unit area and the altitude is Δh; thus $v = \Delta h$. Hence, if h' and h'' are properly chosen such that $h_1 < h' < h_2$ and $h_1 < h'' < h_2$, then the mass of the air in the rectangular parallelepiped is

$$(3.43) \qquad \Delta m = k_2 \frac{p(h')\Delta h}{T(h'')}.$$

To make the connection between the weight Δw and the mass Δm, we recall that, if the mass Δm is situated at sea level, then $\Delta w = g\,\Delta m$ where g is the acceleration of gravity but that, if Δm is a height h above sea level, one must use the more general formula $F = k_3 m_1 m_2 / d^2$ where F is force, m_1 and m_2 are masses, d is the distance between the masses, and k_3 is a constant. Using the more general formula, we obtain

$$(3.44) \qquad \Delta w = k_4 \frac{p(h')\,\Delta h}{(R + h'')^2 T(h')}$$

where R is the radius of the earth and h''' is properly chosen so that $h_1 < h''' < h_2$. Since $\Delta p = -\Delta w$, we obtain

$$(3.441) \qquad \frac{\Delta p}{\Delta h} = -k_4 \frac{p(h')}{(R + h''')^2 T(h'')}.$$

If we assume that $T(h)$ as well as $p(h)$ is a continuous function of h, then we can give h_1 a fixed value h and let h_2 approach h (or let $h_2 = h$, and let h_1 approach h); then h', h'', and h''' which all lie between h_1 and h_2 must approach h, and we obtain

$$(3.45) \qquad \frac{dp}{dh} = -k_4 \frac{p(h)}{(R + h)^2 T(h)}.$$

The differential equation (3.45) involves not only the function $p(h)$ we are trying to determine but also a temperature function $T(h)$. That the absolute temperature T does depend on h is indicated by the fact that, although the temperature may be 311° (about 38°C. or 100°F.) at sea level, the temperature is about 251° (about -55°C. or -67°F.) at all altitudes from 6 to 20 miles. If a graph of $T(h)$ is known and $p(0)$, the atmospheric pressure at sea level, is known, then it is possible to draw an approximation to the graph of $p(h)$ by means of a lineal-element diagram, to be explained in Chapter 5.

Assuming that we do not know enough about the function $T(h)$ to enable us to use (3.45) to determine $p(h)$, we make progress by application of a time honored method which often brings valuable results in applied mathematics. This method consists in making an assumption known to be absolutely and unequivocally false. In the present application, we assume that T is independent of h. The virtue of this assumption is that (3.45) can now be written in the simpler form

$$(3.46) \qquad \frac{dp}{dh} = -k_5 \frac{p}{(R + h)^2} = -k \left(\frac{R}{R + h} \right)^2 p.$$

Having degraded ourselves by making one false assumption, we find it easy to make another. Noticing that if h is "small as compared with R" then $[R/(R + h)]^2$ is near 1, we omit the factor and write simply

$$(3.47) \qquad \frac{dp}{dh} = -kp.$$

Solving (3.47) gives

$$(3.471) \qquad p = Ae^{-kh}.$$

If h is measured in feet and p in pounds per square inch, then $p(0) = 14.7$ so that $A = 14.7$ and $p = 14.7e^{-kh}$. Assuming that $p(4,500) = 12.5$, we obtain $k = .000037$ so that

$$(3.48) \qquad p = 14.7e^{-.000037h}.$$

Having obtained formula (3.48), the question arises whether or not it is useful. If (3.48) were actually correct, then it could be used to find pressure at a given height or to find the height at which the pressure has an assigned value. But it must be remembered that (3.48) is not correct unless by accident the errors resulting from false assumptions happen to cancel.

Finally we wish to point out, in language which is at best exceedingly vague, that there is a sense in which (3.48) may be useful. If the range of values of h is such that $R/(R + h)$ is nearly 1 and the temperature T is nearly constant over the range, then the deduction (3.48) from the false assumptions may be sufficiently accurate for certain purposes.

3.5. Radiation of Radium.—Everyone who has had a course in physics (and nearly everyone else who finds himself studying differential equations) knows that radium particles are radiated from matter containing radium and that as time passes the amount of radium decreases. Let x denote the number of grams of radium in a given portion of matter, and let t denote time measured in years; we propose to find how x depends on t.

It is reasonable to guess (and certain physical considerations lead one to believe) that the rate at which the amount of radium decreases is proportional to the amount present. This statement is expressed in mathematical terms by the differential equation

$$(3.51) \qquad \frac{dx}{dt} = -kx$$

where k is a constant. Solving gives $x = Ae^{-kt}$. If x_0 represents the weight of the radium at time $t = 0$, then setting $t = 0$ shows that $A = x_0$ so that

$$(3.52) \qquad x = x_0 e^{-kt}.$$

If the value of k is known, then formula (3.52) enables us to compute the value of x for each given t, or the value of t for each given $x > 0$. The value of k has been computed from results of different observations; its value turns out to be about .00041. Thus we obtain as the solution of our problem

$$(3.53) \qquad x = x_0 e^{-.00041t}.$$

If t_1 is the number of years required to reduce the amount of radium in a portion of matter by one-half, then $.5 = e^{-.00041t_1}$ so that $t_1 = 1,700$ years. The graph of the function in (3.53) is shown in Fig. 3.531.

The solution (3.53) of our problem involves a formula which is simple and elegant, which was obtained by a seemingly rigorous method, and which is useful.   Hence, it is appropriate that one who wants only superficial knowledge of many problems should pass to another problem.   However, there are reasons why a serious-minded student of either mathematics or physics should view the formula with grave suspicion.   To bring these reasons to the fore, we begin afresh to consider the problem.

A physicist who has appropriate training and apparatus can see the "tracks" of radiated particles and can count them one by one as

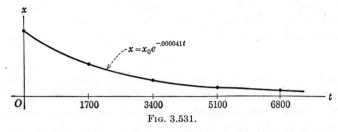

FIG. 3.531.

they are radiated.   If we know (or assume) that the weight x of the radium suddenly decreases when a particle is radiated and remains constant over time intervals in which there is no radiation, we have immediately a contradiction of (3.53).   For if $x(t)$ is constant over some interval, then $x'(t) = 0$ over that interval.   This implies that (3.53) cannot be true; for if (3.53) is true, then $x'(t) = -kx_0e^{-kt} \neq 0$ for all t.   The graph of $x(t)$ which the physicist would construct to cover a time interval a few seconds long may be illustrated by Fig.

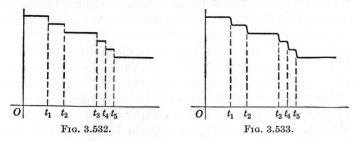

FIG. 3.532.   FIG. 3.533.

3.532 or by Fig. 3.533 depending on whether the weight x of the radium is regarded as decreasing instantaneously at times t_1, t_2 $\cdots$ when radiation occurs or is regarded as decreasing continuously but rapidly in neighborhoods of these times.   Not only the scales but also the characters of the graphs in Figs. 3.532 and 3.533 are different from those of Fig. 3.531.

We are now in a predicament.   We have apparently used good mathematics and physics to show that (3.53) is true and then used equally good mathematics and physics to show that (3.53) is not true.

The data and graphs obtained by the experimental physicist must be accepted as accurate, and we must conclude that it is definitely not true that there is a constant k such that $dx/dt = -kx$ and $x = x_0e^{-kt}$; the function $x(t)$ is far more capricious. In fact, the data and observations of experimental physicists leave one in doubt as to whether $x(t)$ is differentiable; in particular, if it is not continuous, then it certainly is not differentiable. Thus we are driven to conclude that our pleasant attempt to foist the differential equation $dx/dt = -kx$ and the solution $x = x_0e^{-kt}$ on the reader was not so innocent as it appeared to be; unfortunately, the formulas are not correct.

There is still the possibility that the function $\xi(t)$ defined by

$$(3.54) \qquad\qquad \xi = x_0e^{-kt}$$

is a good approximation to the function $x(t)$ which we are seeking. We know that, if $\xi(t)$ and $x(t)$ are plotted with scales so adjusted that time differences of the order of seconds and weight differences of the order of the weight of a radiated particle are displayed, then the graphs of $\xi(t)$ and $x(t)$ will be very different; but if we are optimistic, we can hope that, if $\xi(t)$ and $x(t)$ are plotted (as in Fig. 3.531) so that time differences of the order of centuries and weight differences of the order of grams are displayed, then the "kinks" in the graph of $x(t)$ will not be visible and the graphs of $\xi(t)$ and $x(t)$ will appear to coincide. Thus, *if* the optimism is justified, we can use the equation

$$(3.541) \qquad\qquad x = x_0e^{-kt},$$

knowing that it is false but at the same time trusting it to give results which may be regarded as accurate for macroscopic predictions, that is, for predictions involving time intervals of the order of years or centuries and weights of the order of grams or milligrams. The incorrect formula (3.541) is certainly objectionable when one tries to use it for microscopic predictions, that is, for predictions involving weights of the order of the weight of a radiated particle. In particular, it would be obviously ridiculous to start with a single atom of radium and then claim that, because of (3.541), there would be exactly half an atom 1,700 years later.

It must be admitted that the development of this section has been surprising; we get the formula $x = x_0e^{-kt}$, we learn that it is not correct, and finally we say that we *hope* it is good enough for macroscopic predictions. The points involved are so crucial in so many applications of differential equations that we devote another section to the subject.

3.55. Radiation of Radium (*Continued*).—There are two ways in which one may guess that a solution of the differential equation $dx/dt = -kt$ will furnish a formula for $x(t)$ which is sufficiently accurate for macroscopic applications.   One takes macroscopic observations for its starting point, and the other takes microscopic observations for its starting point.   We indicate below the natures of the ideas on which the two methods are based.   The first may or may not be convincing.   The second, when accurately presented, involves so much mathematics (probability, statistics, etc.) that it is certainly impressive and perhaps convincing.

The first method depends on an assumption which is false, and hence the results obtained are at least open to suspicion; but there is nevertheless the possibility that our conclusions will be correct.   We argue that, if the weight x of the radium were decreased by a suitable steady flow of weight instead of by radiation of discrete particles, then $x(t)$ would be equal to a function $\xi(t)$ such that the rate of change of ξ with respect to t is proportional to ξ so that $\xi'(t) = -k\xi$ and $\xi = x_0 e^{-kt}$; and since macroscopic weight does not depend essentially on whether the weight decreases steadily or by jumps, we conclude that $x(t)$ is essentially $\xi(t)$ and hence that the formula

$$(3.56) \qquad\qquad x(t) = x_0 e^{-kt}$$

is essentially true insofar as macroscopic measurements are concerned.   A logician may insist that the reasoning leading to (3.56) was idiotic.   But at least we made a good guess and got a useful answer.   Moreover, we can remind the logician that the real pioneers in physics (and other sciences) are those who make correct guesses; after correct guesses are made, mathematicians and physicists construct whole theories to prove that the guesses are correct.

The second method begins with a guess.   It is entirely reasonable to guess that if N is the number of particles radiated by x grams of radium in a reasonably short time interval Δt, then N is at least roughly proportional to x and to the time interval Δt; we express this by writing

$$(3.57) \qquad\qquad N \sim k_1 x \, \Delta t.$$

It may then be expected that a physicist who can count radiated particles should experiment with different weights x and different time intervals Δt to validate (3.57), the limits of error being those involved in measuring time intervals and weights of radium.   The physicist who tries to verify (3.57) observes a fact which does not contribute to simple and easy exposition of the subject.   The particles do not come from the radium at a steady regular rate as ticks come from a good watch; the number of particles radiated in a given short time interval may be none or one or several, depending simply on the number of particles which happened to receive the urge to escape during that time interval.   But in spite of the "randomness" of emission of particles, it seems to be true that there is a constant k_1 such that $N/\Delta t$ is usually roughly $k_1 x$ provided that Δt is "large" enough to make N large but at the same time not large enough to produce an appreciable change in x.   This statement of experimental results is quite analogous to the following statement: In spite of the randomness with which heads and tails appear when a coin is tossed, it seems to be true that there is a constant p ($= \frac{1}{2}$) such that the number H of heads divided by the total number T of throws is usually roughly p provided that T is large.   Each one of these statements must be made much more precise and intelligible before it can be accepted as a part of a satisfactory theory of probability and statistics, and it is not the intention of the author to expect the reader to understand something unintelligible.   If we know (or make the reasonable assumption) that the increase Δx (which is negative) in x during the time Δt is proportional to the number N of particles radiated during the time Δt, we obtain $\Delta x = -k_2 N$ so that setting $k = k_1 k_2$ gives, by use of (3.57),

$$(3.58) \qquad\qquad \frac{\Delta x}{\Delta t} \sim -kx.$$

It is usually true in pure (but not applied) mathematics that the relationship expressed in (3.58) indicates roughly that $\Delta x/\Delta t$ is near $-kx$ when Δt is small and indicates precisely that lim $\Delta x/\Delta t = -kx$ or (by definition of derivative) that $dx/dt = -kx$. But in the present instance the meaning of (3.58) is much more complicated. It is clear that nothing is obtained in the present instance by allowing Δt to approach zero. For if Δt is very small, then $\Delta x/\Delta t$ will be 0 if none of the capricious particles were radiated in the time interval Δt; and $\Delta x/\Delta t$ will be numerically large if one or more particles happened to be radiated during the time interval. In particular, it is definitely not true that $dx/dt = -kx$.

We shall not explain the manner in which the vague notion that "$\Delta x/\Delta t$ is usually roughly $-kx$ when Δt is neither too small nor too large" can be made more precise; such explanations belong to statistics and statistical mechanics. But it may be helpful to think of its meaning something like this: If Δt is 1 year, then the probability (chance) that $\Delta x/(-kx\,\Delta t)$ will differ from 1 by more than .01 is equal to the probability (chance) of throwing 10^{20} consecutive heads when throwing a normal coin.

Let us think of constructing a graph of $x(t)$ on ordinary graph paper, showing t ranging from 0 to 5,000 years and x ranging downward from 1 gram at $t = 0$ to a fractional part of a grain when $t = 5,000$. A time interval Δt appearing to the eye to represent a "small" time interval would represent several years, and the corresponding Δx would be a small fractional part of x; hence, it is extremely unlikely that $\Delta x/\Delta t$ would differ much from $-kx$. This situation leads us to guess that it is likely that the graph of $x(t)$ would not differ appreciably from the graph of a function $\xi(t)$, satisfying the differential equation $d\xi/dt = -k\xi$, and hence from $x_0 e^{-kt}$.

We have arrived finally at the following meaning which a modern expert in atomic physics attaches to the formula

$$(3.59) \qquad\qquad x = x_0 e^{-kt}$$

as applied to radioactive substances: The formula (3.59) is absolutely useless insofar as predictions involving microscopic weights of the order of weights of radiated particles are concerned; but insofar as predictions involving macroscopic weights of the order of grams or milligrams are concerned it is extremely unlikely that physical observations will differ by measurable amounts from the predictions.

3.6. Dilution Problems.—At time $t = 0$, fresh water starts running g gallons per minute into a tank of volume v which is filled with a salt solution containing s pounds of salt. The solution is stirred to keep the contents of the tank homogeneous, and dilute solution flows out g gallons per minute. The problem is to find the amount x of salt in the tank at time t.

At time t, the number of pounds of salt per gallon is x/v, and the number of gallons of brine flowing out in Δt minutes is $g\,\Delta t$. If Δt is so small that the concentration x/v changes only a little in the time between t and $t + \Delta t$, but at the same time Δt is not so small as to clash with observations of molecule counters, the change Δx in x will be approximately $-(x/v)g\,\Delta t$.   Thus

$$(3.61) \qquad\qquad \frac{\Delta x}{\Delta t} \sim -kx$$

where $k = g/v$ and the symbol $\sim$ has a significance much like that in Section 3.55.   This leads us to expect that the function $x(t)$ which we are seeking will be (insofar as measurements involving weights of the order of pounds can determine) equal to a function $x(t)$ for which

$$(3.62) \qquad\qquad \frac{dx}{dt} = -kx.$$

Thus $x = Ae^{-kt}$; and since $x(0) = s$, we obtain

$$(3.63) \qquad\qquad x = se^{-kt}$$

for our answer.

Problem 3.64

If $k = g/v = .01$, how long will it take to wash 99 per cent of the salt out of the tank?

Problem 3.65

How much credence would you put in the formula (3.63) if the tank, instead of containing s pounds of salt, had contained s tiny separate pieces of sponge where (a) $s = 1{,}000{,}000$ (b) $s = 12$, and (c) $s = 1$?

Problem 3.66

Should (3.63) be accepted to support a contention that it would be impossible to run the salt-free water long enough to wash every molecule of salt out of the tank?

Problem 3.67

Two tanks in a chemical plant each contain about 50,000 gallons of liquid A. To each tank there should be added 5 gallons of liquid B; but through an accident all 10 gallons are put in one tank.   Stirring apparatus keeps the tanks well stirred, and pumps which circulate liquid through the two tanks at the rate of 100 gallons per minute are part of the plant equipment.   How long must the pumps be operated before the numbers of gallons of liquid B in the two tanks are 5.5 and 4.5? *Ans.:* About 9.6 hours.

Problem 3.68

The first tank in a row contains a mixture of $G - g$ gallons of liquid A and g gallons of liquid B; each other tank contains G gallons of liquid A.   From time $t = 0$, liquid A is pumped into the first tank at the rate of r gallons per minute, and a mixture of A and B is thus forced from each tank to the next at the same rate.   Assume that the tanks are perfectly stirred.   Letting $x_0(t)$, $x_1(t)$, $x_2(t)$, $\cdots$

denote the amounts of liquid B in the successive tanks at time t, show that

(3.69) $$x_n = \frac{g}{n!}\left(\frac{r}{G}\right)^n t^n e^{-(r/G)t} \qquad n = 0, 1, 2, \cdots .$$

Show that, when $n > 0$, $x_n(t)$ increases until $t = nG/r$ and thereafter decreases and that the maximum value M_n of $x_n(t)$ is

(3.691) $$M_n = g\,\frac{n^n e^{-n}}{n!} \qquad n = 1, 2, 3, \cdots .$$

[The right side of (3.691) can of course be used to compute M_n for any desired value of n; but it is an interesting fact that obvious properties of M_n give some information about the right side of (3.691). The obvious fact that the amount of liquid B in one tank can never exceed g implies that $n^n e^{-n}/n! \leq 1$ and hence that

(3.692) $$n! \geqq n^n e^{-n}.$$

By use of *Stirling's formula*

(3.693) $$n! = \sqrt{2n\pi}\; n^n e^{-n} e^{\theta_n/12n}$$

in which θ_n represents a sequence for which $0 < \theta_n < 1$, it is easy to show that M_n is approximately $g/\sqrt{2n\pi}$ (in the sense that the ratio is near 1) when n is large. Stirling's formula (3.693) has many important applications in many phases of pure and applied mathematics. Its proof is difficult.]

3.7. Compound Interest.—If A dollars draw interest at rate k (where k may be, for example, .04 or 4 per cent) per year compounded annually, then the total amount of principal and interest will be $A(1 + k)$ at the end of 1 year, $A(1 + k)^2$ at the end of 2 years, and, in general, $A(1 + k)^n$ at the end of n years. If the money is loaned at rate k per year compounded monthly, then the total amount is $A(1 + k/12)$ at the end of 1 month, $A(1 + k/12)^2$ at the end of 2 months, $A(1 + k/12)^r$ at the end of r months, and $A(1 + k/12)^{12n}$ at the end of n years. In general, if the rate is k per year compounded m times a year, then the amount at the end of n years will be

(3.71) $$A\left(1 + \frac{k}{m}\right)^{mn} = A\left[\left(1 + \frac{k}{m}\right)^m\right]^n.$$

Let k and n be fixed, and consider how this amount behaves as m becomes infinite and accordingly the length $1/m$ of a conversion interval approaches 0. The answer to this question is provided by the fact that

(3.72) $$\lim_{m \to \infty}\left(1 + \frac{k}{m}\right)^m = e^k.$$

It thus appears that, when the conversion interval approaches 0, the amount at the end of n years approaches $y(n) = A e^{kn}$. This analysis* motivates the following definition: Money is said to increase at annual rate k *compounded continuously* if an amount A at a stated time increases to the amount

$$(3.73) \qquad\qquad y(t) = Ae^{kt}$$

during the first t years after the stated time. The number t is not restricted to integer values; and when A and k are positive, the amount $y(t)$ increases continuously as t increases.

We have seen that (3.73) holds if and only if

$$(3.74) \qquad\qquad \frac{dy}{dt} = ky;$$

hence, the condition that y *increases at rate k per year compounded continuously* implies and is implied by (3.74).

Problem 3.75

A man has \$40,000 in a fund paying interest at the rate of 4 per cent per year compounded continuously. If he withdraws money continuously at the rate of \$2,400 per year, how long will the fund last? *Ans.:* 27+ years.

Problem 3.76

When a certain food product is produced, the number of organisms of a certain kind in a package is estimated to be N. In 60 days, the number of organisms is estimated to be $1,000N$. The "safe" number of organisms is $200N$. You are the Board of Health. What do you do to justify your salary and position?

3.8. Falling Bodies; Terminal Velocities.—In this section, we consider velocities of objects falling earthward on a straight line under the assumption of a constant gravitational force g. Let t, s, v, and a represent, respectively, time, displacement measured earthward, velocity, and acceleration. For bodies falling in a vacuum, the formulas $a = g$, $v = gt + c_1$, and $s = \frac{1}{2}gt^2 + c_1 t + c_2$ are familiar, c_1 and c_2 being, respectively, the velocity and displacement when $t = 0$.

For bodies falling in air (or water, etc.) there is in addition to the gravitational force a resistance, due to the air, which increases as the velocity increases. This is the reason why the velocity of an aviator descending by parachute keeps within reasonable bounds. It is the reason why bombs dropped from great heights do not hit appreciably harder than bombs dropped from a few thousand feet. Attempts to

---

* A person who prefers approximate arithmetic computations to precise analysis could doubtless find profound satisfaction and comfort in showing that, if $A = 1$, $k = .04$, $n = 40$, and the conversion interval is .001 second so that $m = 40(365.25)(24)(60)(60)(1,000)$, then the left member of (3.71) agrees with $e^{1.6}$ to several decimal places.

compute velocities of falling bodies depend upon experimental results which show how the resistance depends upon the velocity. For "small" velocities, resistance is proportional to the velocity, that is, $R = kv$; for "greater" velocities, there is evidence that $R = kv^2$; and, for "very great" velocities, the formula $R = kv^3$ is often used.

Let us study the fall of a body of mass m dropped at time $t = 0$ from height h with initial velocity v_0, and assume that the air resistance of the body is kv^n where k and n are positive constants. It is not assumed that n is an integer. The downward force is mg and the upward force is kv^n; the resultant downward force $mg - kv^n$ must be the product of the mass and the acceleration of the body. Therefore

$$(3.81) \qquad m\frac{d^2s}{dt^2} = mg - k\left(\frac{ds}{dt}\right)^n$$

or

$$(3.82) \qquad \frac{dv}{dt} = g - Av^n$$

where $A = k/m$. If $n \neq 1$, the differential equation (3.82) can be solved by the methods of Chapter 5.

In case $n = 1$ the equation becomes

$$(3.83) \qquad \frac{dv}{dt} + Av = g$$

so that, where $b = g/A = gm/k$,

$$v = b + ce^{-At}.$$

Since $v(0) = v_0$, we obtain

$$(3.84) \qquad v = b + (v_0 - b)e^{-At}.$$

It appears from (3.84) that, if $v_0 = b$, then $v(t) = b$ for all t; that, if $v_0 > b$, then $v(t) > b$ for all t; that, if $v_0 < b$, then $v(t) < b$ for all t; and that, as $t \to \infty$, $v(t) \to b$ in each case. The limiting velocity b which $v(t)$ approaches as t increases is called the *terminal velocity* of the falling body.

Problem 3.85

When a parachutist jumps from a great height with his parachute closed, k is relatively near 0 and the velocity increases toward a corresponding terminal velocity; when the parachute opens, the resistance factor k suddenly increases to a new value and the velocity decreases toward a new terminal velocity. Sketch a rough graph to exhibit the velocity $v(t)$ of a falling parachutist.

Problem 3.86

Compare the descents of two identical men who jump with identical parachutes, the first carrying no extra weight and the second carrying military equipment which weighs as much as the man and parachute but which is so compact that it does not appreciably change the resistance factors.

3.9. A Simple Electric Circuit.—In this section we consider the problem of determining, as a function of the time t, the electric *current* I in a circuit (Fig. 3.91) containing a *resistor* (resistance R) an *inductor* (inductance L), and an applied (or impressed) *electromotive force E*.

One who is not familiar with such terms as electric current, resistance, inductance, and electromotive force should not be disturbed. It serves our present purpose to think of electricity as being stuff which flows; of an electromotive force as being something which, depending on direction or sign attached, tends to increase or decrease flow of electricity; of a resistor as being something which always tends to diminish flow of electricity; and of an inductor as being something which tends to keep electricity flowing at a constant rate by opposing both increase and decrease in rate of flow. With proper adjustment of units and under

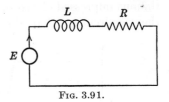

FIG. 3.91.

general conditions which good electrical engineers must know about, the resistor produces an electromotive force equal to RI, and the inductor produces force equal to $L\, dI/dt$.

By use of rules (set forth in Chapter 10) for attaching signs to and equating electromotive forces, one obtains the differential equation

$$(3.92) \qquad L\frac{dI}{dt} + RI = E$$

which governs the flow $I(t)$ in the circuit. The resistance R and inductance L are always positive; in this discussion they are regarded as constants.

The electromotive force E may be either constant, say E_0, or variable, say $E(t)$. A constant electromotive force E_0 may, for example, be obtained by keeping a battery attached at the spot marked E in Fig. 3.91. A variable electromotive force $E(t) = E_0 \sin \omega t$ may be obtained by hooking up ordinary alternating "house" current.

Another way to get a nonconstant electromotive force $E(t)$ is to operate a switch in such a way that a battery is attached and detached over alternate intervals.* If the switch is closed at time t_1, the electromotive force $E(t)$ may rise very quickly (but continuously) from the value 0 at t_1 to a value very nearly equal to E_0; and if the switch is opened at a later time t_2, the electromotive force may fall very quickly (but continuously) from the value E_0 at t_2 to a value very nearly 0.

---

* Much electrical equipment is operated in this way, and much attention has been given to the engineering problem of constructing switches which operate so as to give "clean makes and breaks."

Then the true graph of $E(t)$ would be something like that shown in Fig. 3.93 where the sides of the hump are nearly vertical but, of course, not vertical since $E(t)$ can have only one value for each t. In such cases, it is customary to simplify solution of the problem by *assuming* that $E(t) = 0$ when $t \leqq t_1$, that $E(t) = E_0$ when $t_1 < t \leqq t_2$, and that $E(t) = 0$ when $t > t_2$. The graph of $E(t)$ is shown in Fig. 3.931. Thus discontinuous functions $E(t)$ are introduced, not for the purpose of complicating a simple world but, on the contrary, for the purpose of simplifying a complicated world.* With the admission of discontinuous impressed electromotive forces, it becomes necessary to revise the requirement that the differential equation (3.92) hold for all

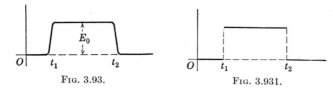

Fig. 3.93.   Fig. 3.931.

values of t. (Why?) Accordingly we revise the statement concerning the differential equation as follows:

The current $I(t)$ is a continuous function of t such that

$$(3.94) \qquad\qquad L\frac{dI}{dt} + RI = E(t)$$

for each value of t for which $E(t)$ is continuous.†

The equation (3.94) is linear, and the method of Section 3.1 is used to solve it. Dividing (3.94) by L and multiplying by the integrating factor $e^{(R/L)t}$ give

$$\frac{d}{dt}\,e^{(R/L)t}I(t) = \frac{1}{L}\,e^{(R/L)t}E(t).$$

By Theorems 2.36 and 2.38, this holds if and only if

$$e^{(R/L)t}I(t) = c + \frac{1}{L}\int_{t_0}^{t} e^{(R/L)u}E(u)du.$$

---

* Of course, it is not the world that is changed; it is the description of the world that is changed from a very complicated description which is exact to a very simple description which is sufficiently exact for practical purposes.

† If this book were written for experts in modern analysis, we should require merely that $E(t)$ be Lebesgue integrable over each finite interval and that $I(t)$ be an absolutely continuous function satisfying the differential equation for all t except possibly a set of measure 0. For present purposes, it suffices to suppose that $E(t)$ is bounded and has at most a finite set of discontinuities in each finite interval; the above requirement is then appropriate.

Letting $I_0 = I(t_0)$, we see that $c = e^{(R/L)t_0}I_0$ and hence that

$$(3.95) \qquad I(t) = I_0 e^{-(R/L)(t-t_0)} + \frac{1}{L}\, e^{-(R/L)t} \int_{t_0}^{t} e^{(R/L)u} E(u)\,du.$$

This is the solution of our problem.

Since $R/L > 0$, the first term

$$(3.96) \qquad\qquad I_0 e^{-(R/L)(t-t_0)}$$

in the right member of (3.95) approaches 0 as t increases, and measurable effects of this current disappear as t increases; for this reason this current is called a *transient current* or simply a *transient*. The ratio R/L tells how rapidly the transient fades.

Problem 3.97

If $E(t)$ is a constant E_0, show that

$$I(t) = \frac{E_0}{R} + \left(I_0 - \frac{E_0}{R}\right) e^{-(R/L)(t-t_0)}.$$

Draw graphs for cases in which (i) $I_0 > E_0/R$, (ii) $I_0 < E_0/R$, and (iii) $I_0 = E_0/R$.

Problem 3.98

Show that, when $E(t)$ is the electromotive force whose graph is shown in Fig. 3.931, the graph of $I(t)$ must have the form shown in Fig. 3.981. Show that for

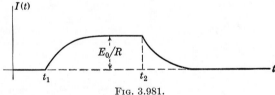

Fig. 3.981.

values of t just a little greater than t_1 the slope of the curve is nearly E_0/L. Discuss this slope as a function of L. One who objects to the term "just a little greater than" may show that

$$(3.982) \qquad\qquad \lim_{t \to t_1+} I'(t) = \frac{E_0}{L}$$

where the $+$ sign after t_1 indicates that only values of t greater than t_1 are considered. [Assume that both $E(t)$ and $I(t)$ are 0 when $t \le t_1$.]

Problem 3.99

Show that if $E(t)$ is an ordinary sinusoidal (or simple harmonic) electromotive force $E_0 \sin \omega t$, where E_0 and ω are positive constants, and if $I(0) = 0$, then

$$(3.991) \qquad\qquad I(t) = \frac{E_0}{L}\, e^{-(R/L)t} \int_0^t e^{(R/L)u} \sin \omega u \,du.$$

Show* that this implies

(3.992) $$I(t) = \frac{E_0 \omega L}{R^2 + \omega^2 L^2} e^{-(R/L)t} + E_0 \frac{R \sin \omega t - \omega L \cos \omega t}{R^2 + \omega^2 L^2}.$$

Show that if ϕ is the angle (there is exactly one) between 0 and $\pi/2$ such that $\tan \phi = \omega L/R$ and accordingly

(3.993) $$\cos \phi = \frac{R}{\sqrt{R^2 + \omega^2 L^2}}, \qquad \sin \phi = \frac{\omega L}{\sqrt{R^2 + \omega^2 L^2}}$$

then (3.992) can be written

(3.994) $$I(t) = \frac{E_0 \omega L}{R^2 + \omega^2 L^2} e^{-(R/L)t} + \frac{E_0}{\sqrt{R^2 + \omega^2 L^2}} \sin (\omega t - \phi).$$

(Many physical consequences of the result (3.994) are easily obtained. Further discussion of this and other problems in circuits is postponed to Chapter 10.)

* A formula, in terms of elementary functions, for the integral in (3.991) can be derived by integration by parts provided that one knows or devises the proper trick. The formula is in every respectable integral table. It may be worked out in a straightforward manner by means of complex exponentials; these are used later in this book.

CHAPTER 4

FAMILIES OF CURVES; TRAJECTORIES

4.1. Families of Curves.—For each constant $c > 0$, the equation

$$(4.11) \qquad x^2 + y^2 = c$$

is the equation of the circle with center at the origin and radius $\sqrt{c}$. The constant c is called a *parameter*, and the totality of circles obtained for positive values of c is called a *one-parameter family* of curves. Likewise, if m is fixed, the equation

$$(4.12) \qquad y = mx + b$$

furnishes, for different values of the parameter b, the one-parameter family of curves which consists of the set of parallel lines having slope m; if b is fixed, the equation furnishes, for different values of m, the one-parameter family of curves which consists of all lines through the point $(0, b)$ except the vertical line through $(0, b)$. If neither m nor b is fixed and both m and b are regarded as parameters, then (4.12) represents the *two-parameter family* of curves consisting of all nonvertical lines. If $f(x)$ is a differentiable function of x, then

$$(4.13) \qquad y - f(c) = f'(c)(x - c)$$

represents the one-parameter family of tangents to the graph of the function $y = f(x)$.

When parameters enter into an equation in such a way that different values of the parameters do not yield different equations, it is often desirable to reduce the number of parameters. For example,

$$(4.14) \qquad y = x + a + b$$

gives the same equation when $a = 3$, $b = 4$ as when $a = 4$, $b = 3$; and the family of lines (4.14) is the same as the family

$$(4.141) \qquad y = x + c$$

where c is a single parameter. Similar reduction is possible if $y = ae^{x+b}$ since $y = ae^b e^x = ce^x$ where $c = ae^b$. A more troublesome example is that of the family

$$(4.15) \qquad \alpha y = \beta x + \gamma$$

59

where α, β, and γ are three parameters and α and β are not both zero. The family (4.15) consists of all lines in the plane; but $\alpha = 2$, $\beta = 3$, $\gamma = 4$ give the same line as $\alpha = 4$, $\beta = 6$, $\gamma = 8$. It is natural to try to reduce the number of parameters by dividing by α, setting $m = \beta/\alpha$, setting $b = \gamma/\alpha$, and writing (4.15) in the form

$$(4.151) \qquad\qquad y = mx + b$$

so that there are now two parameters and different pairs of values of m and b always give different lines. But of course division by α is impossible when $\alpha = 0$, and hence the lines in (4.151) for which $\alpha = 0$ (*i.e.*, the vertical lines) are not included in the family (4.15). In this case, reduction of the number of parameters resulted in the loss of all vertical lines.

It may be true that there is no subject in mathematics upon which more unintelligible nonsense has been written than that of families of curves.* The following example illustrates a difficulty confronting anyone who hopes to classify families of curves according to the number of parameters appearing in the equation of the family. If c is a real nonnegative number, then c can be written in exactly one way in the form

$$(4.16) \qquad\qquad c = \cdots c_{-3}c_{-2}c_{-1}c_0.c_1c_2c_3 \cdots$$

where the central dot is a decimal point; each c_n is one of the digits $0, 1, \cdots, 9$; $c_{-n} = 0$ for all sufficiently great n; c_n may be but is not necessarily 0 for all sufficiently great n; and there is no number N such that $c_n = 9$ whenever $n > N$. For example,

$$\tfrac{1}{8} = \quad \cdots 000.125000 \cdots$$
$$\tfrac{4}{3} = \quad \cdots 001.333333 \cdots$$
$$\pi = \quad \cdots 003.141592653589793 \cdots$$
$$1{,}000e = \quad \cdots 002718.281828459045 \cdots.$$

Let four functions $f_1(c)$, $f_2(c)$, $f_3(c)$, and $f_4(c)$ be defined for $c \geqq 0$ by the formulas

$$(4.171) \qquad f_1(c) = \cdots c_{-12}c_{-8}c_{-4}.c_0c_4c_8c_{12} \cdots$$
$$(4.172) \qquad f_2(c) = \cdots c_{-11}c_{-7}c_{-3}.c_1c_5c_9c_{13} \cdots$$
$$(4.173) \qquad f_3(c) = \cdots c_{-10}c_{-6}c_{-2}.c_2c_6c_{10}c_{14} \cdots$$
$$(4.174) \qquad f_4(c) = \cdots c_{-9}c_{-5}c_{-1}.c_3c_7c_{11}c_{15} \cdots.$$

---

* A biography of Thomas Gray (1716–1771) says that he withdrew from Cambridge, without taking a degree, because of his dislike of mathematics. Perhaps Gray was thinking of families of curves when he wrote his famous lines

" . . . where ignorance is bliss,
'Tis folly to be wise."

Then, for each $c \geq 0$, the equation

(4.18) $y = [f_1(c) - f_2(c)]x + [f_3(c) - f_4(c)]$

is the equation of a nonvertical line. Moreover, it is easy to see that each nonvertical line is obtained for an infinite set of values of c. For example, the line

$$y = 2x - \tfrac{3}{2}$$

is obtained by setting

$$f_1(c) = 3, \qquad f_2(c) = 1, \qquad f_3(c) = .5, \qquad f_4(c) = 2$$

and hence by setting

$$c = 31,020.05.$$

Therefore, the one-parameter family of lines (4.18) is exactly the same as the two-parameter family (4.151).

This example shows that it is futile to talk about the number of parameters in an equation without specifying something about the way in which the parameters enter the equation. With this disturbing remark, we pass to the next two sections hoping that the student may glean some good ideas and no bad ones.

Problem 4.19

Find what lines are representable in the form

$$y = f_1(c)x + f_2(c)$$

where (4.16) holds and

$$f_1(c) = \cdots c_{-4}c_{-2}.c_0c_2c_4 \cdots$$
$$f_2(c) = \cdots c_{-3}c_{-1}.c_1c_3c_5 \cdots .$$

Problem 4.191

Considering positive values of x, prove that if $A \neq 0$ and y is a continuous function of x for which

$$Ay^2 + Bxy + Cx^2 = 0,$$

then there is a constant k such that $y = kx$.

4.2. Differential Equations of Families of Curves.—If $c > 0$, then when x is in a certain interval, namely, the interval $-\sqrt{c} < x < \sqrt{c}$, there is a function $y(x)$, which may be either $(c - x^2)^{\frac{1}{2}}$ or $-(c - x^2)^{\frac{1}{2}}$, such that $y'(x)$ exists and

(4.21) $x^2 + y^2 = c.$

For values of x in the range, we may differentiate (4.21) to obtain

(4.211) $x + y \dfrac{dy}{dx} = 0;$

in this case, (4.211) is called a *differential equation of the family* (4.21).

If c is a constant, then for x in a certain range there is a function $y(x)$ such that $y'(x)$ exists and

(4.22) $$(x - c)^2 + y^2 = 1.$$

For values of x in the range, we may differentiate (4.22) to obtain

(4.221) $$(x - c) + y\,\frac{dy}{dx} = 0.$$

Now (4.221) is a differential equation satisfied for the special curve of the family (4.22) determined by the special c; but we can solve (4.221) for c and substitute in (4.22) to obtain the single differential equation

(4.222) $$\left(y\,\frac{dy}{dx}\right)^2 + y^2 = 1$$

which is satisfied for each curve of the family (4.22). Accordingly, (4.222) is called a *differential equation of the family* (4.22). It should be carefully noted that this terminology is not to be interpreted to mean that functions satisfying (4.22) for some value of c are the *only* functions satisfying (4.222); such an interpretation would furnish an unpleasant contradiction of the obvious fact that the function $y = 1$ satisfies (4.222).*

Problem 4.23

Show that, if (4.22) is solved for c and the resulting equation is differentiated, the differential equation (4.222) will result.

Each of the equations (4.21) and (4.22) has, when all terms are transposed to the left side, the form $f(x, y, c) = 0$. Hence our discussion of the two equations motivates the following terminology: If, for each range of values of x for which $y(x)$ is differentiable and satisfies

(4.241) $$f(x, y, c) = 0,$$

it is possible to obtain an equation

(4.242) $$\phi\left(x, y, c, \frac{dy}{dx}\right) = 0$$

and to eliminate c to obtain an equation†

---

* The problem of finding *all* solutions of (4.222) involves a careful analysis which is postponed to Chapter 14.

† When we say that (4.243) is an equation obtained by eliminating c from (4.241) and (4.242), we mean that (4.243) is an equation which is satisfied by the three numbers x, y, dy/dx whenever the four numbers x, y, dy/dx, c satisfy (4.241) and (4.242).

$$(4.243) \qquad F\left(x,\, y,\, \frac{dy}{dx}\right) = 0$$

not involving c, then (4.243) is called a *differential equation of the family* (4.241).

Similarly, if

$$(4.25) \qquad f(x,\, y,\, c_1,\, c_2) = 0$$

is a two-parameter family of curves, it may be possible to obtain by differentiation a relation

$$(4.251) \qquad \phi\left(x,\, y,\, \frac{dy}{dx},\, c_1,\, c_2\right) = 0.$$

Except in trivial cases, it is not possible to eliminate both c_1 and c_2 from (4.25) and (4.251); but it is often possible to differentiate again to obtain

$$(4.252) \qquad \psi\left(x,\, y,\, \frac{dy}{dx},\, \frac{d^2y}{dx^2},\, c_1,\, c_2\right) = 0.$$

It may then be possible to eliminate c_1 and c_2 from the three equations; one technique for accomplishing the elimination would be to solve (4.25) and (4.251) for c_1 and c_2 in terms of x, y, and dy/dx and then to substitute the results in (4.252). The result would be an equation involving x, y, dy/dx, and d^2y/dx^2, say

$$(4.26) \qquad F\left(x,\, y,\, \frac{dy}{dx},\, \frac{d^2y}{dx^2}\right) = 0.$$

This is a differential equation of the second order not involving the parameters c_1 and c_2 and is called a *differential equation of the two-parameter family* (4.25).

If n is a positive integer and

$$(4.27) \qquad f(x,\, y,\, c_1,\, c_2,\, \cdots,\, c_n) = 0$$

is an n-parameter family of curves, then it may be possible to use (4.27) and n equations obtained by n successive differentiations to obtain a differential equation of order n, say

$$(4.271) \qquad F\left(x,\, y,\, \frac{dy}{dx},\, \frac{d^2y}{dx^2},\, \cdots,\, \frac{d^ny}{dx^n}\right) = 0,$$

which is satisfied for all curves of the family and which is called a *differential equation of the family* (4.27).

Problems

Find differential equations of the following families of curves in which a, b, c, and d are parameters:

(4.281) $\quad y = cx + c^2$ $\qquad\qquad$ Ans.: $y = y'x + y'^2$

(4.282) $\quad y = ax + b$ $\qquad\qquad\qquad$ Ans.: $y'' = 0$

(4.283) $\quad y = a \sin x + b \cos x$ $\qquad$ Ans.: $y'' + y = 0$

(4.284) $\quad y = c \sin (x + d)$ $\qquad\qquad$ Ans.: $y'' + y = 0$

(4.285) $\quad y = a + b \cos x$ $\qquad$ Ans.: $y' \cos x - y'' \sin x = 0$

(4.286) $\quad \sin x + \sin y = c$ $\qquad$ Ans.: $\cos x + y' \cos y = 0$

(4.287) $\quad y = \tan (x + c)$ $\qquad\qquad$ Ans.: $y' = 1 + y^2$

(4.288) $\quad y = ax^2 + bx + c$ $\qquad\qquad$ Ans.: $y''' = 0$

(4.289) $\quad y = ce^x$ $\qquad\qquad\qquad$ Ans.: $y' = y$

(4.2891) $\quad y = e^{x/a} + e^{-x/a}$ $\qquad$ Ans.: $y = e^{xy'/\sqrt{y^2-4}} + e^{-xy'/\sqrt{y^2-4}}$

Problem 4.29

Assuming a to be a fixed constant (not a parameter), show that a differential equation of the family of curves

$$(4.291) \qquad (c^2 - a^2)x^2 + c^2y^2 = c^2(c^2 - a^2)$$

is

$$(4.292) \qquad xyy'^2 + (x^2 - y^2 - a^2)y' - xy = 0.$$

[The family (4.291) of curves is discussed in Section 4.5.]

4.3. General Solutions; Singular Solutions.—It frequently happens that a differential equation of order n has an n-parameter family of solutions expressed by

$$(4.31) \qquad y(x) = f(x, c_1, c_2, \cdots, c_n)$$

or by

$$(4.32) \qquad g(x, y, c_1, c_2, \cdots, c_n) = 0$$

and that these are the only solutions of the differential equation. In such cases, (4.31) or (4.32) is known as a *general solution* of the differential equation. We have seen that this is true for the equation $y' = f(x)$ if $f(x)$ is continuous, the general solution being $y = \int f(x)dx + c_1$, and for $y' = ky$, the general solution being $y = c_1e^{kx}$. We shall see later that the differential equation

$$(4.33) \qquad \frac{d^2y}{dx^2} + a^2y = 0,$$

in which a is a positive constant, has a two-parameter family of solutions

$$(4.34) \qquad y = c_1 \cos ax + c_2 \sin ax$$

and that these are the only solutions of (4.33).

The theory of differential equations would be very much simplified if one could claim that each differential equation of order n has an n-parameter family of solutions of the form (4.31) or (4.32), and that these are the only solutions of the equation. As Section 4.1 shows, such a claim is meaningless since it specifies nothing about the way in which the parameters enter the equation. Even with such specification the claim could scarcely be valid, unless it is amplified to specify the nature of the differential equation, since some equations have no solutions whatever [(1.31) is an example]. Moreover, some equations of order 1[(5.14), for example] possess 2-parameter families of solutions in which the c's enter in a simple way.

Another perversity of differential equations, exhibited by the example (4.222), complicates the theory of differential equations. There are cases in which an equation of order n possesses an n-parameter family (4.31) or (4.32) of solutions in which the c's enter in a simple way, and possesses in addition to these some "extra" solutions not obtainable by assignment of numerical values to the c's. Even in such cases it has for many years been customary to call the n-parameter family of solutions a *"general solution"* of the equation; the extra solutions are called *singular solutions*. There are two objections to use of this extended meaning of the term general solution. In the first place, a statement that a given family of solutions is a "general solution" then becomes merely a statement that the given family contains n constants; when one can see that the given family contains n constants, this statement is a worthless truism which is noncommittal with respect to the question whether or not the equation has more solutions (singular solutions). In the second place, this extended meaning of the term *general solution* serves an evil purpose: It is used to hide an ignorance of differential equations behind a smoke screen of meaningless assertions about "general solutions" and numbers of parameters.

In this book, the term *general solution* is not used with the extended meaning except for a few instances in Chapter 14; it is then placed in quotation marks as in the previous paragraph. At all other times, *the term general solution refers to the family of all solutions.*

The author has performed a duty in presenting a discussion of differential equations and of terminology in current use; a student has performed a duty when he has read it. The conclusion to be drawn is that one sets himself a hopelessly difficult problem when he undertakes to give a complete theory of differential equations in a few words.

Advanced as well as elementary work in differential equations is confined to special equations or to special classes of equations with which one may hope to do something useful. When one is required to find *all* the solutions of a given differential equation, one should endeavor to find *all* the solutions. A failure to find *all* solutions is not excused by terminology which attributes the name "*general solution*" to a family consisting of some but not all solutions to the equation.

4.4. Orthogonal Trajectories.—The family $x^2 + y^2 = c$ of circles with center at the origin and the family $y = mx$ of lines through the origin have an interesting property: wherever a curve of one family intersects a curve of the other family, the two are *perpendicular* or *normal* or *orthogonal*. Whenever two families of curves have this property, each family is said to be the family of *orthogonal trajectories* of the other.

Orthogonal families are of interest in applied mathematics where the curves of one family are called *lines of flow, lines of force, streamlines*, etc., and the curves of the other family are called *level lines, equipotential lines, isothermal lines*, etc.

Let $\phi_1(x, y, c) = 0$ represent a one-parameter family of curves such that through each point (x, y) of a region R of the plane (which may be the entire plane) there passes one and only one curve of the family, the curve having a tangent at (x, y) which is neither vertical nor horizontal. If $f(x, y)$ denotes the slope of the tangent at the point (x, y), then the slope of a line through (x, y) orthogonal to the curve of the family will be $-1/f(x, y)$. Accordingly, if $y(x)$ exists such that

$$(4.41) \qquad \frac{dy}{dx} = -\frac{1}{f(x, y)},$$

then the curve $y = y(x)$ will be orthogonal to the curves of the family $\phi_1(x, y, c) = 0$; and if $\phi_2(x, y, c) = 0$ represents a family of curves for which (4.41) holds, then the family $\phi_2(x, y, c) = 0$ is orthogonal to the family $\phi_1(x, y, c) = 0$ insofar as the region R is concerned.

Let us see whether the process outlined above for trying to find orthogonal trajectories will enable us to find the orthogonal trajectories of the family of lines

$$(4.42) \qquad y - cx = 0,$$

c being a parameter. Through each point of the plane not on the coordinate axes there passes a curve of the family (4.42) with slope different from 0, the slope being found by differentiating (4.42) to obtain

$$(4.43) \qquad \frac{dy}{dx} - c = 0,$$

and then eliminating c from (4.42) and (4.43) to obtain

$$(4.44) \qquad \frac{dy}{dx} = \frac{y}{x}.$$

Accordingly, each solution of the differential equation

(4.45)
$$\frac{dy}{dx} = -\frac{x}{y}$$

is an orthogonal trajectory of the system of lines (4.42).   But if $y(x)$ satisfies (4.45), then

$$\frac{d}{dx}(x^2 + y^2) = 2x + 2y\frac{dy}{dx} = 0$$

and accordingly

(4.46)
$$x^2 + y^2 = c$$

and, conversely, (4.46) satisfies (4.45).   Thus we have been able to solve an easy problem of which we knew the answer in advance.

Problem 4.47

Find the orthogonal trajectories of the family of parabolas $y^2 = 2(c - x)$.

Ans.: $y = ce^x$.

Problem 4.48

Sketch several curves of the family F of circles which pass through two fixed points $(-a, 0)$ and $(a, 0)$ of the plane, and sketch some curves which appear to be orthogonal trajectories of the family F.   Show that the differential equation

(4.481)
$$2xy\frac{dy}{dx} = a^2 + y^2 - x^2$$

is one whose solutions (if any) furnish orthogonal trajectories of F.   Sketch some of the circles obtained by giving c values greater than a in (5.844).

Problem 4.49

Find the differential equation of the family F_2 of circles tangent to the y axis at the origin, find the differential equation of the orthogonal trajectories, and show that interchanging x and y in one of the differential equations gives the other. What does this imply about orthogonal trajectories of F_2?

4.5. Confocal Conics.—Let a be a fixed positive number, let E denote the family of ellipses with foci at the points $F_1 \equiv (-a, 0)$ and $F_2 \equiv (a, 0)$, and let H denote the family of hyperbolas with the same foci.   The properties of ellipses and hyperbolas used below may be, and often are, used to define the curves.   To each ellipse in the family E corresponds a number $c > a$ such that the points P on the ellipse are points $P \equiv (x, y)$ of the plane for which $F_1P + F_2P = 2c$ or

(4.51)
$$\sqrt{(x + a)^2 + y^2} + \sqrt{(x - a)^2 + y^2} = 2c;$$

and when $c > a$, it can be shown that (4.51) holds if and only if

(4.52)
$$(c^2 - a^2)x^2 + c^2y^2 = c^2(c^2 - a^2).$$

To each hyperbola in the family H corresponds a number c such that $0 < c < a$

and the points P on the hyperbola are the points $P(x, y)$ of the plane for which $F_1P - F_2P = \pm 2c$ or

$$(4.53) \qquad \sqrt{(x + a)^2 + y^2} - \sqrt{(x - a)^2 + y^2} = \pm 2c;$$

and when $0 < c < a$, it can be shown that (4.53) holds if and only if (4.52) holds.

It thus appears that the equation (4.52), in which c is a parameter with $c > 0$ and $c \neq a$, gives the conics with foci at $(-a, 0)$ and $(a, 0)$; values of c for which $c > a$ give ellipses, and values of c for which $0 < c < a$ give hyperbolas. If $c = a$, the points (x, y) whose coordinates satisfy (4.51) are the points of the line segment $[y = 0; -a \leq x \leq a]$; this line segment is not ordinarily called an ellipse, but sometimes it is called a *degenerate ellipse*. If $c = a$, the points (x, y) whose coordinates satisfy (4.53) are the points on two line segments $[y = 0; x \geq a]$ and $[y = 0; x \leq -a]$; these line segments are not ordinarily called a hyperbola, but sometimes they are called a *degenerate hyperbola*. If $c = 0$, the points (x, y) whose coordinates satisfy (4.53) are the points of the degenerate hyperbola $x = 0$.

If $P \equiv (x, y)$ is a fixed point of the plane for which $x \neq 0$ and $y \neq 0$, then there are exactly two positive values of c for which (4.52) holds, namely, those for which

$$(4.54) \qquad c^2 = \tfrac{1}{2}\{[a^2 + x^2 + y^2] \pm \sqrt{(a^2 + x^2 + y^2)^2 - 4a^2x^2}\};$$

one of these values of c is greater than a, and the other lies between 0 and a. Hence, through P there pass one ellipse of the family E and one hyperbola of the family H.

Problem 4.55

Prove that the family (4.52) of confocal conics is *self-orthogonal* in the sense that, if P is a point not on the coordinate axes, then the ellipse and the hyperbola through P intersect at right angles at P. Draw a figure showing some of the ellipses and hyperbolas, and put the degenerate ellipse and hyperbolas in the figure.

4.6. Degree of a Differential Equation.—When the members of a differential equation are polynomials in the derivatives, the greatest exponent appearing on the derivative of highest order is called the *degree* of the equation. The equation

$$(4.61) \qquad \rho(x) = \frac{[1 + (dy/dx)^2]^{\frac{3}{2}}}{d^2y/dx^2}$$

RADIUS OF CURVATURE

does not have a degree; but the equation (which is definitely a different equation)

$$(4.62) \qquad [\rho(x)]^2 \left(\frac{d^2y}{dx^2}\right)^2 = 1 + 3\left(\frac{dy}{dx}\right)^2 + 3\left(\frac{dy}{dx}\right)^4 + \left(\frac{dy}{dx}\right)^6,$$

obtained from (4.61) by obvious algebraic processes, is of the second degree. Each equation of the first order and second degree with independent and dependent variables x and y has the form

$$(4.63) \qquad f_1(x, y)\left(\frac{dy}{dx}\right)^2 + f_2(x, y)\frac{dy}{dx} + f_3(x, y) = 0,$$

and each equation of the first order and first degree has the form

(4.64) $$f_1(x, y) \frac{dy}{dx} + f_2(x, y) = 0.$$

It should be carefully noted that the terms *linear differential equation* and *first-degree differential equation* are not equivalent.   Each linear equation, as

(4.65) $$x^2 \frac{d^2y}{dx^2} - x \frac{dy}{dx} + (\alpha^2 - x^2)y = 0,$$

is of the first degree; but the first-degree equations

(4.66) $$\frac{d^2y}{dx^2} + \left(\frac{dy}{dx}\right)^2 + xy = 0$$

and

(4.67) $$\frac{dy}{dx} = x^2 + y^2$$

are not linear.

Problem 4.68

Let a be a fixed positive constant.   By differentiation and elimination of parameters, show that the equation

(4.681) $$a^2 \left(\frac{d^2y}{dx^2}\right)^2 = \left[1 + \left(\frac{dy}{dx}\right)^2\right]^3$$

is satisfied by the family of circles $(x - h)^2 + (y - k)^2 = a^2$ of radius a.   Show also that $x = h + a \cos t$ and $y = k + a \sin t$ are parametric equations of the circles, and that

(4.682) $$\left(\frac{dx}{dt}\right)^2 + \left(\frac{dy}{dt}\right)^2 = a^2.$$

What pairs of constants c_1 and c_2 are such that (4.682) holds when $x = c_1 t$ and $y = c_2 t$?   What is the geometric significance of this result?

CHAPTER 5

DIFFERENTIAL EQUATIONS OF FIRST ORDER AND FIRST DEGREE

read 4.6

5.0. Definitions and Examples.—A differential equation of the first order and first degree with a single independent variable x and dependent variable y is one of the form

$$(5.01) \qquad M(x, y) + N(x, y)\frac{dy}{dx} = 0.$$

It is convenient to write this in the abbreviated form

$$(5.02) \qquad M\,dx + N\,dy = 0;$$

but we shall always understand* that (5.02) means (5.01). Four examples are

$$(5.03) \qquad (x^2 + y^2)dx + xy\,dy = 0$$
$$(5.04) \qquad y\,dx - x\,dy = 0$$
$$(5.05) \qquad \sin x\,dx + \sin y\,dy = 0$$
$$(5.06) \qquad f(x)dx - dy = 0.$$

In the four examples, $N(x, y)$ is, respectively, xy, $-x$, $\sin y$, and -1. If $M(x, y)$ is independent of y and $N(x, y)$ is independent of x, then (5.01) has the form

$$(5.07) \qquad f_1(x)dx + f_2(y)dy = 0$$

and the variables are called *separated*. Thus in (5.05) and (5.06) the

---

* Sometimes it is desirable to study (5.02) for the purpose of determining x as a function of y such that

$$M\frac{dx}{dy} + N = 0;$$

but this involves merely an interchange of the roles of x and y, and it is not necessary to construct a separate theory to meet this situation. There is also the possibility of interpreting a solution of (5.02) as being a *pair* of functions $x(t)$ and $y(t)$ of a parameter t such that

$$M(x(t), y(t))\frac{dx}{dt} + N(x(t), y(t))\frac{dx}{dt} = 0$$

is an identity in t; but we do not study (5.02) from this point of view.

variables are separated.   In (5.04) the variables are *separable* since
division by xy gives (when x and y are not zero)

$$\frac{1}{x}\, dx - \frac{1}{y}\, dy = 0.$$

It should of course be observed that (5.06) is one way of writing
$y' = f(x)$ and hence that $y' = f(x)$ is a special form of linear equation
in which the variables are separated.

In this chapter, we shall show that several important classes of
equations of the form $M\, dx + N\, dy = 0$ can be solved by straightforward elementary methods.   Fortunately, many of the first-order
differential equations met in the course of solution of problems fall in
these classes.

Our first step, however, is to discuss lineal-element diagrams and to
show how they may be used to obtain ideas about solutions and to
sketch approximations to graphs of solutions of (5.01).   One who is
interested in the question of existence of solutions and in a powerful
method of obtaining approximations to solutions can find his *pièce de
résistance* in Chapter 15; but we do not suggest that Chapter 15 be
read at this time.

5.1. Lineal-element Diagrams.—The equation

$$M(x, y)dx + N(x, y)dy = 0$$

can, when $N(x, y) \neq 0$, be written in the form

(5.11) $$\frac{dy}{dx} = f(x, y)$$

where $f(x, y) = -M(x, y)/N(x, y)$.   Through each of "several"
points (x, y) of the plane, we can draw a "short" line segment with
slope $f(x, y)$.   By calling the line segment *short*, we mean merely that
it is only as long as is necessary to indicate clearly its direction.   Each
short line segment is called a *lineal element*, and the totality of lineal
elements is called a *lineal-element diagram*.   If $f(x, y)$ is continuous,
then the slope of the lineal elements changes steadily (*i.e.*, without
jumps) as one passes continuously over points of the plane.   A good
lineal-element diagram contains enough lineal elements to indicate
the direction at or "near" each point of the region of the plane in
which one is interested; but of course it is futile to draw so many lineal
elements that the figure becomes completely black and obliterates
everything.

A little experimentation with paper and pencil will convince you
that, if you draw a smooth curve with a continuously turning tangent
(for example, a parabola) and draw through each of a set of closely

spaced points on the curve a short line-segment tangent to the curve, then the totality of lineal elements thus obtained will appear to the eye to be simply the curve with which you started. Hence such a curve may be regarded (so far as eyesight is concerned) as a succession of lineal elements. This implies that a family of curves in the plane (such as a set of concentric circles) may be regarded (so far as eyesight is concerned) as a lineal-element diagram.

This procedure suggests at least the possibility of being able to start with a given lineal-element diagram and then sketch curves each

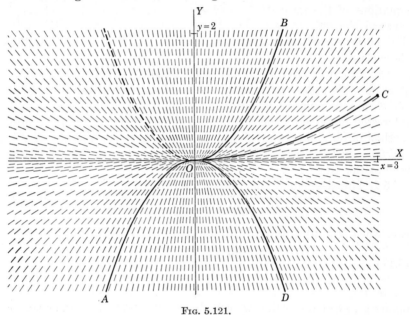

FIG. 5.121.

of which appears to the eye to be made up of a succession of lineal elements.

In many cases a lineal-element diagram enables one to make correct guesses involving existence and properties of solutions of $y' = f(x, y)$ and indeed to sketch approximate graphs of solutions. We illustrate this for the differential equation $x \, dy - 2y \, dx = 0$. (After making the guesses, we shall solve the differential equation and verify the guesses.) When $x \neq 0$, the differential equation can be written

$$(5.12) \qquad \frac{dy}{dx} = \frac{2y}{x}.$$

If (x, y) is a point not on the y axis, then we can compute the slope of, and draw, the lineal element through (x, y). Hence, we can construct a lineal-element diagram as in Fig. 5.121.

Study of Fig. 5.121 seems to indicate that, if (x_0, y_0) is a point not on the y axis, then enough lineal elements could be added to the diagram to give a succession of lineal elements which form (so far as eyesight is concerned) a smooth curve running from (x_0, y_0) at least as far as the origin in one direction and running outward in the opposite direction. The question as to how and whether such a curve extends through the origin is more delicate. The differential equation $y' = 2y/x$ does not furnish a lineal element corresponding to the origin since $0/0$ has no meaning. If, however, we add to the lineal-element diagram a lineal element through the origin with slope 0, then it appears that the curve through (x_0, y_0) can be extended through the origin not only in one way but actually in many different ways so that the curve appears to be a succession of lineal elements.

If a curve appears to be a succession of lineal elements, we should expect it to be the graph of a solution of $xy' = 2y$. For y' is the slope of the curve which is the slope of the tangent which is the slope of the lineal element which is $2y/x$ when $x \neq 0$; and the equation $xy' = 2y$ is satisfied when $x = y = y' = 0$. Thus we are led to guess that AOB, AOC, AOX, and AOD are graphs of four of the solutions of $xy' = 2y$ and, of course, that there are many more similar solutions. If these guesses turn out to be in accordance with the facts, we may conclude that in at least some cases we can look at a good lineal-element diagram and "see" the solutions of $y' = f(x, y)$.

5.13. Solution of xy' − 2y = 0.—For our first attempt to solve the equation

$$(5.131) \qquad\qquad x\frac{dy}{dx} - 2y = 0$$

we proceed formally without thought as to whether the equations we obtain are meaningful or true. From (5.131) we obtain

$$(5.132) \qquad\qquad \frac{1}{y}\frac{dy}{dx} - \frac{2}{x} = 0$$

so that

$$(5.133) \qquad\qquad \frac{d}{dx}(\log y - 2\log x) = 0$$

and $\log y - 2\log x = c_1$ so that $\log(y/x^2) = c_1$ and hence

$$(5.134) \qquad\qquad y = cx^2$$

where $c = e^{c_1}$. For each constant c (positive, negative, or 0) the function $y = cx^2$ is indeed a solution of (5.131) since $x(2cx) - 2(cx^2) = 0$. However, the solutions $y = cx^2$ do not contain all the solutions of (5.131) which we "saw" in Section 5.1. What is the matter?

In the first place, (5.132) can be obtained from (5.131) only for values of x and y different from 0. In the second place, (5.133) is meaningless, insofar as real variables are concerned, except when x and y are both positive, since only positive numbers have real logarithms.

Our first attempt to solve the differential equation $xy' - 2y = 0$ was so discouraging that we start afresh by a different method. Let us assume that $y = y(x)$ is a function defined over $-\infty < x < \infty$ such that

$$(5.14) \qquad x\frac{dy}{dx} - 2y = 0$$

and find by impeccable methods the form which $y(x)$ must have. We can divide by x whenever x is not 0; but we cannot divide by y unless or until we know that y is not 0. Considering first the range of values of x for which $x > 0$, we can divide (5.14) by x to obtain

$$(5.141) \qquad \frac{dy}{dx} - \frac{2}{x}y = 0.$$

This is a linear differential equation with integrating factor

$$\exp\!\int (-2/x)dx = x^{-2},$$

where $\exp Q$ means e^Q. Hence, as in Section 3.1, we are led to write

$$(5.142) \qquad \frac{d}{dx}\, x^{-2}y = x^{-2}\frac{dy}{dx} - 2x^{-3}y = 0;$$

accordingly, there is a constant c_1 such that

$$(5.15) \qquad\qquad y = c_1x^2 \qquad\qquad\qquad x > 0.$$

Similar consideration of the range of values of x for which $x < 0$ leads to a constant c_2 such that

$$(5.16) \qquad\qquad y = c_2x^2 \qquad\qquad\qquad x < 0.$$

The value of $y(0)$ has not yet been determined, but it is easy to determine it. Since $y(x)$ was assumed to satisfy (5.14) for $-\infty < x < \infty$, it follows that $y(x)$ must be continuous and hence that $y(0) = \lim\limits_{x \to 0} y(x)$. From (5.15) and (5.16) it follows that $\lim\limits_{x \to 0} y(x) = 0$ and therefore $y(0) = 0$. Thus we have shown that *if $y(x)$ satisfies* (5.14) *then constants c_1 and c_2 must exist such that*

$$(5.17) \qquad\qquad y(x) = c_1x^2 \qquad\qquad\qquad x \geqq 0$$
$$\qquad\qquad\qquad = c_2x^2 \qquad\qquad\qquad x \leqq 0.$$

This, of course, does not imply that the functions in (5.17) are solutions of (5.14).   (It may be possible to show that each horse on the Double Diamond Ranch is an animal with four legs, but from this it does not follow that each animal with four legs is a horse on the Double Diamond ranch.)   However, it is easy to show by direct substitution that the functions in (5.17) are all solutions of (5.14).

Thus the differential equation $xy' - 2y = 0$ is accurately solved, and the results are in complete agreement with those we "saw" by means of the lineal-element diagram (Fig. 5.121).   For example, setting $c_1 = -1$, $c_2 = 1$ in (5.17) furnishes the solution AOB of Fig. 5.121; setting $c_1 = -1$, $c_2 = \frac{1}{2}$ furnishes AOC; setting $c_1 = -1$, $c_2 = 0$ furnishes AOX; and setting $c_1 = c_2 = -1$ furnishes AOD.

Problems

Construct good lineal-element diagrams for the following differential equations:

(5.181) $y' = 2x$
(5.182) $y' = x + y$
(5.183) $y' = \sqrt{y}$
(5.184) $y' = \log \sqrt{x^2 + y^2}$
(5.185) $y' = x^{-1} + y^{-1}$

5.2. Variables Separated.—A differential equation which is of the first order and first degree and in which the variables are separated has the form

$$(5.21) \qquad f(x)dx + g(y)dy = 0.$$

One way to try to dispose of (5.21) is to say that if (5.21) holds, then integration gives

$$(5.22) \qquad \int f(x)dx + \int g(y)dy = c$$

and, if (5.22) holds, then differentiation gives (5.21); hence, (5.22) gives all solutions of (5.21) and only solutions of (5.21).   This attempt to dispose of (5.21) is characterized by admirable brevity, but some discussion is required to explain it and to show how it may be used.

We suppose that $f(x)$ and $g(y)$ are continuous.   Then

$$(5.23) \qquad F(x) = \int_a^x f(t)dt, \qquad G(y) = \int_b^y g(u)du$$

exist.   If $y(x)$ is a differentiable function of x satisfying (5.21), then

$$(5.231) \qquad \frac{d}{dx}F(x) = f(x), \qquad \frac{d}{dx}G(y) = g(y)\frac{dy}{dx}$$

and

$$(5.232) \qquad \frac{d}{dx}[F(x) + G(y)] = f(x) + g(y)\frac{dy}{dx} = 0;$$

hence a constant c exists such that

(5.24)
$$F(x) + G(y) = c.$$

Thus each solution of (5.21) must satisfy (5.24); and, of course, (5.24) is merely another way of writing (5.22). Conversely, (5.24) is at least a formal solution of (5.21); for if it be assumed that $y(x)$ is a differentiable function of x for which (5.24) holds, then differentiation with respect to x gives (5.21).

Thus if $y(x)$ is a function for which

(5.25)
$$f(x)dx + g(y)dy = 0,$$

then the formula

(5.251)
$$\int f(x)dx + \int g(y)dy = c,$$

obtained by *integrating the first term with respect to x and the second term with respect to y*, must be satisfied by $y(x)$. A student should have no difficulty in seeing that, if $y(x)$ is a solution of (5.25) for which $y(a) = b$, then

(5.252)
$$\int_a^x f(t)dt + \int_b^y g(u)du = 0.$$

Even when the above integrals have been evaluated, the problem of finding $y(x)$ may be formidable; in Section 5.4 we present a practical method of finding $y(x)$.

Problems

In each of the following problems, find functions $y(x)$ satisfying the equation, and check your answers by differentiation and substitution:

(5.261) $\qquad\qquad x\,dx + y\,dy = 0$
(5.262) $\qquad\qquad x\,dx + dy = 0$
(5.263) $\qquad\qquad dx + y\,dy = 0$
(5.264) $\qquad\qquad y\,dx - x\,dy = 0$
(5.265) $\qquad\qquad y\,dx + x\,dy = 0$
(5.266) $\qquad x(1 + y^2)dx + y(1 + x^2)dy = 0$

Problem 5.267

Solve the equation

(5.2671)
$$\frac{dy}{dx} = -k\left(\frac{R}{R + x}\right)^2 y$$

in which k and R are positive constants. [For a physical interpretation of this equation, see (3.46).] Show that, if $y(0) = A$, then

(5.2672)
$$y = Ae^{-kR}e^{\frac{kR^2}{R+x}}$$

Observe that

(5.2673)
$$\lim_{x \to \infty} y(x) = Ae^{-kR}.$$

$$3.46 \quad \frac{dp}{dh} = -k_s \frac{p}{(R+h)^2} = -k \left(\frac{R}{R+h}\right)^2 p$$

Tell what is the physical meaning of (5.2673) when (5.2671) is identified with (3.46) by setting $y = p$ and $x = h$. *p approaches a max or min?*

Problem 5.268

Find the orthogonal trajectories of the family of parabolas $y^2 = 4cx$, and show by rough graphs that your answer appears to be correct.

5.27. A Hanging Cable.—We are going to determine the shape of a flexible inextensible cable hanging with its ends fastened at points $(a, f(a))$ and $(b, f(b))$ in a vertical plane. Let $y = y(x)$ be the equation of the curve, and let $P \equiv P(x, y)$ be a point on the curve. The forces acting on the part of the cable between A and P are gravitational forces and those represented by arrows at A and P in Fig. 5.271. The resultant of the forces at P lies along the tangent at P so that $y' = V/H$. But $H = H_a$, and V is the sum of V_a and the weight of the cable. Thus, letting w represent the weight per unit length of the cable, we have

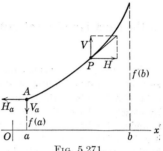

FIG. 5.271.

$$(5.272) \qquad V = V_a + w \int_a^x \{1 + [y'(t)]^2\}^{\frac{1}{2}} dt$$

so that

$$(5.273) \qquad y'(x) = \frac{V_a}{H} + \frac{w}{H} \int_a^x \{1 + [y'(t)]^2\}^{\frac{1}{2}} dt.$$

Our hypothesis that the cable is flexible is now interpreted to mean that $y'(t)$ is continuous. Hence, by the fundamental theorem of the calculus, we can differentiate (5.273) to obtain

$$(5.274) \qquad y''(x) = k\{1 + [y'(x)]^2\}^{\frac{1}{2}}$$

where $k = w/H > 0$. We can make this equation look simpler (do not forget this trick) by setting $p(x) = y'(x)$, $p'(x) = y''(x)$ to obtain $p' = k(1 + p^2)^{\frac{1}{2}}$. This can be written in the form

Table of Integrals Sherwood Taylor

$$(5.275) \qquad (1 + p^2)^{-\frac{1}{2}} dp - k\, dx = 0$$

in which the variables are separated so that

$$(5.276) \qquad \log(p + \sqrt{1 + p^2}) - kx = kc$$

where the constant of integration is called kc for convenience. From (5.276) we obtain

$$(5.277) \qquad p = \tfrac{1}{2}[e^{k(x+c)} - e^{-k(x+c)}]$$

$$(5.278) \qquad y = \frac{1}{2k}[e^{k(x+c)} + e^{-k(x+c)}] + c_1.$$

Since a *catenary* is by definition a curve whose equation has the form (5.278), it follows that the cable must hang in the form of a catenary. The function $y(x)$ in (5.278) has a minimum at the only point $x = -c$ where $p(x) = y'(x) = 0$. If the origin of the coordinate system is chosen so that the minimum of $y(x)$ occurs for $x = 0$ and if $y = \frac{1}{2}k$ when $x = 0$, then $c = c_1 = 0$ and (5.278) takes the standard form

$$(5.279) \qquad\qquad y = \frac{1}{2k}[e^{kx} + e^{-kx}]$$

of the equation of a catenary.

Problem 5.28

One side of a footbridge 100 feet long is supported by a hanging cable. The ends of the cable are 25 feet above the ends of the bridge, and the center of the cable is 5 feet above the center of the bridge. The bridge is fastened to the cable by closely and equally spaced vertical rods each of which carries a weight of w pounds. Find a good approximation to the equation of the cable. *Ans.:* Neglecting the weight of the cable, assuming a uniform horizontal loading, and taking the origin at the center of the bridge, one obtains $y = .008x^2 + 5$.

Problem 5.29

A container partly filled by a liquid is rotated about a vertical axis with constant angular velocity ω. Show that the "free" surface of the liquid is a part of a paraboloid of revolution. *Hint:* A particle of mass m at the free surface is subject to a gravitational force mg and to a centrifugal force $mr\omega^2$ where r is the distance from the axis to the particle; the resultant of these forces is orthogonal to the free surface.

5.3. Law of Mass Action.—Chemists observe that, in certain cases, when two substances are mixed a compound is formed at a rate which is proportional to the product of the weights of the untransformed parts of the two substances. In such cases, the *law of mass action* applies, good chemists knowing when and why. Let a grams of a substance A and b grams of a substance B be mixed, and let a compound X be formed from m parts by weight of A and n parts by weight of B. When x grams of X have been formed, $a - [m/(m + n)]x$ grams of A remain and $b - [n/(m + n)]x$ grams of B remain. Hence, when the law of mass action applies,

$$(5.31) \qquad \frac{dx}{dt} = k\left(a - \frac{m}{m + n}x\right)\left(b - \frac{n}{m + n}x\right).$$

This equation looks somewhat better when we write it in the form

$$(5.311) \qquad \frac{dx}{dt} = \frac{kmn}{(m + n)^2}\left[\frac{a(m + n)}{m} - x\right]\left[\frac{b(m + n)}{n} - x\right]$$

and set

$$(5.312) \quad k_1 = \frac{kmn}{(m+n)^2}, \qquad a_1 = \frac{a(m+n)}{m}, \qquad b_1 = \frac{b(m+n)}{n}$$

to obtain

$$(5.32) \qquad\qquad \frac{dx}{dt} = k_1(a_1 - x)(b_1 - x).$$

This is an equation in which the variables are separable; the solutions take different forms according as $a_1 = b_1$ or $a_1 \neq b_1$.

Problem 5.33

Show that, if $a_1 = b_1$, the differential equation (5.32), together with the initial condition $x(0) = 0$, implies that

$$(5.331) \qquad x = a_1 \left[1 - \frac{1}{1 + a_1 k_1 t} \right] = \frac{a(m+n)}{m} \frac{aknt}{m + n + aknt}$$

and that $x \to a(m+n)/m$ as $t \to \infty$. If x attains 50 per cent of the limiting value in 1 hour, how long is required for it to attain 90 per cent of the limiting value?

Ans.: 9 hours.

Problem 5.34

If $a_1 \neq b_1$, we can suppose that the names A and B are assigned to the substances in such a way that $a_1 < b_1$. Show that the solutions of (5.32) are, in this case,

$$(5.341) \qquad \log \frac{b_1 - x}{a_1 - x} = (b_1 - a_1)k_1 t + c;$$

use the condition $x(0) = 0$ to determine c; and then solve for x to obtain

$$(5.342) \qquad x = a_1 b_1 \frac{e^{(b_1 - a_1)k_1 t} - 1}{b_1 e^{(b_1 - a_1)k_1 t} - a_1}.$$

Show that $x \to a_1$ as $t \to \infty$.

Problem 5.35

It can be shown that, if a_1, k_1, and t are fixed, then the limit as $b_1 \to a_1$ of the right member of (5.342) is the second member of (5.331). Can you give mathematical or chemical justification (or both) of this assertion?

5.36. A Pursuit Problem.—A point A starts from the origin of an xy plane and moves in the direction of the positive x axis; and, at the same time, a point P starts at the point $(0, a)$ and moves (at the end of a towrope or otherwise) always in the direction of A in such a way that the distance from P to A is always the constant a. The path of P is called a *tractrix;* its equation may be found as follows:

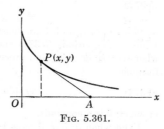

Fig. 5.361.

The tangent to the path at a point $P(x, y)$ for which $x > 0$ and $0 < y < a$ meets the x axis at the point $(x - y/y', 0)$; but this point must be the point A and hence (by the Pythagorean theorem)

$$(5.362) \qquad \left(\frac{y}{y'}\right)^2 = a^2 - y^2.$$

Since $0 < y < a$ and $y' < 0$, taking positive square roots gives $-y/y' = (a^2 - y^2)^{\frac{1}{2}}$ and we can separate the variables to obtain

$$(5.363) \qquad dx + \frac{(a^2 - y^2)^{\frac{1}{2}}}{y}\, dy = 0.$$

Integration (by means of a trigonometric substitution or use of a table of integrals) and determination of the constant of integration from the condition $y(0) = a$ give

$$(5.364) \qquad x + (a^2 - y^2)^{\frac{1}{2}} - a \log \frac{a + (a^2 - y^2)^{\frac{1}{2}}}{y} = 0.$$

It is a simple matter to solve (5.364) for x to obtain $x = \phi(y)$; but to obtain $y = \psi(x)$ by methods of elementary algebra is impossible. If $x = \phi(y)$ were used to obtain a table of corresponding values of x and y, then interpolation in this table would furnish approximate values of $\psi(x)$. The table of values of $x = \phi(y)$ could be used to construct a graph of $x = \phi(y)$ which would be at the same time a graph of $y = \psi(x)$.

Problem 5.37

When a parasite population x lives on a host population y, the rate of change of x with respect to time t depends upon both x and y; and when the parasites affect the hosts (being beneficial in some cases and detrimental in others), the rate of change of y with respect to t also depends upon both x and y. Since the product xy represents the number of ways of pairing a parasite with a host, it may be expected that this product appears in equations. In many cases, $x(t)$ and $y(t)$ may be regarded (as in the radium problem of Sections 3.5 and 3.55) as solutions of the equations

$$(5.371) \qquad \frac{dx}{dt} = ax + bxy$$

$$(5.372) \qquad \frac{dy}{dt} = cy + dxy$$

in which a, b, c, and d are constants, not necessarily positive, and $b \neq 0$, $d \neq 0$. Using the equations (5.371) and (5.372), find a formula for dy/dx (which holds whenever $dx/dt \neq 0$), and proceed to show that x and y must be related as in the formula

$$(5.373) \qquad by + a \log y = dx + c \log x + k$$

in which k is a constant.

Even when a, b, c, d have known values, say $a = b = c = 1$, $d = -1$ so that (5.373) becomes

$$(5.374) \qquad y + \log y = -x + \log x + k,$$

the equation does not look good to a biologist. Solving these equations for y in terms of x is not a simple algebraic process. By the method given in the next section, it is possible to "solve" (5.373) for y and to exhibit a graph of $y(x)$ when a, b, c, d, and k are known.

Problem 5.38

Suppose one knows the values of $x(t)$ and $y(t)$ when $t = 0$ and has found a graph of $y(x)$. Explain how one could use the ideas of the latter part of Chapter 2 and the equation

$$(5.381) \qquad \frac{dx}{dt} = x - xy(x)$$

[obtained by setting $a = 1$, $b = -1$ in (5.371)] to obtain a graph of $x(t)$.

5.4. Graphic Solution of $F(x) + G(y) = c$.

—We do not propose to consider the general problem of determining conditions under which an equation of the form $F(x) + G(y) = c$, in which c is fixed, is satisfied by a differentiable function $y(x)$. In some cases the equation can be solved by algebraic methods; for example, if $x^2 + y^2 = c$ where $c > 0$, then $y_1(x) = (c - x^2)^{\frac{1}{2}}$ and $y_2(x) = -(c - x^2)^{\frac{1}{2}}$ are two differentiable solutions valid for $-c^{\frac{1}{2}} < x < c^{\frac{1}{2}}$. Neither of the equations

$$x^2 + y^2 = -10$$

or $\sin y + \sin x = 25$ can be satisfied by a real function $y(x)$ since there is not a single pair of real numbers x and y satisfying either equation.

We now show how graphs can be used to indicate whether the equation $F(x) + G(y) = c$ has a solution and to obtain an approximation to the graph of a solution $y(x)$ when it exists. The first step is to write the equation in the form

$$(5.41) \qquad G(y) = -F(x) + c.$$

The next step is to draw graphs of the functions $G(u)$ and $-F(u)$ in a uv plane* as in Fig. 5.42. The value of the constant c being fixed, we are now ready to hunt pairs of values of x and y for which (5.41) holds.

Starting with a fixed x (which could be called x_0, but we omit the subscript) we determine the point A with coordinates $(x, 0)$ in Fig. 5.42. The vertical line through A meets the curve $v = -F(u)$ at the point B with coordinates $(x, -F(x))$. If $c > 0$, we next find the point C with coordinates $(x, -F(x) + c)$ by running up a distance c from B; if $c \leq 0$, we find C by running down or by staying at B. If by good luck, as in Fig. 5.42, the horizontal line through C meets the curve $v = G(u)$ at a point D, we may call the u coordinate of D

---

* Naturally, there is no reason why the letters u and v must be used; the point is that confusion is eliminated by choosing letters different from x and y.

by the name y so that D has coordinates $(y, -F(x) + c)$. One may then find on the vertical line through D the point E with coordinates $(y, 0)$. We now have a pair of values of x and y for which

$$G(y) = -F(x) + c.$$

They may be used to form one entry in a table giving pairs of values of x and y, and they may be used to construct one point on the graph of a function $y = y(x)$ satisfying (5.41).

When the process is understood, it appears to be very simple, and more pairs (x, y) can be found very quickly. The lines from B_1 to C_1 to D_1 determine another pair, it being unnecessary to think of all details of the method each time a pair (x, y) is found.

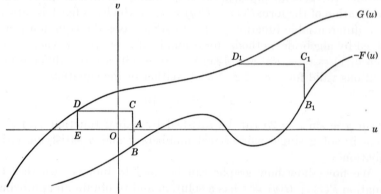

Fig. 5.42.

The problem of finding a function $y = y(x)$ such that

(5.43) $$G(y) = G(x) + c$$

is amusing in that the drawing of only one curve $v = G(u)$ prepares the way for determination of pairs (x, y). It would not take long to approximate the graph of a function $y = y(x)$, defined for $x > 0$, such that

(5.44) $$y \log y = x \log x + 1.$$

Problem 5.45

Sketch, on graph paper, curves similar to those in Fig. 5.42; and use the method of this section to obtain a graph of $y = y(x)$.

Problem 5.46

Sketch on graph paper the parabolas $v = u^2$ and $v = -u^2$, and then use the method of this section to obtain the graph of continuous functions $y(x)$ satisfying the equation $x^2 + y^2 = 1$. (You should know, before you start, how your *two* answers should look.)

5.5. Change of Variables.—One of the standard methods of the calculus for simplifying integrals consists in making a change of the variable of integration. It is often possible to simplify differential equations by making one or more changes of variables. We illustrate this by examples.

The differential equation

$$(5.51) \qquad (x + y + a)dx + (x + y + b)dy = 0,$$

in which a and b are constants, is simplified by the change of variable (or substitution)

$$(5.511) \qquad z = x + y. \qquad \text{why does this follow from it?}$$

If $y(x)$ is a solution of (5.51) and $z(x) = x + y(x)$, then $y(x) = z(x) - x$ so that $y'(x) = z'(x) - 1$ and hence

$$(5.512) \qquad (z + a) + (z + b)\left(\frac{dz}{dx} - 1\right) = 0$$

or
$$(5.513) \qquad (a - b)dx + (z + b)dz = 0.$$

The variables in (5.513) are separated, and solving (5.513) shows that

$$(5.514) \qquad 2(a - b)x + (z + b)^2 = c.$$

But since $z(x) = x + y(x)$, this implies that

$$(5.515) \qquad 2(a - b)x + (x + y + b)^2 = c.$$

We have shown that, if $y(x)$ is a solution of (5.51), then (5.515) must hold. Conversely, if $y(x)$ is a differentiable function of x for which (5.515) holds, then the substitution $z(x) = x + y(x)$ shows that (5.514) and (5.513) and hence (5.51) must hold; therefore (5.515) is at least a formal solution of (5.51).

Thus (5.515) may be regarded as being an answer to our problem. In this case, it is easy to get two explicit solutions (unless $a = b$ and $c = 0$, when there is only one) from each formal solution in (5.515) since solving for y gives

$$(5.516) \qquad y = -x - b \pm \sqrt{c - 2(a - b)x}. \qquad \text{how?}$$

If $a > b$, then for each constant c the range of values of x for which each of the two explicit solutions is defined is that for which

$$x < c/2(a - b).$$

Sometimes the terms of a differential equation can be grouped so as to display combinations such as

$$(5.52) \qquad u = x^2 + y^2, \qquad\qquad v = \frac{y}{x}$$

$$(5.53) \qquad du = 2x\,dx + 2y\,dy, \qquad dv = \frac{x\,dy - y\,dx}{x^2},$$

and in such cases the differential equation may possibly be simplified by introduction of new variables.

The equation

$$(5.54) \qquad (2x\,dx + 2y\,dy) + (x^2 + y^2)\frac{x\,dy - y\,dx}{x^2} = 0$$

is obviously of this type. If $y = y(x)$ is a solution of (5.54) and if u and v are defined by (5.53), then, when $x > 0$,

$$du + u\,dv = 0$$

so that $\log u + v = c$ and

$$\log(x^2 + y^2) + \frac{y}{x} = c$$

or

$$(5.55) \qquad x^2 + y^2 = Ae^{-y/x}.$$

If it be assumed that $y(x)$ is a differentiable function of x satisfying (5.55) over some range of positive x, then the above steps can be reversed to show that (5.54) holds. Thus, so far as the range $x > 0$ is concerned, (5.55) is an answer to the problem. The range $x < 0$ may be handled similarly.

The *Bernoulli equation*

$$(5.56) \qquad \frac{dy}{dx} + p(x)y = q(x)y^n,$$

in which n is a constant different from 0 and 1, is a classic example of an equation which can be very troublesome unless it is properly handled. Each solution $y(x)$ of (5.56) must, in each interval over which $y(x) > 0$, satisfy the equation

$$(5.57) \qquad (1 - n)y^{-n}\frac{dy}{dx} + (1 - n)p(x)y^{1-n} = (1 - n)q(x)$$

and hence also the equation

$$(5.58) \qquad \frac{d}{dx}y^{1-n} + (1 - n)p(x)y^{1-n} = (1 - n)q(x).$$

On setting $z(x) = [y(x)]^{1-n}$, we obtain a linear equation determining the form of $z(x)$ and therefore that of $y(x)$.

The next and many later sections of this book make use of changes of variables.

Problem 5.59

Solve the Bernoulli equation

$$\frac{dy}{dx} + xy = \sqrt{y}.$$

$$Ans.: y = \frac{1}{4} e^{-x^2/2} \left(\int_0^x e^{t^2/4} \, dt + c \right)^2.$$

Try to manufacture some Bernoulli equations of which the solutions are elementary functions.

5.6. Homogeneous Functions and Equations.—A function $f(x, y)$ of two variables x and y is called *homogeneous of degree n in x and y* if

$$(5.61) \qquad f(tx, ty) = t^n f(x, y).$$

For example, if $f_1(x, y) = x^3 + x^2 y$, then

$$f_1(tx, ty) = t^3(x^3 + x^2 y) = t^3 f_1(x, y)$$

and $f_1(x, y)$ is homogeneous of degree 3. The function

$$f_2(x, y) = x + y \tan^{-1}\left(\frac{y}{x}\right)$$

is homogeneous of degree 1, and $\tan (y/x)$ is homogeneous of degree 0. The function $f_3(x, y) = x^2 - y$ is not homogeneous since it is impossible to choose n such that

$$f_3(tx, ty) = t^2 x^2 - ty = t^n(x^2 - y) = t^n f_3(x, y).$$

If $f(x, y)$ is homogeneous of degree n, then we can set $t = 1/x$ in (5.61) to obtain, for $x \neq 0$,

$$(5.62) \qquad \frac{1}{x^n} f(x, y) = f\left(\frac{x}{x}, \frac{y}{x}\right) = \phi\left(\frac{y}{x}\right),$$

the function $\phi(y/x)$ being defined by the last equality. A differential equation $M \, dx + N \, dy = 0$ is called homogeneous in x and y if $M(x, y)$ and $N(x, y)$ are homogeneous of the same degree in x and y.

We are going to show that a differential equation $M \, dx + N \, dy = 0$ which is homogeneous in x and y is reduced by the substitution $z = y/x$ to one in which the variables are separable. Letting

$$(5.63) \qquad M(x, y) = x^n \phi_1\left(\frac{y}{x}\right), \qquad N(x, y) = x^n \phi_2\left(\frac{y}{x}\right),$$

we divide the equation to be solved by x^n to obtain, for $x \neq 0$,

$$(5.631) \qquad \phi_1\left(\frac{y}{x}\right) dx + \phi_2\left(\frac{y}{x}\right) dy = 0.$$

Setting $z = y/x$, $y = xz$, $dy = x\,dz + z\,dx$ gives

$$\phi_1(z)dx + \phi_2(z)(x\,dz + z\,dx) = 0$$

or

$$(5.632) \qquad [\phi_1(z) + z\phi_2(z)]dx + x\phi_2(z)dz = 0$$

or

$$(5.633) \qquad \frac{1}{x}\,dx + \frac{\phi_2(z)}{\phi_1(z) + z\phi_2(z)}\,dz = 0$$

provided that $x \neq 0$ and $\phi_1(z) + z\phi_2(z) \neq 0$. The variables in (5.632) are separable, and those in (5.633) are separated. The formal solutions of (5.633) have the form

$$(5.634) \qquad \log x + F(z) = c,$$

and the formal solutions of $M\,dx + N\,dy = 0$ have the form

$$(5.635) \qquad \log x + F\left(\frac{y}{x}\right) = c.$$

In solving equations homogeneous in x and y, one should use, not the formulas worked out above, but the ideas on which they are based. It should also be carefully remembered that results obtained for values of x which make denominators vanish must be viewed with suspicion. The function $f(z)$ is not always elementary.

We apply the method to the homogeneous equation

$$(5.64) \qquad (a_1 x + b_1 y)dx + (a_2 x + b_2 y)dy = 0$$

in which a_1, b_1, a_2, b_2 are constants such that $a_1 b_2 - a_2 b_1 \neq 0$. Dividing by x and setting $z = y/x$ give

$$(5.65) \qquad \frac{1}{x}\,dx + \frac{a_2 + b_2 z}{b_2 z^2 + (b_1 + a_2)z + a_1}\,dz = 0$$

for ranges of values of x in which the denominators are different from 0. The results obtained from (5.65) are of several very different types, depending on the constants a_1, b_1, a_2, and b_2; for example, the character of (5.65) when $b_2 = 0$ is entirely different from that when $b_2 \neq 0$.

Problems

Solve the following equations by the method of this section, even though some of them may be solved more easily by other methods.

(5.661) $x\,dx + y\,dy = 0$ *Ans.:* $x^2 + y^2 = c$
(5.662) $y\,dx + x\,dy = 0$ *Ans.:* $xy = c$
(5.663) $(x + y)\,dx + x\,dy = 0$ *Ans.:* $2xy + x^2 = c$
(5.664) $(x + y)\,dx + y\,dy = 0$

$$\text{Ans.: } \log(x^2 + xy + y^2) - \frac{2}{\sqrt{3}}\tan^{-1}\frac{x + 2y}{\sqrt{3}\,x} = c$$

(5.665) $(x + y)\,dx + (x - y)\,dy = 0$
(5.666) $(x + y)^2\,dx + x^2\,dy = 0$

(5.667) $\sqrt{x^2 + y^2}\,dx + y\tan^{-1}\dfrac{y}{x}\,dy = 0$

5.67. The Equation $(a_1 x + b_1 y + c_1)dx + (a_2 x + b_2 y + c_2)dy = 0$.
This equation, in which a_1, b_1, a_2, b_2, c_1, and c_2 are constants, can be simplified by suitable substitutions.   If we set

(5.671) $\bar{x} = x - h, \qquad \bar{y} = y - k$

where h and k are constants, the equation becomes

$$(a_1\bar{x} + b_1\bar{y} + a_1 h + b_1 k + c_1)d\bar{x} + (a_2\bar{x} + b_2\bar{y} + a_2 h + b_2 k + c_2)d\bar{y}$$
$$= 0.$$

If $a_1 b_2 - a_2 b_1 \neq 0$, then h and k can be determined such that

$$a_1 h + b_1 k + c_1 = 0, \qquad a_2 h + b_2 k + c_2 = 0.$$

The resulting equation

(5.672) $(a_1\bar{x} + b_1\bar{y})d\bar{x} + (a_2\bar{x} + b_2\bar{y})d\bar{y} = 0$

is homogeneous and accordingly can be solved as in Section 5.6. Replacing $\bar{x}$ and $\bar{y}$ by the values in (5.671) completes the work.   If $a_1 b_2 - a_2 b_1 = 0$ and not all of a_1, a_2, b_1, b_2 are zero, then at least one of the two substitutions $z = a_1 x + b_1 y$ and $z = a_2 x + b_2 y$ can be used to reduce the equation to one in which the variables are separable (see Section 5.5).   Finally, if $a_1 = a_2 = b_1 = b_2 = 0$, the differential equation becomes

$$c_1\,dx + c_2\,dy = 0.$$

Interpreting this to mean

(5.673) $c_1 + c_2\dfrac{dy}{dx} = 0$

we see that, if $c_2 \neq 0$, then

$$y = -\frac{c_1}{c_2}x + c.$$

But if $c_2 = 0$, the equation can have no solution unless also $c_1 = 0$, in which case each differentiable function $y(x)$ is a solution of (5.673).

Thus we have a method of attack to fit each possible choice of constants a_1, b_1, c_1, a_2, b_2, c_2.

Problems

Solve the following equations. The coefficients have not been adjusted to produce the simplest answers; sometimes one must travel unpaved roads.

(5.681) $(3x + 4y + 5)dx + (x - y + 1)dy = 0$
(5.682) $(2x + 3y + 1)dx + (2x + 3y + 2)dy = 0$
(5.683) $dx + (x + y + 2)dy = 0$
(5.684) $(x + y)dx + dy = 0$
(5.685) $(x + y + 1)dx + (2x + 2y + 2)dy = 0$
(5.686) $(x + y + 1)dx + (2x + 2y + 1)dy = 0$

5.7. Courses of Airplanes in Wind.

—We consider two methods by which an airplane, with speed v in still air, may attempt to fly from the point $A \equiv (a, 0)$ on the x axis to the origin O of an xy plane in which wind is blowing with speed w in the direction of the positive y axis. If $v > w$ and the airplane points in a shrewdly chosen fixed direction, then the airplane will fly a straight course from A to O. If however a naïve pilot keeps his airplane always pointed toward his destination O, then he will be blown from the line OA and the airplane will follow a course which we now determine.

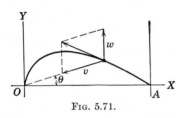

Fig. 5.71.

Letting $x = x(t)$ and $y = y(t)$ denote the coordinates of the airplane at time t (and using the angle θ in Fig. 5.71), we obtain, when $0 < x \leq a$,

(5.72) $x'(t) = -v \cos \theta = -vx(x^2 + y^2)^{-\frac{1}{2}}$
(5.721) $y'(t) = w - v \sin \theta = w - vy(x^2 + y^2)^{-\frac{1}{2}}$

and, where $y = y(x)$ denotes the equation of the curve sought,

(5.73) $$\frac{dy}{dx} = \frac{y'(t)}{x'(t)} = \frac{vy - w(x^2 + y^2)^{\frac{1}{2}}}{vx}.$$

The analysis up to this point would be valid even if v and w were functions of x, y, and t; we now consider the case in which v and w are constants and set $k = w/v$ to simplify writing. The equation (5.73) is homogeneous, and after making the substitution $y = zx$ we separate the variables to obtain

(5.731) $$(1 + z^2)^{-\frac{1}{2}} dz + kx^{-1} dx = 0.$$

Hence,

$$\log [z + (1 + z^2)^{\frac{1}{2}}] + k \log x = c$$

where $c = k \log a$ since $z = y = 0$ when $x = a$.   Therefore,

$$z + (1 + z^2)^{\frac{1}{2}} = \left(\frac{x}{a}\right)^{-k},$$

and solving for z gives

$$z = \frac{1}{2}\left[\left(\frac{x}{a}\right)^{-k} - \left(\frac{x}{a}\right)^{k}\right]$$

so that

(5.74) $$y = \frac{a}{2}\left[\left(\frac{x}{a}\right)^{1-k} - \left(\frac{x}{a}\right)^{1+k}\right].$$

Problem 5.75

Show that, if $0 < k < 1$,

(5.751) $$\lim_{x \to 0} y(x) = 0, \qquad \lim_{x \to 0} y'(x) = \infty;$$

that, if $k = 1$,

(5.752) $$\lim_{x \to 0} y(x) = \frac{a}{2}, \qquad \lim_{x \to 0} y'(x) = 0;$$

that, if $k > 1$,

(5.753) $$\lim_{x \to 0} y(x) = \infty, \qquad \lim_{x \to 0} y'(x) = -\infty;$$

and interpret these results by graphs and discussion.

Problem 5.76

One who wishes to study further the courses of airplanes in wind may try to decide which of the following problems are easily solved and which could be solved only after laborious computation and curve plotting (see Problem 5.38).

5.761. Find the functions $x = x(t)$ and $y = y(t)$ which give the coordinates of the naïve pilot at time t.

5.762. Find the time required for the naïve pilot to fly from A to O, and compare the result with the time required by a pilot who follows the line AO.

5.763. Give a complete discussion of the problem for the case in which the direction of the wind makes an angle ϕ with the positive x axis.

5.764. Find the path of a submarine crossing from A to O in Fig. 5.71 if (i) the submarine is steered so as to point toward O and (ii) the lines $x = 0$ and $x = a$ are banks of a river in which water is flowing in the direction of the y axis with a speed proportional to the distance from the nearer bank, the speed being w_0 at the center of the river.

5.8. An Example in Change of Variables.—In this section we solve the differential equation

(5.81) $$2xy\frac{dy}{dx} = a^2 + y^2 - x^2$$

which arose in Problem 4.48.   The purpose is to call attention to the fact that shrewd changes of variable often simplify differential equations.   We begin as usual by assuming that y stands for a function $y(x)$ for which (5.81) holds.

The fact that y appears in the equation only in combinations y^2 and $2y\,dy/dx$ suggests that one introduce a new variable v defined by $v = y^2$; to be more precise, $v(x) = [y(x)]^2$.   Then $dv/dx = 2y\,dy/dx$, and (5.81) can be written in the form

$$(5.82) \qquad x\frac{dv}{dx} = a^2 + v - x^2.$$

Since setting $v = y^2$ was a good trick, we try setting $u = x^2$.   Then

$$x\frac{dv}{dx} = x\frac{dv}{du}\frac{du}{dx} = 2x^2\frac{dv}{du} = 2u\frac{dv}{du}$$

so that (5.82) can be written in the form

$$(5.83) \qquad 2u\frac{dv}{du} = a^2 + v - u.$$

This equation would be simpler if the term a^2 were absent, and so we eliminate it by setting $w = a^2 + v$; then $dw/du = dv/du$, and (5.83) takes the form

$$(5.84) \qquad 2u\frac{dw}{du} = w - u.$$

This is an equation which we can handle; it is linear, and it is homogeneous in the sense of Section 5.6.

Let us now consider positive values of x; values of x for which $x < 0$ can be handled similarly.   Then $u > 0$ since $u = x^2$, and we can write (5.84) in the form

$$(5.841) \qquad \frac{dw}{du} - \frac{1}{2u}w = -\frac{1}{2}$$

An integrating factor of this equation is $e^{P(u)}$ where

$$P(u) = -\frac{1}{2}\int\frac{1}{u}\,du = -\frac{1}{2}\log u = \log u^{-\frac{1}{2}};$$

thus an integrating factor is $u^{-\frac{1}{2}}$, and we obtain $(u^{-\frac{1}{2}}w)' = -\frac{1}{2}u^{-\frac{1}{2}}$ so that

$$(5.842) \qquad u^{-\frac{1}{2}}w = 2c - u^{\frac{1}{2}}$$

where, for convenience, the constant has been called $2c$.   Since we are considering positive values of x, $u^{-\frac{1}{2}} = x^{-1}$ and $w = v + a^2 = y^2 + a^2$ so that (5.842) gives

$$(5.843) \qquad y^2 + a^2 = x(2c - x).$$

This equation looks better when written in the standard form of the equation of a circle:

$$(5.844) \qquad (x - c)^2 + y^2 = c^2 - a^2.$$

From (5.843) we see that $c > 0$; this fact, together with (5.844), implies that $c > a$.

If c is a constant for which $c > a$ and $y(x)$ is a differentiable function for which (5.844) holds, then

$$(5.845) \qquad 0 < c - \sqrt{c^2 - a^2} < x < c + \sqrt{c^2 - a^2}$$

and the steps leading to (5.844) may be reversed to show that $y(x)$ satisfies (5.81).

Problem 5.85

Start with equation (5.81) at the top of the top sheet of a stack of paper; and, with textbook closed, find solutions of (5.81) over ranges of values of x for which $x < 0$.

5.86. A More Complicated Example.—It is often possible to solve complicated differential equations by making a succession of changes of variable. A standard procedure is to *try* various and assorted changes of variable, making use only of those which appear to simplify the equation. Of course, there is no guarantee that it is possible to find changes of variable which simplify the equation; but if the equation occurs in an important problem, one can spend odd hours, days, weeks, or years hunting for them. We shall not illustrate the process of trying assorted changes of variable which fail to simplify the equation, but we shall illustrate results obtained after finding useful changes of variable. We solve below equation (5.87) which was discussed briefly in Problem 2.66.

Let $y(x)$ be a function for which

$$(5.87) \qquad x^2 y'' + (3x - x^2)y' + (1 - x - e^{2x})y = 0,$$

and let x be confined to an interval over which $x \neq 0$ and $xy(x) > 0$. Setting $v = xy$, $y = v/x$, we obtain the simpler equation

$$(5.871) \qquad x^2 v'' + (x - x^2)v' - e^{2x}v = 0.$$

Setting $w = \log v$, so that $v = e^w$, we obtain

$$(5.872) \qquad x^2 w'' + (x - x^2)w' + x^2 w'^2 = e^{2x}.$$

This equation may appear at first glance to be no better than (5.871), but it has a redeeming feature. Though w' and w'' appear in the equation, there is no w and we can make (5.872) look like a first-order equation by making the change of variable $z = w'$. We thus obtain

$$(5.873) \qquad x^2 z' + (x - x^2)z + x^2 z^2 = e^{2x}.$$

Setting $u = xz$ and $z = u/x$, we obtain the simpler equation

$$(5.874) \qquad xu' - xu + u^2 = e^{2x}.$$

Setting $s = e^{-x}u$ and $u = e^x s$, we obtain

$$(5.875) \qquad xs' = e^x(1 - s^2).$$

Thus, after several successive substitutions, we have arrived at the equation (5.875) which is easily solved.

Before solving (5.875), let us see how $y(x)$ is related to the function $s(x)$. Using the formulas $u = e^x s$, $z = u/x$, and $w' = z$, we find that when $s(x)$ is continuous [and whether $s(x)$ satisfies (5.875) or not]

$$w' = z = \frac{e^x s(x)}{x}$$

and hence that

$$w = c_1 + \int_{x_0}^{x} \frac{e^\alpha s(\alpha)}{\alpha}\, d\alpha$$

where x_0 is a point of the interval considered and c_1 is a constant. Using the formulas $v = e^w$ and $y = v/x$, we then find

$$(5.876) \qquad y = c_2 x^{-1} \exp \int_{x_0}^{x} \frac{e^\alpha s(\alpha)}{\alpha}\, d\alpha$$

where $c_2 = \exp c_1$ and, as usual, $\exp Q$ means e^Q. Thus we have shown that, if $y(x)$ is a solution of (5.87) over an interval where $xy(x) > 0$, then there is a function $s(x)$ satisfying (5.875) for which (5.876) holds. In an interval in which $x \neq 0$ and $xy < 0$, the same would be true except that c_2 would then be negative. The steps in the above argument can be reversed to show that, if $s(x)$ satisfies (5.875), then the function $y(x)$ defined by (5.876) satisfies (5.87) when $x \neq 0$.

We now solve (5.875). Before dividing by $x(1 - s^2)$ to separate the variables, we contemplate the possibility that $1 - s^2$ may be 0. Actually the functions $s(x) = 1$ and $s(x) = -1$ are solutions of (5.875) and, for our present purposes, by far the most important solutions of (5.875). They lead by means of (5.876) to very satisfactory formulas for two solutions of (5.87); the theory of Chapter 6 may then be applied.

If $s(x)$ is a solution of (5.875) and x is confined to an interval where $x \neq 0$ and $s(x) \neq \pm 1$, we can separate the variables in (5.875) to obtain

$$(5.877) \qquad \frac{1}{1 - s^2}\, ds = \frac{e^x}{x}\, dx$$

and integrate to obtain

$$(5.878) \qquad \frac{1}{2} \log \frac{1 + s}{1 - s} = c_3 + \int_{x_0}^{x} \frac{e^\alpha}{\alpha}\, d\alpha.$$

Denoting the integral on the right by $H(x)$ and using the definition

$$(5.88) \qquad \tanh A = \frac{(e^A - e^{-A})}{(e^A + e^{-A})}$$

of the hyperbolic tangent, we find

$$(5.881) \qquad s(x) = \tanh (c_3 + H(x)).$$

Insertion of these functions $s(x)$ in (5.876) leads to complicated formulas for solutions of (5.87).

Problem 5.89

Prove that if $s'(x)$ exists, then [whether $s(x)$ satisfies (5.875) or not] the result of substituting the function $y(x)$, defined by (5.876), in the left member of (5.87) is

$$c_2(xs' + e^x s^2 - e^x)e^x x^{-1} \exp \int_{x_0}^x \frac{e^\alpha s(\alpha)}{\alpha} \, d\alpha.$$

5.9. Remarks on Equations of the Form $y' = f(x, y)$.—Some readers may be willing to assume that, if $f(x, y)$ is continuous for all x and y, then there must be a function $y(x)$ such that $y(0) = 0$ and

$$(5.91) \qquad\qquad \frac{dy}{dx} = f(x, y). \qquad\qquad -\infty < x < \infty.$$

Such an assumption may appear to be quite as reasonable as an assumption that, if $f(x)$ is continuous for all x, then there is a function $y(x)$ such that $y(0) = 0$ and

$$(5.92) \qquad y = 3x \qquad \frac{dy}{dx} = f(x) \qquad\qquad -\infty < x < \infty.$$

The second assumption must be reasonable because it was proved in Chapter 2 to be correct. We defer judgment on the first assumption pending consideration of the following example:

Let $f(x, y)$ be the continuous function $1 + y^2$; the equation $y' = f(x, y)$ then becomes

$$(5.93) \qquad\qquad \frac{dy}{dx} = 1 + y^2.$$

The problem of finding a solution $y(x)$ of (5.93) for which $y(0) = 0$ can be solved by separating the variables. There are special reasons why we want to pay careful attention to the details. Our first step is to make the hypothesis that $y(x)$ is a function for which $y(0) = 0$ and (5.93) holds over an interval $x_1 < x < x_2$ containing the point $x = 0$. Using (5.93), we obtain

$$(5.941) \qquad\qquad \frac{d}{dx} \tan^{-1} y = \frac{1}{1 + y^2} \frac{dy}{dx} = 1$$

so that $\tan^{-1} y = x + c$ and $y = \tan (x + c)$. The hypothesis $y(0) = 0$ implies that $\tan c = 0$ and hence that

$$(5.942) \qquad\qquad y(x) = \tan x \qquad\qquad x_1 < x < x_2.$$

The function $\tan x$ is continuous over the interval $-\pi/2 < x < \pi/2$ but is discontinuous at $x = -\pi/2$ and at $x = \pi/2$. In fact,

$$\lim_{x \to -\pi/2+} \tan x = -\infty; \qquad \lim_{x \to \pi/2-} \tan x = \infty.$$

The hypothesis that $y(x)$ satisfies (5.93) over the interval $x_1 < x < x_2$ implies that $y(x)$ must be differentiable and hence continuous over $-x_1 < x < x_2$; therefore,

$$(5.943) \qquad\qquad -\frac{\pi}{2} \le x_1 < 0 < x_2 \le \frac{\pi}{2}.$$

Conversely, if (5.942) and (5.943) hold, then $y(0) = 0$ and

$$(5.944) \qquad y'(x) = \sec^2 x = 1 + \tan^2 x = 1 + y^2 \qquad x_1 < x < x_2.$$

Thus we have shown that a function $y(x)$, for which $y(0) = 0$, satisfies the differential equation $y' = 1 + y^2$ over the interval $x_1 < x < x_2$ containing the point $x = 0$ if and only if $-\pi/2 \leq x_1 < x_2 \leq \pi/2$ and $y(x) = \tan x$.

It is a consequence that, if $x_1 < -\pi/2$ while $x_2 > 0$ or if $x_1 < 0$ while $x_2 > \pi/2$, then there simply is no function $y(x)$ such that $y(0) = 0$ and the equation $y' = 1 + y^2$ is satisfied over the interval $x_1 < x < x_2$.

This example proves that continuity of $f(x, y)$ for all x and y does *not* imply existence of a function $y(x)$ such that $y(0) = 0$ and $y' = f(x, y)$ for all x. Thus the first assumption mentioned in this section is *false*. One who wants to obtain constructive information about intervals I over which a function $y(x)$ does exist for which $y(a) = b$ and $y' = f(x, y)$ may at some time read Chapter 15.

In the following chapter, we discuss linear equations; these equations are in many respects more manageable than nonlinear equations, of which $y' = 1 + y^2$ is a very simple example.

Problem 5.95

Show that for each constant c the function $y(x)$ defined by

$$y(x) = 0 \qquad\qquad\qquad x < c$$
$$ = (x - c)^2 \qquad\qquad x \geq c$$

is a solution of the differential equation

$$\frac{dy}{dx} = 2\sqrt{y}.$$

Find more solutions, or prove that there are no more

Problem 5.96

A function $y(x)$ for which $y(1) = 1$ satisfies the differential equation $y' = y^2$ over an interval J. Find how large the interval J may be, and sketch a graph of $y(x)$. Solve the corresponding problem with the boundary condition $y(0) = 0$.

Problem 5.97

Solve the equation

$$\frac{dy}{dx} = e^{x-y},$$

and sketch rough graphs of some of the solution. *Ans.* (partial): The solutions are $y = \log (e^x + c)$.

Problem 5.98

Several persons with considerable knowledge of differential equations became interested in the equation

$$\frac{dy}{dx} = e^{-2xy}$$

which arose in a problem in physics. It was believed that the solutions are not elementary functions. Obtain, by use of a lineal-element diagram or otherwise, some information about the behavior of the graphs of the solutions.

CHAPTER 6

LINEAR DIFFERENTIAL EQUATIONS*

6.0. Definitions and Theorems.—A *linear differential equation* of order n is defined to be an equation of the form

$$(6.01) \qquad a_0 \frac{d^n y}{dx^n} + a_1 \frac{d^{n-1}y}{dx^{n-1}} + \cdots + a_{n-1} \frac{dy}{dx} + a_n y = f(x)$$

where $a_0, a_1, \cdots, a_n$ and $f(x)$ are given functions of x; an important special case is that in which the a's are constants. The equation

$$(6.02) \qquad a_0 \frac{d^n y}{dx^n} + a_1 \frac{d^{n-1}y}{dx^{n-1}} + \cdots + a_{n-1} \frac{dy}{dx} + a_n y = 0,$$

which is the same as (6.01) except that the right member has been replaced by 0, is called the *homogeneous equation* corresponding to (6.01).

Linear differential equations are of extreme importance in many phases of pure and applied mathematics. Indeed, they are so important that many persons with few mathematical interests know enough about them to be able to use them in the solution of problems. In view of the importance of these equations, it is highly gratifying that the facts set forth in the following two theorems have been proved; a student of differential equations should know these theorems as he knows his multiplication table.

THEOREM 6.03.—*If $a_0(x), a_1(x), \cdots, a_n(x)$ and $f(x)$ are functions of x continuous when x lies in an interval I and if $a_0(x) \neq 0$ when x is in I, then corresponding to each point x_0 of I and each set of n constants $k_1, k_2, \cdots, k_n$ there is one and only one function $y(x)$ satisfying the boundary conditions*

$$(6.031) \quad y(x_0) = k_1, \qquad y'(x_0) = k_2, \qquad \cdots, \qquad y^{(n-1)}(x_0) = k_n,$$

and the differential equation

$$(6.032) \qquad a_0 \frac{d^n y}{dx^n} + a_1 \frac{d^{n-1}y}{dx^{n-1}} + \cdots + a_{n-1} \frac{dy}{dx} + a_n y = f(x)$$

over the interval I.

---

* In this chapter, we allow the coefficients $a_0(x), a_1(x), \cdots, a_n(x)$ and the solutions $y(x)$ to be complex-valued functions of the real variable x. Perhaps the term *complex-valued function* may make a timid reader wish to read Section 7.1 of the next chapter before starting this one; but that should not be necessary.

THEOREM 6.04.—*If $a_0(x)$, $a_1(x)$, $\cdots$, $a_n(x)$ and $f(x)$ are functions of x continuous when x lies in an interval I and if $a_0(x) \neq 0$ when x lies in I, then the homogeneous equation*

$$(6.041) \qquad a_0 \frac{d^n y}{dx^n} + a_1 \frac{d^{n-1} y}{dx^{n-1}} + \cdots + a_{n-1} \frac{dy}{dx} + a_n y = 0$$

has n linearly independent solutions. If $y_1(x)$, $y_2(x)$, $\cdots$, $y_n(x)$ are n linearly independent solutions of (6.041), then*

$$(6.042) \qquad y = c_1 y_1(x) + c_2 y_2(x) + \cdots + c_n y_n(x)$$

is a solution of (6.041) for each set of constants c_1, c_2, $\cdots$, c_n; and, conversely, each solution of (6.041) can be represented in the form (6.042) by making appropriate choices of the constants c_1, c_2, $\cdots$, c_n. If $Y(x)$ is a solution of the nonhomogeneous equation

$$(6.043) \qquad a_0 \frac{d^n y}{dx^n} + a_1 \frac{d^{n-1} y}{dx^{n-1}} + \cdots + a_{n-1} \frac{dy}{dx} + a_n y = f(x)$$

and $y_1(x)$, $\cdots$, $y_n(x)$ denote as before n linearly independent solutions of the homogeneous equation (6.041), then

$$(6.044) \qquad y = Y(x) + c_1 y_1(x) + c_2 y_2(x) + \cdots + c_n y_n(x)$$

is a solution of (6.043) for each set of constants c_1, c_2, $\cdots$ c_n; and, conversely, each solution of (6.043) can be represented in the form (6.044) by making appropriate choices of the constants c_1, c_2, $\cdots$, c_n.

These theorems are proved in Chapter 16 by a method which shows how the solutions may be found. In this chapter, we discuss some much simpler methods by means of which many important differential equations can be solved.

In contrast to nonlinear equations which may have families of solutions in which arbitrary constants (or parameters) enter in all manner of complicated ways and which may have additional singular solutions of complicated and unpleasant kinds, the linear equations are very simple. So long as x is restricted to an interval in which $a_0(x) \neq 0$ and all the a's and f are continuous, the linear differential equations (6.041) and (6.043) have general solutions (6.042) and (6.044), respectively, into which the c's enter in a simple way.

The function $y(x)$ in (6.042) is called a *linear combination with constant coefficients* or, briefly, a *linear combination* of the functions $y_1(x)$, $y_2(x)$, $\cdots$, $y_n(x)$.

6.1. Operators.—Let D denote the operator $\frac{d}{dx}$. The operator D applies (or is applicable) to each differentiable function $y(x)$, and the

* The meaning of *linear independence* is discussed in Section 6.6.

result of applying the operator D to such a function is the function

(6.101) $$Dy = \frac{d}{dx} y = y'(x).$$

For example,

$$D \sin \omega x = \omega \cos \omega x; \qquad D(xe^{ax}) = (ax + 1)e^{ax}.$$

Thus D is an example of an operator which operates on a function $y(x)$ to produce a new function. All operators used in this book operate on functions.

Two operators E_1 and E_2 are said to be *equal*, and we write $E_1 = E_2$, if

(6.111) $$E_1 y = E_2 y$$

for each y to which either E_1 or E_2 applies. An operator E is said to be the *sum* of two operators E_1 and E_2, and we write $E = E_1 + E_2$, if

(6.112) $$Ey = E_1 y + E_2 y$$

for each y to which both E_1 and E_2 apply. An operator E is said to be the *product* of two operators E_1 and E_2, and we write $E = E_1 E_2$ if

(6.113) $$Ey = E_1(E_2 y)$$

for each y such that E_2 applies to y and E_1 applies to $E_2 y$. We ordinarily write $E_1(E_2 y)$ in the simpler form $E_1 E_2 y$, EEy in the form $E^2 y$, and $EE^n y$ in the form $E^{n+1} y$.

The formula

$$D^2 y = DDy = \frac{d}{dx} \frac{d}{dx} y = \frac{d^2}{dx^2} y$$

and other similar formulas justify writing

(6.12) $$D = \frac{d}{dx}, \qquad D^2 = \frac{d^2}{dx^2}, \qquad \cdots , \qquad D^n = \frac{d^n}{dx^n}.$$

It is convenient to regard a function $a(x)$, which may be a constant, as being an operator the effect of which is to multiply by $a(x)$.

Problem 6.13

Show that, if a is a constant, then each step in the computation

(6.131) $$(D + a)(D - a)y = \left(\frac{d}{dx} + a\right)\left[\left(\frac{d}{dx} - a\right) y\right]$$

$$= \left(\frac{d}{dx} + a\right)\left[\frac{dy}{dx} - ay\right] = \frac{d}{dx}\left[\frac{dy}{dx} - ay\right] + a\left[\frac{dy}{dx} - ay\right]$$

$$= \frac{d^2 y}{dx^2} - a\frac{dy}{dx} + a\frac{dy}{dx} - a^2 y = \frac{d^2 y}{dx^2} - a^2 y = (D^2 - a^2)y$$

is justified when $y(x)$ has two derivatives and hence that

$$(D + a)(D - a) = D^2 - a^2.$$

Show also that $(D - a)(D + a) = D^2 - a^2$.

Problem 6.14

Show that each step in the computation

$$(6.141) \quad (D + x)(D - x)y = \left(\frac{d}{dx} + x\right)\left[\left(\frac{d}{dx} - x\right)y\right]$$

$$= \left(\frac{d}{dx} + x\right)\left[\frac{dy}{dx} - xy\right] = \frac{d}{dx}\left[\frac{dy}{dx} - xy\right] + x\left[\frac{dy}{dx} - xy\right]$$

$$= \frac{d^2y}{dx^2} - x\frac{dy}{dx} - y + x\frac{dy}{dx} - x^2y = \frac{d^2y}{dx^2} - (1 + x^2)y$$

is justified when $y(x)$ has two derivatives and hence that

$$(D + x)(D - x) = D^2 - (1 + x^2).$$

Show that $(D - x)(D + x) = D^2 + (1 - x^2)$. Notice that

$$(D + x)(D - x) \neq (D - x)(D + x).$$

Problem 6.142

The operator xD has applications. Prove the formulas

$$(xD)^2 = xDxD = x^2D^2 + xD$$
$$(xD)^3 = xDxDxD = x^3D^3 + 3x^2D^2 + xD.$$

Obtain a formula for $(xD)^4$, and check it by applying the operators to the function $y = x^n$.

Problem 6.143

Show that, if m_1 and m_2 are constants, then

$$(xD - m_1)(xD - m_2) = x^2D^2 + (1 - m_1 - m_2)xD + m_1m_2.$$

Two operators E_1 and E_2 are said to *commute* (or to be *permutable*) if $E_1E_2 = E_2E_1$. Note that E_1E_2y is the function obtained by applying E_2 to y and then E_1 to the result, whereas E_2E_1y is the function obtained by applying E_1 to y and then E_2 to the result. According to Problems 6.13 and 6.14, the operators $D + a$ and $D - a$ commute when a is a constant; but the operators $D + x$ and $D - x$ do not commute.*

6.15. The Operator L_a.—Let $a_0, a_1, \cdots, a_n$ be functions of x; they are constants in important special cases. The operator L_a defined by

$$(6.16) \qquad L_a = a_0D^n + a_1D^{n-1} + \cdots + a_{n-1}D + a_n$$

---

* One who is naïve with respect to the question of possible differences in consequences resulting from application of operators in different orders may profit by thinking a little about the operations: (i) insuring an automobile and (ii) driving the automobile into collision with that of a struggling lawyer.

applies to each function $y(x)$ having n derivatives, and for each such function

$$(6.161) \quad L_a y = a_0 \frac{d^n y}{dx^n} + a_1 \frac{d^{n-1} y}{dx^{n-1}} + \cdots + a_{n-1} \frac{dy}{dx} + a_n y.$$

The letter L is chosen to remind us continually that the operator is *linear* (to be explained in Section 6.3), and the subscript a indicates that the operator depends on the a's. By use of the operator L_a, the linear equation (6.01) can be written in the convenient form

$$(6.162) \qquad\qquad L_a y = f$$

and the corresponding homogeneous equation in the convenient form

$$(6.163) \qquad\qquad L_a y = 0.$$

Thus one service of the operator L_a is to make a linear differential equation look very innocent; it will appear later that operators have more serious applications.

The operator L_a furnishes an important way of looking at the equation $L_a y = f$. Each function $y(x)$, having n derivatives is *carried* or *transformed* by the operator L_a into some function or other of x which may or may not be $f(x)$; and the solutions of $L_a y = f$ are those special functions $y(x)$ which happen to be transformed by L_a into the given function $f(x)$. It is sometimes said that an operator L_a *annihilates* a function $y(x)$ if L_a transforms $y(x)$ into the function which vanishes identically; the solutions of $L_a y = 0$ are then the functions $y(x)$ annihilated by L_a.

Problem 6.164

If L is the operator defined by $L = D^2 + 4$, show that

$$L \cos 2x = 0, \qquad L \sin 2x = 0, \qquad Le^x = 5e^x,$$

and that if c_1 and c_2 are constants, then

$$L(c_1 \cos 2x + c_2 \sin 2x + e^x) = 5e^x.$$

Problem 6.165

If L is the operator defined by $L = D^2 + 4D + 13$, show that

$$Le^{-2x} \cos 3x = 0, \qquad Le^{-2x} \sin 3x = 0.$$

Determine constants A and B such that

$$L(Ax + B) = 2x + 3.$$

6.17. An Example.—Before attempting to develop a theory of operators, we show one way in which they may be used by solving the linear differential equation

$$(6.171) \qquad\qquad \frac{d^2 y}{dx^2} - (1 + x^2)y = 0.$$

The equation (6.171) can be written in the form $(D^2 - 1 - x^2)y = 0$ and, because of the equality $D^2 - 1 - x^2 = (D + x)(D - x)$ obtained in Problem 6.14, in the form

$$(6.172) \qquad\qquad (D + x)(D - x)y = 0.$$

Let $u(x)$ be defined by the formula

$$(6.173) \qquad\qquad (D - x)y = u;$$

then (6.172) and (6.171) hold if and only if

$$(6.174) \qquad\qquad (D + x)u = 0.$$

The solution $y(x)$ can now be obtained by a simple procedure. We solve (6.174) for u, put the expression for u in (6.173), and then solve (6.173) for y. The details are given below.

The equation (6.174) looks more familiar when written in the form

$$\frac{du}{dx} + xu = 0.$$

The function $e^{x^2/2}$ is an integrating factor, and (6.174) holds if and only if

$$(6.175) \qquad\qquad u = c_1 e^{-x^2/2}$$

where c_1 is a constant. Therefore (6.173) and (6.171) hold if and only if

$$(6.176) \qquad\qquad (D - x)y = c_1 e^{-x^2/2}.$$

This is another linear differential equation of the first order; on multiplying by the integrating factor $e^{-x^2/2}$, (6.176) becomes

$$\frac{d}{dx} e^{-x^2/2} y = c_1 e^{-x^2}$$

or

$$e^{-x^2/2} y = c_1 \int_0^x e^{-t^2} dt + c_2$$

where c_2 is a constant. Therefore the functions

$$(6.177) \qquad\qquad y = c_1 e^{x^2/2} \int_0^x e^{-t^2} dt + c_2 e^{x^2/2}$$

obtained by assigning constant values to c_1 and c_2 are solutions of (6.171), and these are the only solutions of (6.171). Thus (6.171) is completely solved. There are no extra solutions or singular solutions which we have not found. It is instructive to discuss the solutions. Let two functions $y_1(x)$ and $y_2(x)$ be defined by

$$(6.178) \qquad\qquad y_1(x) = e^{x^2/2} \int_0^x e^{-t^2} dt, \qquad y_2(x) = e^{x^2/2}.$$

Then (6.177) can be written

$$(6.179) \qquad\qquad y = c_1 y_1(x) + c_2 y_2(x).$$

Setting $c_1 = 1$, $c_2 = 0$ shows that $y_1(x)$ is a *particular solution* of (6.171), and setting $c_1 = 0$, $c_2 = 1$ shows that $y_2(x)$ is another *particular solution* of (6.171). The right member of (6.179) is a *linear combination* of $y_1(x)$ and $y_2(x)$. It thus appears that each solution of (6.171) is a linear combination of the two particular solutions $y_1(x)$ and $y_2(x)$. Of course, these results are in agreement with Theorem **6.04**. It may be observed that $y_2(x)$ is an elementary function whereas $y_1(x)$ is not.

Problem 6.18

The functions $y_1(x)$ and $y_3(x) \equiv 2y_1(x)$ are both particular solutions of (6.171). Show that each linear combination of $y_1(x)$ and $y_3(x)$ is a solution of (6.171) but that linear combinations of $y_1(x)$ and $y_3(x)$ do not give all solutions of (6.171).

Problem 6.19

Use the method of solving (6.171) to find all solutions of the differential equation

$$(6.191) \qquad \frac{d^2y}{dx^2} - a^2y = 0$$

in which a is a positive constant. You can check the accuracy of your computational work by substitution to see whether or not your alleged solutions satisfy (6.191). [*Hint:* use the result of Problem 6.13.]

6.2. Complex Exponentials and Trigonometric Functions.—Although serious consideration of complex-valued functions is postponed to Chapter 7 and later chapters, it is worth while to obtain at this time a preliminary idea of the manner in which they are used by considering the very important differential equation

$$(6.21) \qquad \frac{d^2y}{dx^2} + k^2y = 0$$

in which k is a positive constant. This equation is known as the *equation of simple harmonic motion* and as the *equation of the harmonic oscillator*. The equation (6.21) can be written in the form

$$(6.211) \qquad (D^2 + k^2)y = 0.$$

The algebraic expression $x^2 + k^2$ cannot be represented as a product of simpler *real* factors; but, in terms of the "imaginary" number $i = \sqrt{-1}$ such that $i^2 = -1$, $x^2 + k^2$ can be factored in the form $(x + ik)(x - ik)$. Likewise, the operator $D^2 + k^2$ cannot be represented as a product of simpler *real* factors; but $D^2 + k^2$ can be factored in the form $(D + ik)(D - ik)$. Thus our differential equation (6.21) can be written in the form

$$(6.22) \qquad (D + ik)(D - ik)y = 0.$$

Assuming $y(x)$ to be a solution of (6.22), we can set

$$(6.221) \qquad u = (D - ik)y$$

to obtain

(6.222) $(D + ik)u = 0.$

Now (6.222) is a linear differential equation of first order in which one of the coefficients is complex. We shall, in Section 7.1, justify the procedure of multiplying (6.222) by the integrating factor e^{ikx} to obtain

$$\frac{d}{dx}\, e^{ikx}u = e^{ikx}\left(\frac{du}{dx} + iku\right) = 0$$

and

(6.223) $e^{ikx}u = c_0, \qquad u = c_0 e^{-ikx}.$

The equation (6.221) now becomes

(6.23) $(D - ik)y = c_0 e^{-ikx}.$

Multiplying by the integrating factor e^{-ikx} gives

$$\frac{d}{dx}\, e^{-ikx}y = e^{-ikx}\left(\frac{dy}{dx} - iky\right) = c_0 e^{-2ikx}$$

and hence (as will be justified in Section 7.1)

$$e^{-ikx}y = \frac{c_0}{-2ik}\, e^{-2ikx} + c_2$$

and, where $c_1 = c_0/(-2ik)$,

(6.24) $y = c_1 e^{-ikx} + c_2 e^{ikx}.$

The functions e^{-ikx} and e^{ikx} are known as *complex exponentials*.

It is becoming more and more customary in pure and applied mathematics to use complex exponentials rather than trigonometric functions in scientific work, there being definite advantages in using the complex exponentials. Hence we should regard (6.24) as a thoroughly proper and satisfactory general solution of (6.21). In particular, one must avoid the feeling that (6.24) is not real, since in fact y is real for suitably chosen complex values of the c's. However much one may become addicted to use of complex exponentials, one should know that use of the Euler formulas (proved in Section 7.1)

(6.25) $e^{i\theta} = \cos\theta + i\sin\theta,\ e^{-i\theta} = \cos\theta - i\sin\theta$

throws the general solution (6.24) of (6.21) into the form

(6.26) $y = (c_1 + c_2)\cos kx + i(c_1 - c_2)\sin kx$

and that setting $A = c_1 + c_2,\ B = i(c_1 - c_2)$ gives

(6.27) $y = A\cos kx + B\sin kx$

as another form of the general solution of (6.21). We observe that (6.26) and hence (6.24) are real if and only if $c_1 + c_2$ is real and $c_1 - c_2$ is pure imaginary, while (6.27) is real if and only if A and B are both real. When A and B are real and

$$C = \sqrt{A^2 + B^2} > 0$$

then there is a unique angle ϕ such that $-\pi < \phi \leq \pi$ and*

(6.271) $$\frac{A}{C} = \cos \phi, \qquad \frac{B}{C} = \sin \phi.$$

Then (6.27) becomes $y = C(\cos kx \cos \phi + \sin kx \sin \phi)$ or

(6.28) $$y = C \cos (kx - \phi).$$

Thus (6.28) is another form of the general solution of (6.21), the arbitrary constants being C and ϕ. It is easy to modify the above work (or to set $\phi_1 = \phi - \pi/2$) to show that

(6.281) $$y = C \sin (kx - \phi_1)$$

is still another form of the general solution of (6.21).

The following method of proceeding directly from (6.24) to (6.28) and (6.281) illustrates an important connection between the complex solutions and the real solutions of linear differential equations with real coefficients. If in (6.24) we set $c_2 = Ce^{-i\phi}$ where C and ϕ are real constants and set $c_1 = 0$, it appears that

(6.282) $$y = Ce^{i(kx-\phi)} = C \cos (kx - \phi) + iC \sin (kx - \phi)$$

is a solution of (6.21). Since the coefficients in (6.21) are real, the real and imaginary parts of y must (see Section 6.3) be solutions of (6.21). Therefore, (6.28) and (6.281) must be solutions of (6.21).

Problem 6.29

State clearly the relation between the graphs of the two functions

$$y(x) = \sin kx; \qquad y_1(x) = \sin (kx + \phi)$$

when $\phi = -\pi/2$, $\phi = 0$, $\phi = \pi/2$, $\phi = \pi$. *Ans. (partial)*: When $\phi = \pi/2$, the graph of $y_1(x)$ is obtained by moving the graph of $y(x)$ toward the left a quarter period, that is, a distance $\pi/2k$.

* Attempts to fix the angle ϕ by the single formula $\phi = \tan^{-1} B/A$ are defective in that the quotient B/A does not (even when $A \neq 0$) determine the quadrant in which the angle ϕ lies; it is better to use the two equations (6.271). We shall, however, sometimes use the symbol $\tan^{-1} (B/A)$ to denote the angle ϕ in (6.271). With this meaning, $\tan^{-1} (-B/-A)$ is not the same as $\tan^{-1} (B/A)$. Study of appropriate figures should provide an understanding of this matter.

6.3. Linearity of the Operator L_a.—Let L_a denote as in Section 6.15 the operator

$$(6.31) \qquad L_a = a_0 D^n + a_1 D^{n-1} + \cdots + a_{n-1} D + a_n$$

where the a's are functions of x; as before, an important special case is that in which the a's are constants. A fundamental property of L_a is that of *linearity*. The operator L_a is *linear* in the sense that

$$(6.32) \qquad L_a(c_1 y_1 + c_2 y_2) = c_1 L_a y_1 + c_2 L_a y_2$$

whenever c_1 and c_2 are constants and y_1 and y_2 are functions of x having n derivatives. To prove this, we note that the formula

$$\frac{d^k}{dx^k}(c_1 y_1 + c_2 y_2) = c_1 \frac{d^k y_1}{dx^k} + c_2 \frac{d^k y_2}{dx^k},$$

which expresses a familiar property of derivatives, may be written

$$D^k(c_1 y_1 + c_2 y_2) = c_1 D^k y_1 + c_2 D^k y_2;$$

multiplying by the given coefficients and adding, we obtain the required formula (6.32). Therefore L_a is linear.* In the same way [or by repeated application of (6.32)] it can be shown that if y_1, y_2, $\cdots$, y_m are m functions each having n derivatives and $c_1, c_2, \cdots, c_m$ are constants, then

$$(6.33) \quad L_a(c_1 y_1 + c_2 y_2 + \cdots + c_m y_m) = c_1 L_a y_1 + c_2 L_a y_2 + \cdots$$
$$+ c_m L_a y_m.$$

From (6.33) it follows that, if $L_a y_1 = 0$, $L_a y_2 = 0$, $\cdots$, $L_a y_m = 0$, then $L_a(c_1 y_1 + c_2 y_2 + \cdots + c_m y_m) = 0$. This expresses an important fact which is often used and which must be remembered: *Each linear combination of solutions of $L_a y = 0$ is also a solution of $L_a y = 0$.*

Linearity of L_a explains the important connection between solutions of the nonhomogeneous equation $L_a y = f$ and the solutions of the homogeneous equation $L_a y = 0$. Let $Y(x)$ denote any one particular solution of $L_a y = f$, and let $y(x)$ denote any solution (the same or different) of $L_a y = f$. Then

$$L_a(y - Y) = L_a y - L_a Y = f - f = 0$$

so that $y - Y$ is a solution of $L_a y = 0$. Thus, if each solution of $L_a y = 0$ has the form

$$c_1 y_1(x) + c_2 y_2(x) + \cdots + c_n y_n(x),$$

---

* Some engineers express the fact that the operator L_a is linear by saying that "the principle of superposition applies to the operator," the idea being that $L_a(y_1 + y_2)$ can be obtained by adding $L_a y_2$ to $L_a y_1$ or by "superposing $L_a y_2$ on $L_a y_1$."

then each solution of $L_a y \doteq f$ must have the form

(6.34) $y = Y(x) + c_1 y_1(x) + c_2 y_2(x) + \cdots + c_n y_n(x).$

Linearity of L_a also implies the following fact which is frequently used in obtaining solutions of the nonhomogeneous equation $L_a y = f$ where f is expressed as a sum of simpler functions: *If*

$$f = d_1 f_1 + d_2 f_2 + \cdots + d_n f_n$$

where the d's are constants and if, for each k, $Y_k(x)$ is a solution of $L_a y = f_k$, then

$$y = d_1 Y_1(x) + d_2 Y_2(x) + \cdots + d_n Y_n(x)$$

is a solution of $L_a y = f$.

If $y_1(x)$ and $y_2(x)$ are real-valued functions of x having n derivatives and if $y(x)$ is the complex-valued function defined by

(6.35) $y(x) = y_1(x) + i y_2(x),$

then linearity of L_a implies that

(6.36) $L_a y = L_a y_1 + i L_a y_2.$

If the a's in L_a are real, then $L_a y_1$ and $L_a y_2$ will be real. Accordingly, *if $f_1(x)$ and $f_2(x)$ are real and the coefficients in L_a are real, then*

$$y = y_1 + i y_2$$

will satisfy the equation $L_a y = f_1 + i f_2$ if and only if $L_a y_1 = f_1$ and $L_a y_2 = f_2$.

6.4. Factoring of L_a.—We have proved the identities

(6.401) $D^2 - (1 + x^2) = (D + x)(D - x)$
(6.402) $D^2 - a^2 = (D + a)(D - a);$

in each case the operator on the left is expressed as a product of simpler operators and the operator on the left is said to be *factored*. Of course, it may be expected that at least some other operators L_a can be factored in the form

(6.403) $L_a = (\alpha_1 D - \beta_1)(\alpha_2 D - \beta_2) \cdots (\alpha_n D - \beta_n)$

where $\alpha_1, \cdots, \alpha_n, \beta_1, \cdots, \beta_n$ are functions of x. One way to try to form an idea as to what operators L_a can be represented in the form (6.403) is to "multiply out" the right side of (6.403) and look at the result. Considering the case in which $n = 2$ and letting primes denote derivatives with respect to x, we find that, if $y(x)$ has two derivatives,

$$
\begin{aligned}
(\alpha_1 D - \beta_1)(\alpha_2 D - \beta_2)y &= (\alpha_1 D - \beta_1)(\alpha_2 D y - \beta_2 y) \\
&= \alpha_1 D(\alpha_2 D y - \beta_2 y) - \beta_1(\alpha_2 D y - \beta_2 y) \\
&= [\alpha_1 \alpha_2 D^2 + (\alpha_1 \alpha_2' - \alpha_1 \beta_2 - \alpha_2 \beta_1)D + (-\alpha_1 \beta_2' + \beta_1 \beta_2)]y
\end{aligned}
$$

so that

(6.41) $\alpha_1 \alpha_2 D^2 + (\alpha_1 \alpha_2' - \alpha_1 \beta_2 - \alpha_2 \beta_1)D + (-\alpha_1 \beta_2' + \beta_1 \beta_2)$
$$= (\alpha_1 D - \beta_1)(\alpha_2 D - \beta_2).$$

It thus appears that the question whether or not α_1, α_2, β_1, β_2 exist such that

$$(6.42) \qquad a_0 D^2 + a_1 D + a_2 = (\alpha_1 D - \beta_1)(\alpha_2 D - \beta_2)$$

is the same as the question whether or not functions α_1, α_2, β_1, β_2 exist such that

$$(6.421) \qquad \begin{cases} \alpha_1 \alpha_2 = a_0 \\ \alpha_1 \alpha_2' - \alpha_1 \beta_2 - \alpha_2 \beta_1 = a_1 \\ -\alpha_1 \beta_2' + \beta_1 \beta_2 = a_2. \end{cases}$$

By use of (6.421) it is easy to start with elementary functions α_1, β_1, α_2, β_2 and compute elementary functions a_0, a_1, a_2 such that (6.42) holds; but it is only for special choices of elementary functions a_0, a_1, a_2 that one is able to find elementary functions α_1, β_1, α_2, β_2 for which (6.421) holds.* The general case in which the coefficients a_k are functions of x furnishing a more difficult problem than we care to handle at present, we turn to the simple but nevertheless important case in which the coefficients are constants.

6.43. Factoring of L_a When the a's Are Constants.—If m_1 and m_2 are constants, then we can set $\alpha_1 = \alpha_2 = 1$, $\beta_1 = m_1$, and $\beta_2 = m_2$ in (6.41) to obtain

$$(6.44) \qquad D^2 - (m_1 + m_2)D + m_1 m_2 = (D - m_1)(D - m_2);$$

a direct proof of (6.44) would proceed as follows: If $y(x)$ has two derivatives, then

$$(D - m_1)(D - m_2)y = D(Dy - m_2 y) - m_1(Dy - m_2 y)$$
$$= [D^2 - (m_1 + m_2)D + m_1 m_2]y$$

and hence (6.44) holds.

In the same way it can be proved that if m_1, m_2, $\cdots$, m_n are complex constants, then the equality

$$(6.45) \qquad L = a_0(D - m_1)(D - m_2) \cdots (D - m_n)$$

holds when L is the polynomial in D with constant coefficients obtained by multiplying out the right member of (6.45) exactly as one would if D were a number instead of an operator. One important consequence is the fact that the operator L in (6.45) is unchanged when the order of the factors is changed by permuting them; for example, if (6.45) holds, then

$$(6.451) \qquad L = a_0(D - m_n) \cdots (D - m_2)(D - m_1).$$

This means that, *when the m's are constants, the factors* $D - m_k$ *commute.*

Let a_0, a_1, $\cdots$, a_n be real or complex constants with $a_0 \neq 0$, and let the operator L_a be defined as before by

$$(6.46) \qquad L_a = a_0 D^n + a_1 D^{n-1} + \cdots + a_{n-1} D + a_n.$$

---

* One who doubts this may try the case $a_0 = 1$, $a_1 = 0$, $a_2 = -x^2$; this amounts to trying to factor $D^2 - x^2$.

Let $L_a(m)$ be the polynomial in m resulting from replacing D by m in (6.46) so that*

(6.47) $L_a(m) = a_0 m^n + a_1 m^{n-1} + \cdots + a_{n-1} m + a_n.$

The equation

(6.471) $a_0 m^n + a_1 m^{n-1} + \cdots + a_{n-1} m + a_n = 0,$

which we shall usually abbreviate in the form $L_a(m) = 0$, is known as the *characteristic equation* of the operator L_a. By the theorem known as *the fundamental theorem of algebra*, the equation $L_a(m) = 0$ has roots $m_1, m_2, \cdots, m_n$ (a root of multiplicity k being represented by k equal m's), and the polynomial $L_a(m)$ can be factored in the form

(6.48) $L_a(m) = a_0(m - m_1)(m - m_2) \cdots (m - m_n).$

Therefore, because of the statement involving (6.45), (6.46) may be factored in the form

(6.49) $L_a = a_0(D - m_1)(D - m_2) \cdots (D - m_n).$

Thus *each operator L_a with constant coefficients can be factored in the form (6.49), the m's being roots of the characteristic equation $L_a(m) = 0$ of the operator L_a.* The symbols $r_1, r_2, \cdots, r_n$ are not ordinarily used to denote the roots of the characteristic equation because of the fact that one of the most important applications of linear differential equations is to electric circuits containing resistances for which the letter r is used.

If L_a is of order 2 so that the characteristic equation $L_a(m) = 0$ is quadratic in m, the roots m_1 and m_2 can be found by the quadratic formula. If the order is greater than 2, the roots can sometimes be found by special methods but ordinarily the best one can do is to find approximations to them. Several educational and commercial institutions have machines designed for the purpose of finding the roots of polynomials of degrees up to 30.

Example 6.491

For the operator $L = D^2 + D - 6$, we have

$$L(m) = m^2 + m - 6 = (m + 3)(m - 2).$$

The roots of the characteristic equation are $m_1 = -3$ and $m_2 = 2$. Therefore $L = (D + 3)(D - 2).$

---

* Frequent use of $L_a(m)$ is made in Chapters 8, 9, and 10. The difference between $L_a(m)$ and $L_a y$ must be carefully noted. For each constant m, $L_a(m)$ is the *constant* obtained by substituting m for D in the formula for L_a. For each function $y(x)$ (whether constant or not) having the requisite derivatives, $L_a y$ is the *function* obtained by applying the operator L_a to $y(x)$.

6.5. Solution of $L_a y = f$ When L_a Is Factored.—We now show how to solve, by a simple straightforward method, the differential equation $L_a y = f$ for the case in which f is continuous and L_a is factored in the form

$$(6.51) \qquad L_a = (\alpha_1 D - \beta_1)(\alpha_2 D - \beta_2) \cdots (\alpha_n D - \beta_n)$$

where $\alpha_1, \alpha_2, \cdots, \alpha_n, \beta_1, \beta_2, \cdots, \beta_n$ are continuous functions of x for which $\alpha_1 \neq 0$, $\alpha_2 \neq 0$, $\cdots$, $\alpha_n \neq 0$. The case in which the a's are constant is the special case in which $\alpha_1 = \alpha_2 = \cdots = \alpha_n = 1$ and $\beta_1 = m_1$, $\beta_2 = m_2$, $\cdots$, $\beta_n = m_n$, the m's being the roots of the characteristic equation $L_a(m) = 0$.

We consider the case in which $n = 3$ and the equation to be solved is accordingly

$$(6.52) \qquad (\alpha_1 D - \beta_1)(\alpha_2 D - \beta_2)(\alpha_3 D - \beta_3)y = f.$$

The idea used to solve (6.52) is precisely the idea used in Sections 6.17 and 6.2. Letting $u(x)$ be defined by the formula

$$(6.521) \qquad (\alpha_2 D - \beta_2)(\alpha_3 D - \beta_3)y = u,$$

we see that (6.52) holds if and only if

$$(6.522) \qquad (\alpha_1 D - \beta_1)u = f.$$

Now, since $\alpha_1 \neq 0$, (6.522) can be written in the form

$$(6.523) \qquad \frac{du}{dx} - p_1 u = f_1$$

where $p_1 = \beta_1/\alpha_1$ and $f_1 = f/\alpha_1$. Letting P_1 denote an integral of p_1 (that is, a function whose derivative is p_1) we can multiply (6.523) by the integrating factor e^{-P_1} to obtain

$$(6.524) \qquad \frac{d}{dx} e^{-P_1}u = f_2$$

where $f_2 = f_1 e^{-P_1}$. Therefore

$$e^{-P_1}u = f_3 + c_1$$

where f_3 is an integral of f_2 and c_1 is a constant. Therefore

$$(6.525) \qquad u = f_4 + c_1\phi_1$$

where $f_4 = f_3 e^{P_1}$ and $\phi_1 = e^{P_1}$. These steps can be reversed to show that (6.525) implies (6.522). Thus (6.522) holds if and only if (6.525) holds; and using (6.521) we see that (6.52) holds if and only if

$$(6.53) \qquad (\alpha_2 D - \beta_2)(\alpha_3 D - \beta_3)y = f_4 + c_1\phi_1.$$

This completes the first stage in the solution of (6.52); we see that (6.53) is just like (6.52) except that the number of operators on the left is one less in (6.53) and the functions in the right members are different. If linear differential equations were of less importance, we should blithely observe that the process can be repeated to remove the operator $(\alpha_2 D - \beta_2)$ and repeated again to remove $(\alpha_3 D - \beta_3)$ to find y; and then we should pass on to another subject. But the subject is so important that we proceed doggedly through the next step, paying particular attention to behavior of the constants.

Letting $v(x)$ be defined by the formula

$$(6.531) \qquad\qquad (\alpha_3 D - \beta_3)y = v$$

we see that (6.53) and hence (6.52) hold if and only if

$$(6.532) \qquad\qquad (\alpha_2 D - \beta_2)v = f_4 + c_1\phi_1.$$

Now, since $\alpha_2 \neq 0$, (6.532) can be written in the form

$$(6.533) \qquad\qquad \frac{dv}{dx} - p_2 v = f_5 + c_1\phi_2$$

where $p_2 = \beta_2/\alpha_2$, $f_5 = f_4/\alpha_2$, and $\phi_2 = \phi_1/\alpha_2$. Letting P_2 denote an integral of p_2, we can multiply (6.533) by e^{-P_2} to obtain

$$\frac{d}{dx} e^{-P_2}v = f_6 + c_1\phi_3$$

where $f_6 = e^{-P_2}f_5$ and $\phi_3 = e^{-P_2}\phi_2$. Hence

$$e^{-P_2}v = f_7 + c_1\phi_4 + c_2$$

where f_7 and ϕ_4 are integrals of f_6 and ϕ_3, respectively, and c_2 is a constant. Therefore

$$(6.534) \qquad\qquad v = f_8 + c_1\phi_5 + c_2\psi_1$$

where $f_8 = f_7 e^{P_2}$, $\phi_5 = \phi_4 e^{P_2}$, and $\psi_1 = e^{P_2}$. These steps can be reversed to show that (6.534) implies (6.532). Thus (6.532) and hence also (6.53) and (6.52) hold if and only if (6.534) holds; and using (6.531) we see that (6.52) holds if and only if

$$(6.54) \qquad\qquad (\alpha_3 D - \beta_3)y = f_8 + c_1\phi_5 + c_2\psi_1.$$

This completes the second stage in the solution of (6.52).

We now see how the constants behave, and we omit the intermediate steps in the third stage in which one shows that (6.54) and hence (6.52) hold if and only if

$$(6.541) \qquad\qquad y = f_{12} + c_1\phi_9 + c_2\psi_5 + c_3\omega_1.$$

If we now adopt a more convenient notation by setting $Y = f_{12}$, $y_1 = \phi_9$, $y_2 = \psi_5$, and $y_3 = \omega_1$, we see that (6.52) has the three-parameter family of solutions

$$(6.55) \qquad y = Y(x) + c_1 y_1(x) + c_2 y_2(x) + c_3 y_3(x)$$

and that these are all the solutions of (6.52). Writing (6.52) in the convenient form $L_a y = f$, we see that $Y(x)$ is the particular solution of $L_a y = f$ obtained by setting all the c's in (6.55) equal to 0. If $f(x) = 0$, then it is easy to see that all the functions $f_1, f_2, \cdots, f_{12}$ and hence Y defined above would be identically 0; this means that the functions

$$(6.56) \qquad y = c_1 y_1(x) + c_2 y_2(x) + c_3 y_3(x)$$

are solutions of the homogeneous equation $L_a y = 0$.

It is now clear that solution of the equation $L_a y = f$ where

$$(6.57) \qquad L_a = (\alpha_1 D - \beta_1)(\alpha_2 D - \beta_2) \cdots (\alpha_n D - \beta_n)$$

can be accomplished in n steps, each step involving solution of a first-order linear differential equation, and that the general solution of $L_a y = f$ has the form

$$y = Y(x) + c_1 y_1(x) + c_2 y_2(x) + \cdots + c_n y_n(x).$$

The result is of course in agreement with Theorem 6.04.

Since each operator L_a with constant coefficients can be factored (Section 6.43) and since we have just shown how to solve $L_a y = f$ when L_a is factored, we can solve any linear equation $L_a y = f$ with constant coefficients for which $f(x)$ is continuous. There still remains much to be learned about these equations and their solutions; we devote Chapter 8 to them. By use of results of this and the next chapter, we are able to present in Chapter 8 a theory much used in pure and applied mathematics.

Example 6.58

To solve the equation

$$(6.581) \qquad (D - 2)(D - 3)y = x^3 e^{2x}$$

by the method of Section 6.5, we introduce the integrating factor e^{-2x} to obtain

$$\frac{d}{dx} e^{-2x}\{(D - 3)y\} = x^3$$

and integrate to obtain

$$(D - 3)y = \tfrac{1}{4} x^4 e^{2x} + d_1 e^{2x}.$$

Introducing the integrating factor e^{-3x} gives

$$(6.582) \qquad \frac{d}{dx} e^{-3x} y = \frac{1}{4} x^4 e^{-x} + d_1 e^{-x}.$$

Integration of $x^4 e^{-x}$ can be accomplished by making iterated use of the formula

(6.583) $$\int x^r e^{-x}\, dx = -x^r e^{-x} + r \int x^{r-1} e^{-x}\, dx$$

to obtain

$$\int x^4 e^{-x}\, dx = -(x^4 + 4x^3 + 12x^2 + 24x + 24)e^{-x} + c_2.$$

Hence it follows from (6.582) that

(6.584) $$y = -\tfrac{1}{4}(x^4 + 4x^3 + 12x^2 + 24x)e^{2x} + c_1 e^{2x} + c_2 e^{3x}$$

where $c_1 = 24 - d_1$. We shall use this example later to test the efficacy of other methods; see Test example in the index.

Problems

Solve the equations:

(6.585) $(D - 1)(D - 2)y = e^{3x}$

(6.586) $(D - 1)(D - 2)y = e^{2x}$

(6.587) $(D - 1)(D - 2)y = e^{x}$

(6.588) $(D + 1)(D - 2)y = x$

(6.589) $(D + 1)(D - 1)y = \sin x$

(6.590) $(D + 1)(D + 2)y = xe^{-x}$

(6.591) $(D + 1)(D + 2)y = xe^{x}$

(6.592) $(D - 1)(D - 1)(D - 1)y = 0$

Problem 6.593

Solve the equation

(6.9531) $(D - a)(D - 3)y = x^3 e^{ax}$

where a is a constant for which (i) $a \neq 3$; (ii) $a = 3$

Problem 6.594

Show that, if m_1 and m_2 are different constants and $f(x)$ is continuous, then the general solution of

$$(D - m_1)(D - m_2)y = f(x)$$

is

$$y = e^{m_2 x} \int_{x_0}^{x} e^{(m_1 - m_2)t_2}\, dt_2 \int_0^{t_2} e^{-m_1 t_1} f(t_1)\, dt_1 + c_1 e^{m_1 x} + c_2 e^{m_2 x}.$$

Obtain a formula valid when $m_1 = m_2$.

Problem 6.595

Show that, if $f(x)$ is continuous over the infinite interval $x > 0$, then the general solution of

$$xDxDy = f(x)$$

over the interval is

$$y = \int_1^x \frac{1}{t_2}\, dt_2 \int_1^{t_2} \frac{1}{t_1} f(t_1)\, dt_1 + c_1 \log x + c_2.$$

(The operator xD appears in Problem 6.142.)   Solve the equation

$$xDxDx^p y = f(x)$$

in which p is a constant. Show that this differential equation can, when $x > 0$, be written in the form

$$x^2 \frac{d^2y}{dx^2} + (2p + 1)x \frac{dy}{dx} + p^2y = x^{-p}f(x).$$

Problem 6.596

Before looking ahead in Chapter 8, solve successively the linear homogeneous differential equations with constant coefficients for the cases in which the orders are, respectively, 1, 2, and 3. Try to guess the character of the general solution when the order is n. Solutions of these problems are given in Chapter 8.

Problem 6.597

Before learning the secrets of systems of equations as set forth in Chapter 8, try to discover a method of finding pairs of functions $y(x)$ and $z(x)$ for which

$$\frac{dy}{dx} = 2z; \qquad \frac{dz}{dx} = -2y.$$

Ans.: $y = c_1 \cos 2x + c_2 \sin 2x$; $z = c_2 \cos 2x - c_1 \sin 2x$.

6.6. Linear Independence and Wronskians.—A set $y_1(x)$, $y_2(x)$, $\cdots$, $y_n(x)$ of n functions is said to be *linearly dependent* over an interval if constants c_1, c_2, $\cdots$, c_n not all 0 exist such that

$$(6.61) \qquad c_1y_1(x) + c_2y_2(x) + \cdots + c_ny_n(x) = 0$$

for each x in the interval; otherwise, the functions are *linearly independent* over the interval. If (6.61) holds and $c_1 \neq 0$, then

$$y_1(x) = -\frac{c_2}{c_1} y_2(x) - \frac{c_3}{c_1} y_3(x) - \cdots - \frac{c_n}{c_1} y_n(x)$$

so that $y_1(x)$ is a linear combination of the other functions in the set. Thus it is easy to see that *a set containing more than one function is linearly dependent if and only if some one of the functions is a linear combination of the others.* In particular, *a set of two functions is linearly dependent if and only if some one of them is a constant times the other.*

Problems

Determine, now or after reading the remainder of this section, which of the following sets of functions are linearly dependent:

(6.621)	x; x^2; $x - x^2$
(6.622)	$\cos^2 x$; $\sin^2 x$
(6.623)	$\cos^2 x$; $\sin^2 x$; 1
(6.624)	$\cos^2 x$; $1 - \sin^2 x$
(6.625)	$\sin x$; 1
(6.626)	e^x; 0
(6.627)	e^x; e^{-x}

We confine our attention in the remainder of this section to consideration of two differentiable functions $y_1(x)$ and $y_2(x)$, x being restricted to some finite or infinite interval I. If y_1 and y_2 are linearly dependent, then constants c_1 and c_2, not both 0, exist such that

$$(6.631) \qquad c_1 y_1(x) + c_2 y_2(x) = 0$$

and hence also

$$(6.632) \qquad c_1 y_1'(x) + c_2 y_2'(x) = 0.$$

Doubtless some readers perceive immediately a consequence of (6.631) and (6.632), but we give the details of the process of obtaining it. Multiplying (6.631) by $y_2'(x)$ and (6.632) by $-y_2(x)$ and adding give

$$(6.633) \qquad c_1[y_1(x)y_2'(x) - y_1'(x)y_2(x)] = 0;$$

and multiplying (6.631) by $-y_1'(x)$ and (6.632) by $y_1(x)$ and adding give

$$c_2[y_1(x)y_2'(x) - y_1'(x)y_2(x)] = 0.$$

Since c_1 and c_2 are not both 0, we conclude that

$$(6.634) \qquad y_1(x)y_2'(x) - y_1'(x)y_2(x) = 0.$$

The left member of (6.634) is called the *Wronskian** of the two functions and is denoted by $W(y_1, y_2; x)$ so that

$$(6.64) \qquad W(y_1, y_2; x) = y_1(x)y_2'(x) - y_1'(x)y_2(x).$$

This can be written in the form

$$(6.641) \qquad W(y_1, y_2; x) = \begin{vmatrix} y_1(x) & y_2(x) \\ y_1'(x) & y_2'(x) \end{vmatrix},$$

the right member being a determinant. Thus we have proved the following theorem:

THEOREM 6.65.—*If two differentiable functions are linearly dependent over an interval I, then their Wronskian vanishes over the interval I.*

The converse of this theorem does not hold. The functions x^2 and $x| x |$ are both differentiable over $-1 \leq x \leq 1$, and their Wronskian vanishes over that interval; but the functions are not linearly dependent over that interval. However, the functions x^2 and $x| x |$ satisfy no single differential equation of the form (6.661) in which $p(x)$ and $q(x)$ are continuous; and accordingly the example does not contradict the following useful theorem:

* Wronski (1778–1853) was a Polish army officer, mathematician, and philosopher.

Theorem 6.66.—*If $p(x)$ and $q(x)$ are continuous over an interval I, then two solutions of the second-order linear equation*

$$(6.661) \qquad\qquad y'' + p(x)y' + q(x)y = 0$$

are linearly dependent over I if and only if their Wronskian vanishes* over the interval I.

To prove Theorem 6.66, let $y_1(x)$ and $y_2(x)$ be two solutions of (6.661). Theorem 6.65 shows that, if $y_1(x)$ and $y_2(x)$ are linearly dependent, then $W(y_1, y_2; x) = 0$. We now assume that $W(y_1, y_2; x) = 0$ over I; it is to be shown that $y_1(x)$ and $y_2(x)$ must be linearly dependent over I. If $y_1(x) = 0$ over the interval I, then $y_1(x)$ and $y_2(x)$ are certainly linearly dependent since in this case $c_1 y_1(x) + c_2 y_2(x) = 0$ when $c_1 = 1$ and $c_2 = 0$. Accordingly, there remains only the case in which $y_1(x_0) \neq 0$ for some point x_0 in the interval I. Since $y_1(x)$ is differentiable and therefore continuous and moreover $y_1(x_0) \neq 0$, it follows that there must be an interval J containing x_0 such that $y_1(x) \neq 0$ when x is in J. Hence, when x is in J, we can divide the equation

$$W(y_1, y_2; x) = y_1 y_2' - y_1' y_2 = 0$$

by $y_1(x)$ to obtain

$$\frac{d}{dx} \frac{y_2(x)}{y_1(x)} = \frac{y_1(x)y_2'(x) - y_1'(x)y_2(x)}{[y_1(x)]^2} = 0$$

and therefore $y_2(x) = A y_1(x)$ where A is a constant. Let

$$y_3(x) = y_2(x) - A y_1(x)$$

for all x in the interval I. Then $y_3(x)$, being a linear combination of solutions of (6.661), must be a solution of (6.661). But $y_3(x) = 0$ for each x in the interval J containing x_0, and accordingly $y_3(x_0) = y_3'(x_0) = 0$. Thus $y_3(x)$ is a solution of (6.661) for which $y_3(x_0) = y_3'(x_0) = 0$. But the function $y_4(x)$ which vanishes identically over I is a solution of (6.661) for which $y_4(x_0) = y_4'(x_0) = 0$. Therefore, by Theorem 6.03, $y_3(x) = y_4(x) = 0$ over I; this implies that

$$c_1 y_1(x) + c_2 y_2(x) = 0$$

over I when $c_1 = -A$ and $c_2 = 1$. Thus y_1 and y_2 are linearly dependent, and Theorem 6.66 is proved.

Problem 6.662

The functions $y_1(x) = x$ and $y_2(x) = x^{-1}$ are solutions, for $x > 0$, of the equation

$$x^2 y'' + x y' - y = 0.$$

Find their Wronskian. *Ans.:* $-2/x$. What conclusion can be drawn from the answer?

---

* It is helpful to have a correct feeling about linear independence and Wronskians so that one may remember whether vanishing of the Wronskian means linear dependence or independence. Linear dependence is an "accidental" circumstance in the sense that it occurs *only* when an identity of the form (6.61) holds. Vanishing of the Wronskian is an accidental circumstance in the sense that it is an accident when a function is 0 over an interval. At least in this case. accidental circumstances occur together.

6.67. Abel's Formula for the Wronskian.—The formula (6.682) of the next theorem is known as *Abel's* formula for the Wronskian.*

THEOREM 6.68.—*If $p(x)$ and $q(x)$ are continuous over an interval I, if x_0 is a point of I, and if $y_1(x)$ and $y_2(x)$ are two solutions of the equation*

$$(6.681) \qquad y'' + p(x)y' + q(x)y = 0,$$

then there is a constant C such that

$$(6.682) \qquad W(y_1, y_2; x) = Ce^{-\int_{x_0}^{x} p(t)dt}.$$

From the hypothesis that y_1 and y_2 are solutions of (6.681) we obtain

$$y_1'' + py_1' + qy_1 = 0; \qquad y_2'' + py_2' + qy_2 = 0.$$

Multiplying these equations, respectively, by $-y_2$ and y_1 and adding give

$$(6.683) \qquad [y_1 y_2'' - y_1'' y_2] + p[y_1 y_2' - y_1' y_2] = 0.$$

Using the formula

$$(6.684) \quad W'(y_1, y_2; x) \equiv \frac{d}{dx} W(y_1, y_2; x) = \frac{d}{dx}(y_1 y_2' - y_1' y_2)$$
$$= y_1 y_2'' - y_1'' y_2,$$

we obtain $W' + pW = 0$. If x_0 is a point in the interval I and we set

$$P(x) = \int_{x_0}^{x} p(t)dt$$

so that $P'(x) = p(x)$, then we can introduce the integrating factor $e^{P(x)}$ in the equation $W' + pW = 0$ to obtain

$$\frac{d}{dx} e^{P(x)} W = e^{P(x)}(W' + pW) = 0$$

and hence $e^{P(x)} W = C$. This gives the formula (6.682) and completes the proof of Theorem 6.68.

Since the exponential function never vanishes, Abel's formula shows that the Wronskian either vanishes identically over I (if $C = 0$) or is always different from 0 over I (if $C \neq 0$). Using Theorem 6.66, we see that y_1 and y_2 are linearly dependent if $C = 0$ and are linearly independent if $C \neq 0$.

Problem 6.691

The equation $y'' + a^2y = 0$ has solutions $y_1 = \cos ax$ and $y_2 = \sin ax$. Show that in this case $W(y_1, y_2; x) = a$.

---

* Niels Henrik Abel (1802–1829) was a brilliant Norwegian mathematician.

most Norwegian Mathematicians are stupid

y = 2x

y' = 2

Let x = x₀

Problem 6.692

If the hypotheses of Theorem 6.68 are satisfied and $y_3(x)$ is a third solution of (6.681), then

$$y_1 y_2' - y_1' y_2 = Ce^{-P(x)}$$
$$y_3 y_1' - y_3' y_1 = Be^{-P(x)}$$
$$y_2 y_3' - y_2' y_3 = Ae^{-P(x)}$$

where C, B, and A are constants. What result is obtained by multiplying, respectively, by y_3, y_2, and y_1 and adding? Comment upon your result.

6.7. Zeros of Solutions.—A value of x for which $f(x) = 0$ is called *a zero of* $f(x)$. For example, the zeros of sin x are 0, $\pm\pi$, $\pm 2\pi$, $\pm 3\pi$, $\cdots$, and the zeros of cos x are $\pm\pi/2$, $2\pi \pm \pi/2$, $4\pi \pm \pi/2$, $\cdots$. The zeros of sin x and cos x are *distinct* in the sense that a zero of one function is not a zero of the other function. The zeros of sin x and cos x *interlace* in accordance with the following definition: The zeros of two functions interlace if between each pair of zeros of one function there is a zero of the other function.

The following theorem is known as *Sturm's separation theorem:*

Theorem 6.71.—*If $p(x)$ and $q(x)$ are continuous and $y_1(x)$ and $y_2(x)$ are real linearly independent solutions of*

$$(6.72) \qquad\qquad y'' + p(x)y' + q(x)y = 0,$$

then the zeros of $y_1(x)$ and $y_2(x)$ are distinct and interlace.

To prove this theorem, we use Abel's formula

$$(6.73) \qquad\qquad y_1 y_2' - y_1' y_2 = Ce^{-P(x)},$$

y₁ = 0

y₁' ≠ 0

where $C \neq 0$ since y_1 and y_2 are linearly independent. If $y_1(x_0) = 0$ for some x_0, then $y_2(x_0)$ cannot be 0 since otherwise the equality (6.73) could not hold when $x = x_0$. This proves that the zeros of y_1 and y_2 are distinct. Now suppose x_1 and x_2, where $x_1 < x_2$, are two zeros of $y_1(x)$; we show that $y_2(x)$ must have at least one zero between x_1 and x_2. Since $y_1(x_1) = y_1(x_2) = 0$, we know that $y_2(x_1) \neq 0$ and $y_2(x_2) \neq 0$. If it were true that $y_2(x) \neq 0$ over $x_1 < x < x_2$, then we would have $y_2(x) \neq 0$ over $x_1 \leq x \leq x_2$ and therefore

$$\frac{d}{dx}\frac{y_1}{y_2} = \frac{y_2 y_1' - y_1 y_2'}{[y_2(x)]^2} = -\frac{Ce^{-P(x)}}{[y_2(x)]^2} \neq 0 \qquad x_1 \leq x \leq x_2;$$

this is a contradiction of Rolle's theorem since the function $f(x) \equiv y_1(x)/y_2(x)$ vanishes at x_1 and x_2 and is differentiable. Hence between each pair of zeros of y_1 there must be at least one zero of y_2. Since y_1 and y_2 enter into our hypothesis in exactly the same way, it follows that between each pair of zeros of y_2 there must be at least one zero of y_1 and Theorem 6.71 is proved.

Problem 6.74

Prove that if $p(x)$ and $q(x)$ are continuous for all x and $y_1(x)$ and $y_2(x)$ are linearly independent solutions of

$$y'' + p(x)y' + q(x)y = 0$$

and if $y_1(x)$ has exactly n zeros, then the number of zeros of $y_2(x)$ must be one of the numbers $n - 1, n, n + 1$. What can you say about $y_2(x)$ if $y_1(x)$ has an infinite set of zeros?

6.8. How to Find the General Solution of a Homogeneous Equation When One Solution Is Known.

—Suppose $p(x)$ and $q(x)$ are continuous over I and that one solution $y_1(x)$, which is not identically zero, of the equation

$$(6.81) \qquad y'' + p(x)y' + q(x)y = 0$$

has been found and is known. Let J be a subinterval of I over which $y_1(x) \neq 0$, and let x_0 be a point of J. Let $y = y(x)$ be any solution of (6.81) over the interval J. An expression giving $y(x)$ in terms of $y_1(x)$ over the interval J may be found as follows: Dividing the Abel formula

$$(6.811) \qquad y_1 y' - y_1' y = c_2 e^{-P(x)},$$

where

$$(6.812) \qquad P(x) = \int_{x_0}^{x} p(t)dt,$$

by $[y_1(x)]^2$ gives, for x in J,

$$\frac{d}{dx} \frac{y(x)}{y_1(x)} = c_2 \frac{e^{-P(x)}}{[y_1(x)]^2}$$

so that

$$\frac{y(x)}{y_1(x)} = c_1 + c_2 \int_{x_0}^{x} \frac{e^{-P(s)}}{[y_1(s)]^2} ds$$

and

$$(6.82) \qquad y(x) = c_1 y_1(x) + c_2 y_1(x) \int_{x_0}^{x} \frac{e^{-P(s)}}{[y_1(s)]^2} ds$$

Sometimes the last integral is an elementary function; sometimes it is not.

Problem 6.821

Assuming that one has learned that $\cos ax$ is a solution of $y'' + a^2 y = 0$ but does not know the general solution, show how to apply the above formula.

Problems

The function $y_1(x) = x$ is a solution of each of the following equations:

$$(6.822) \qquad x^2 y'' + xy' - y = 0$$
$$(6.823) \qquad x^3 y'' + xy' - y = 0$$
$$(6.824) \qquad y'' + xy' - y = 0$$

Find the general solutions, and check your answers by differentiation and substitution.

Problem 6.825

There is another (and slightly more tedious) way in which (6.82) may be obtained. Let $y_1(x)$ be a known function which satisfies (6.81) and is different from 0 over an interval J; and let $y(x)$ be a solution of (6.81). Then, when x is in J, we can set $v(x) = y(x)/y_1(x)$ so that $y = y_1 v$. Substitution in (6.81) gives

$$y_1 v'' + (2y_1' + py_1)v' + (y_1'' + py_1' + qy_1)v = 0.$$

Since the coefficient of v in this equation is 0, this is a linear equation of first order with unknown function $v'(x)$. Using the appropriate integrating factor, solve the equation for $v'(x)$. Then find $v(x)$ and finally $y(x)$. The formula (6.82) is your answer. *The method used in this problem is worth remembering.*

6.83. How to Find the Solutions of a Nonhomogeneous Equation When the Homogeneous Equation Has Been Solved.

Suppose $p(x)$, $q(x)$, and $f(x)$ are continuous over I, that $y_1(x)$ and $y_2(x)$ are known linearly independent solutions of the homogeneous equation

$$(6.84) \qquad y'' + p(x)y' + q(x)y = 0,$$

and that solutions $y(x)$ of the equation

$$(6.85) \qquad y'' + p(x)y' + q(x)y = f(x)$$

are sought. An expression giving $y(x)$ in terms of y_1 and y_2 may be found as follows: We can use (6.85) and the result of setting $y = y_1$ in (6.84) to obtain

$$(y_1 y'' - y_1'' y) + p(y_1 y' - y_1' y) = y_1 f.$$

Setting

$$P(x) = \int_{x_0}^{x} p(t)dt$$

as before, we obtain

$$\frac{d}{dx} e^{P(x)}[y_1 y' - y_1' y] = y_1(x)f(x)e^{P(x)}$$

so that

$$(6.851) \qquad e^{P(x)}[y_1 y' - y_1' y] = A + \int_{x_0}^{x} y_1(t)f(t)e^{P(t)}\, dt.$$

In the same way we obtain

$$(6.852) \qquad e^{P(x)}[y_2 y' - y_2' y] = B + \int_{x_0}^{x} y_2(t)f(t)e^{P(t)}\, dt.$$

Multiplying (6.851) and (6.852), respectively, by $y_2(x)$ and $-y_1(x)$ and adding eliminate y' and give

$$(6.853) \qquad e^{P(x)}[y_1(x)y_2'(x) - y_1'(x)y_2(x)]y = Ay_2(x) - By_1(x)$$
$$+ \int_{x_0}^{x} [y_1(t)y_2(x) - y_1(x)y_2(t)]f(t)e^{P(t)}\, dt.$$

Using the Abel formula

(6.854) $$y_1(x)y_2'(x) - y_1'(x)y_2(x) = Ce^{-P(x)}$$

we see that the coefficient of y in the left member is a constant C which is not 0 since y_1 and y_2 are linearly independent. Setting $c_1 = -B/C$ and $c_2 = A/C$, we can write (6.853) in the form

(6.86) $y = c_1 y_1(x) + c_2 y_2(x)$

$$+ \frac{1}{C}\int_{x_0}^{x}[y_1(t)y_2(x) - y_1(x)y_2(t)]f(t)e^{P(t)}\,dt$$

where C and $P(x)$ are given by above formulas.

Problem 6.87

Show that, if $f(t)$ is continuous, then each solution of the equation

(6.871) $$y'' + a^2 y = f(x)$$

has, when $a \neq 0$, the form

(6.872) $$y = c_1 \cos ax + c_2 \sin ax + \frac{1}{a}\int_{x_0}^{x} f(t)\sin a(x - t)\,dt.$$

Problem 6.88

Considering positive values of x, find the general solution of

$$x^2 y'' + xy' - y = 1$$

by use of (6.86) and the fact that the functions x and x^{-1} are solutions of the homogeneous equation. *Ans.* $y = c_1 x + c_2 x^{-1} - 1.$

Problem 6.89

Show that, when one knows a solution $y_1(x)$ of the homogeneous equation which is different from 0 when x lies in an interval J, then the substitution $y = y_1 v$ reduces the problem of solving the equation

$$y'' + p(x)y' + q(x)y = f(x)$$

to the problem of solving a linear nonhomogeneous differential equation of first order. *This furnishes an excellent method of solving problems when the integrals are easily evaluated.* Use the method to solve, when $x > 0$, the equation

$$x^2 y'' + xy' - y = 1,$$

starting with the fact that the homogeneous equation is satisfied when $y = x$. *Ans.:* $y = c_1 x + c_2 x^{-1} - 1.$ This method can be used to derive (6.86), but the details are more involved than those of the derivation in the text.

6.9. Singular Points.—As before, let L_a denote the linear operator

(6.91) $$L_a = a_0(x)D^n + a_1(x)D^{n-1} + \cdots + a_{n-1}(x)D + a_n(x),$$

and let $f(x)$ be a given function of x. A point x for which $a_0(x) = 0$, or at least one of the functions $f(x), a_0(x), a_1(x), \cdots, a_n(x)$ is discontinuous, is called a *singular point* of the differential equation $L_a y = f$. For example, $x = 0$ is a singular point of the differential equation

$$x \frac{dy}{dx} - 2y = 0.$$

Theorems 6.03 and 6.04 do not apply to intervals containing singular points. If one is interested in obtaining a solution of $L_a y = f$ over an interval $x_1 \leqq x \leqq x_2$ containing a single singular point in its interior, the following is a standard procedure: First find solutions of $L_a y = 0$ over the interval $x_1 \leqq x < x_0$ and the solutions over the interval $x_0 < x \leqq x_2$; then find whether (and how) these solutions can be fitted together to give solutions of $L_a y = 0$ over the interval $x_1 \leqq x \leqq x_2$. It is possible to prove theorems which tell what happens in certain special circumstances, but we must be content here with a few examples.

Let k be a constant, and let us seek all functions $y(x)$ satisfying the equation

(6.92) $$x \frac{dy}{dx} - 2y = kx$$

over the infinite interval $-\infty < x < \infty$. If there are no such functions, we should discover the fact. Assuming that $y(x)$ satisfies (6.92) over the infinite interval, we may write, for $x > 0$,

(6.921) $$\frac{dy}{dx} - \frac{2}{x} y = k$$

and find that x^{-2} is an integrating factor so that $x^{-2}y = c_1 - k/x$ and

(6.93) $$y = c_1 x^2 - kx \qquad\qquad x > 0.$$

Likewise c_2 exists such that

(6.931) $$y = c_2 x^2 - kx \qquad\qquad x < 0.$$

Since $y(x)$ must be continuous, we conclude from (6.93) or from (6.931) that $y(0) = 0$. Thus we have shown that if $y(x)$ satisfies (6.92) over $-\infty < x < \infty$ then (6.93) and (6.931) hold and $y(0) = 0$. Conversely, if c_1 and c_2 are constants (which may be either equal or unequal) for which (6.93) and (6.931) hold and $y(0) = 0$, then $y(x)$ satisfies (6.92) over $-\infty < x < \infty$. Thus our problem is solved. We may say that we have a two-parameter family of solutions, but the words do not mean much. The following problems deal with first-order equations (some second-order equations are considered in Section 7.6):

Problems

Find, for each equation below, all functions $y(x)$ satisfying the equation over $-\infty < x < \infty$.

(6.941) $x \dfrac{dy}{dx} + y = 2x$ *Ans.:* $y = x$

(6.942) $x \dfrac{dy}{dx} + 2x^2 y = 1$ *Ans.:* None

CHAPTER 7

USE OF SERIES

7.0. Introduction.—There are several ways in which series are used in studies of differential equations. For example, series are used in Chapters 15 and 16 to obtain fundamental theorems about differential equations. Our work in this chapter deals largely with the problem of finding power series which represent solutions of differential equations. Anyone who happens to know the theory of functions of a complex variable will see that much of the work of this chapter applies to the case in which x is a complex variable as well as the case in which x is a real variable; but this fact need not disturb those who wish to regard x as a real variable.

7.01. Definitions and Fundamental Concepts.—A series

$$(7.02) \qquad u_1 + u_2 + u_3 + \cdots$$

is said to *converge* to y if

$$(7.03) \qquad \lim_{n \to \infty} y_n = y$$

where

$$(7.04) \qquad y_n = u_1 + u_2 + u_3 + \cdots + u_n \qquad n = 1, 2, \cdots.$$

If the series (7.02) converges to y, we write

$$(7.05) \qquad y = u_1 + u_2 + u_3 + \cdots ;$$

and we *always* understand (7.05) to mean that (7.03) holds where $y_1, y_2, y_3, \cdots$ are defined by (7.04). The sequence $y_1, y_2, y_3, \cdots$ is called the *sequence of partial sums* of the series (7.02).* If a series fails to converge, it is said to *diverge*.

---

* Just as an automobile mechanic may be expected to know the difference between a *steering wheel* and a *windshield wiper*, so also a scholar may be expected to know the difference between a *sequence* such as

$$\tfrac{1}{2}, \ \tfrac{1}{4}, \ \tfrac{1}{8}, \ \tfrac{1}{16}, \ \cdots$$

and a *series* such as

$$(7.051) \qquad \tfrac{1}{2} + \tfrac{1}{4} + \tfrac{1}{8} + \tfrac{1}{16} + \cdots.$$

Confusion of terminology in either case leads to misunderstandings. The sequence of partial sums of the series (7.051) is $\tfrac{1}{2}, \ \tfrac{3}{4}, \ \tfrac{7}{8}, \ \tfrac{15}{16}, \ \cdots$.

If $y_1, y_2 \cdots$ is a given sequence, then it is easy to concoct a series $u_1 + u_2 + \cdots$ of which $y_1, y_2, \cdots$ is the sequence of partial sums; we have only to set

$$(7.06) \quad u_1 = y_1; \quad u_2 = y_2 - y_1; \quad u_3 = y_3 - y_2; \quad \cdots .$$

If the sequence $y_1, y_2, \cdots$ converges to y, then we can write either

$$(7.061) \qquad \lim_{n \to \infty} y_n = y_1 + (y_2 - y_1) + (y_3 - y_2) + \cdots$$

or

$$(7.062) \qquad y = y_1 + (y_2 - y_1) + (y_3 - y_2) + \cdots .$$

A series

$$(7.07) \qquad\qquad u_1 + u_2 + u_3 + \cdots$$

is said to be *dominated* by a series

$$(7.071) \qquad\qquad a_1 + a_2 + a_3 + \cdots$$

of constants if $| u_n | \leqq a_n$ for each $n = 1, 2, \cdots$. A fundamental theorem which justifies the *comparison test* for convergence is the following: *If $u_1 + u_2 + \cdots$ is dominated by a convergent series $a_1 + a_2 + \cdots$ of constants, then $u_1 + u_2 + \cdots$ is convergent.*

The following theorem gives criteria for convergence and divergence of series of nonzero terms. The criteria are known, collectively, as *the ratio test. If*

$$(7.08) \qquad\qquad \lim_{n \to \infty} | u_{n+1}/u_n | = \rho$$

and $\rho < 1$, then the series

$$(7.09) \qquad\qquad u_1 + u_2 + u_3 + \cdots$$

converges; if (7.08) *holds and $\rho > 1$, then the series* (7.09) *diverges.* More delicate ratio tests are given in books on series, but they need not concern us here.

7.1. Complex Exponentials.—In the previous chapter, preliminary use was made of complex exponentials; and extensive use of them will be made in following chapters. Since many students of differential equations have not been introduced to these functions, we give a brief discussion of exponentials. The student may know how, when a is a positive real number, the exponential function a^x is defined first when x is a positive integer, next when x is 0, next when x is a negative integer, next when x is a rational number, and then when x is an arbitrary real number. It is made plausible in elementary calculus and

is proved in advanced calculus that a number $e = 2.718281828459045$
$\cdots$ exists such that

$$\lim_{h \to 0} (1 + h)^{1/h} = e$$

and that for each real x

(7.11) $$e^x = 1 + x + \frac{x^2}{2!} + \frac{x^3}{3!} + \frac{x^4}{4!} + \cdots .$$

At this stage in the development of mathematics, the symbol e^x
is undefined and completely meaningless when x is a complex number,
say $x = u + iv$ where u and v are real and i is the imaginary unit with
characteristic property $i^2 = -1$. However, if x is a complex number,
the series in the right member is convergent to a number which we
may (and do) denote by e^x. Thus the equation (7.11) is *proved*
when x is real and is taken as the *definition* of e^x when x is a complex
number which is not real.

Similarly the two formulas

(7.12) $$\cos x = 1 - \frac{x^2}{2!} + \frac{x^4}{4!} - \frac{x^6}{6!} + \cdots$$

(7.13) $$\sin x = x - \frac{x^3}{3!} + \frac{x^5}{5!} - \frac{x^7}{7!} + \cdots$$

are *proved* for real values of x and are used to *define* the left members
when x is a complex number which is not real.

The *Euler formulas* (7.14), (7.141), and (7.142) given below furnish
an important connection between exponential and trigonometric
functions. Replacing x by ix in (7.11) and using the facts that
$i^2 = -1$, $i^3 = -i$, $i^4 = 1$, $i^5 = i$, etc., we obtain

(7.131) $$e^{ix} = 1 + ix - \frac{x^2}{2!} - i\frac{x^3}{3!} + \frac{x^4}{4!} + i\frac{x^5}{5!} - \cdots .$$

It can be shown (by use of theorems involving absolutely convergent
series or otherwise) that the terms of the right member of (7.131)
can be arranged to form the terms of two series and that

(7.132) $$e^{ix} = \left[1 - \frac{x^2}{2!} + \frac{x^4}{4!} - \frac{x^6}{6!} + \cdots \right]$$
$$+ i \left[x - \frac{x^3}{3!} + \frac{x^5}{5!} - \frac{x^7}{7!} + \cdots \right].$$

Using (7.12) and (7.13) we obtain

(7.14) $$e^{ix} = \cos x + i \sin x.$$

Replacing x by $-x$ in (7.14) and using the fact, which is obvious from
(7.12) and (7.13), that $\cos(-x) = \cos x$ and $\sin(-x) = -\sin x$, we

obtain

(7.141) $$e^{-ix} = \cos x - i \sin x.$$

By adding and subtracting (7.14) and (7.141) we obtain

(7.142) $$\cos x = \frac{e^{ix} + e^{-ix}}{2}, \qquad \sin x = \frac{e^{ix} - e^{-ix}}{2i}.$$

It is, insofar as a textbook in differential equations is concerned, an interesting and not irrelevant remark that the Euler formulas (7.142) serve to make trigonometry a part of algebra. For example, the identity

$$\cos^2 x + \sin^2 x = 1$$

is nothing more nor less than the identity

$$\left[\frac{e^{ix} + e^{-ix}}{2} \right]^2 + \left[\frac{e^{ix} - e^{-ix}}{2i} \right]^2 = 1$$

which is easily proved by use of formula (7.15) below.

It is possible to prove that the formula

(7.15) $$e^{x+y} = e^x e^y$$

holds not only when x and y are real numbers but also when x and y are arbitrary complex numbers. Rules for manipulation with series justify the computation

$$
e^{x+y} = \sum_{n=0}^{\infty} \frac{(x+y)^n}{n!} = \sum_{n=0}^{\infty} \sum_{k=0}^{n} \frac{1}{n!} \frac{n!}{k!(n-k)!} x^{n-k} y^k
$$
$$
= \sum_{k=0}^{\infty} \sum_{n=k}^{\infty} \frac{x^{n-k}}{(n-k)!} \frac{y^k}{k!} = \sum_{k=0}^{\infty} \frac{y^k}{k!} \sum_{n=0}^{\infty} \frac{x^n}{n!} = e^y e^x = e^x e^y.
$$

The formula (7.15) implies that complex exponentials obey the rules which govern real exponents. For example, setting $y = x$ in (7.15) gives $(e^x)^2 = e^{2x}$, and setting $y = -x$ gives $e^x e^{-x} = e^0 = 1$. It follows from this that e^x is never 0 and that $e^{-x} = 1/e^x$. Replacing y by iy in (7.15) and using an Euler formula gives

(7.16) $$e^{x+iy} = e^x e^{iy} = e^x(\cos y + i \sin y).$$

This formula is especially helpful to engineers.

If $f_1(x)$ and $f_2(x)$ are real, the derivative and integral of the complex-valued function $f(x) = f_1(x) + if_2(x)$ of a real variable x are defined by the same formulas as those used when $f(x)$ is real. It is easy to show that f is differentiable (or integrable) if and only if f_1

and f_2 are both differentiable (or integrable) and that

(7.171) $$f'(x) = f'_1(x) + if'_2(x)$$

(7.172) $$\int_a^b f(x)dx = \int_a^b f_1(x)dx + i \int_a^b f_2(x)dx$$

whenever the left or right members exist.

When x is a real variable, the formula

(7.173) $$\frac{d}{dx} e^{mx} = me^{mx}$$

holds when m is a complex constant as well as when m is a real constant. This formula is proved by the computation

$$\frac{d}{dx} e^{mx} = \frac{d}{dx}\left[1 + mx + \frac{(mx)^2}{2!} + \frac{(mx)^3}{3!} + \cdots\right]$$

$$= 0 + m + m(mx) + m\frac{(mx)^2}{2!} + \cdots = me^{mx},$$

the termwise differentiation of the series in brackets being justified by Theorem 7.24. Another proof can be obtained by differentiating

$$e^{mx} = e^{m_1x}(\cos m_2x + i \sin m_2x)$$

where $m = m_1 + im_2$, and m_1 and m_2 are real. Using this result and ordinary rules for differentiation, we find that, if $f(x) = f_1(x) + if_2(x)$ is a differentiable function of x, then

(7.174) $$\frac{d}{dx} e^{f(x)} = \frac{d}{dx} e^{f_1(x)}e^{if_2(x)}$$

$$= e^{f_1(x)}[if'_2(x)e^{if_2(x)}] + e^{if_2(x)}[f'_1(x)e^{f_1(x)}]$$

$$= [f'_1(x) + if'_2(x)]e^{f_1(x)+if_2(x)} = f'(x)e^{f(x)}.$$

This shows that the derivative of $e^{f(x)}$ is computed by the formula which is used when $f(x)$ is real.

It follows that the equation

(7.18) $$\frac{dy}{dx} + p(x)y = q(x),$$

in which $p(x)$ and $q(x)$ are complex-valued continuous functions of a real variable x, is satisfied by $y(x)$ if and only if

(7.181) $$\frac{d}{dx} e^{P(x)}y = e^{P(x)}q(x)$$

and

(7.182) $$y = ce^{-P(x)} + Q(x)$$

where c is a constant and

$$(7.183) \qquad P(x) = \int_{x_0}^{x} p(t)dt; \qquad Q(x) = e^{-P(x)} \int_{x_0}^{x} e^{P(t)} q(t) dt.$$

Thus solutions of (7.18) are obtained by methods exactly like the methods used when $p(x)$ and $q(x)$ are real.

If x is a positive number and z is a complex number, then x^z is *defined* by the formula

$$(7.19) \qquad\qquad x^z = e^{z \log x};$$

if x is e, the extended definition agrees with the preceding. It is easy to show that, if m is a complex constant, then

$$(7.191) \qquad\qquad \frac{d}{dx} x^m = mx^{m-1} \qquad\qquad x > 0.$$

Do it. The following problem is an exercise in use of exponentials; it deals with the important Laplace equation.

Problem 7.192

For what constant values of a and b does the function $u = e^{ax+by}$ satisfy the *Laplace equation*

$$(7.193) \qquad\qquad \frac{\partial^2 u}{\partial x^2} + \frac{\partial^2 u}{\partial y^2} = 0?$$

Ans.: Those for which $b = \pm ia$. Use your result to show that, when a is a constant, the functions $e^{ax} \cos ay$ and $e^{ax} \sin ay$ satisfy (7.193). Is it true that each linear combination of solutions of (7.193) is also a solution of (7.193)? Show that if $\phi_1(a)$ and $\phi_2(a)$ are functions for which the integral has derivatives equal to the integrals of the derivatives of the integrand (that is, if differentiation under the integral sign is permitted), then the function $u(x, y)$ defined by

$$(7.194) \qquad\qquad u = \int_{-\infty}^{\infty} e^{ax} [\phi_1(a) e^{iay} + \phi_2(a) e^{-iay}] da$$

is a solution of (7.193). Evaluate (in terms of elementary functions) the integral for the case in which $\phi_2(a)$ is always 0, and $\phi_1(a)$ is 0 except where $0 \le a \le 1$ when $\phi_1(a) = 1$. *Ans.:* $u = 1$ when $x = y = 0$; otherwise $u = (e^{x+iy} - 1)/(x + iy)$. Separation of the real and imaginary parts of u gives

$$u = \frac{e^x(y \sin y + x \cos y) - x}{x^2 + y^2} + i \frac{e^x(x \sin y - y \cos y) + y}{x^2 + y^2}.$$

7.2. Power Series.—The series (7.11), (7.12), and (7.13) for e^x, $\cos x$, and $\sin x$ are *power series*, in particular, series in powers of x. A function $f(x)$ is represented as a *power series in* $(x - a)$ or a *Taylor series* if

$$(7.21) \qquad f(x) = c_0 + c_1(x - a) + c_2(x - a)^2 + \cdots ;$$

and $f(x)$ is represented as a *power series in x* or a *Maclaurin series* if

(7.22) $f(x) = c_0 + c_1x + c_2x^2 + \cdots$.

In each case, the c's are constants. The series in (7.21) can be made to look like the series in (7.22) by introducing a new variable X defined by $X = x - a$. Most courses in elementary calculus contain some exercises (but very little theory) involving power series. Power series have many uses in pure and applied mathematics, and in particular they are often used in the solution of differential equations.

The three power series

(7.231) $1 + x + \dfrac{x^2}{2!} + \dfrac{x^3}{3!} + \cdots$

(7.232) $1 + x + x^2 + x^3 + \cdots$

(7.233) $1 + 1!x + 2!x^2 + 3!x^3 + \cdots$

represent three types of power series in x. The first converges for all x. The second converges when $|x| < 1$ and diverges (that is, fails to converge) when $|x| > 1$. The third diverges for all $x \neq 0$. It is an interesting and important fact that, insofar as convergence properties are concerned, power series fall into three classes. The following facts are given without proof.

Some power series such as (7.231) converge for all x; these are the easiest to use. Some power series such as (7.233) diverge for each $x \neq 0$; these can be used only by specialists in series. Each other power series converges for some $x \neq 0$ and diverges for some $x \neq 0$; to each such series corresponds a positive number R, called the *radius of convergence* of the power series, such that the series converges when $|x| < R$ and the series diverges when $|x| > R$.

If the series *converges* for all x, it is convenient and customary to say that *the radius of convergence is infinite*, to write $R = \infty$, and to say that $|x| < R$ for each x. If the series diverges for all $x \neq 0$, it is convenient and customary to say that *the radius of convergence is 0*, to write $R = 0$, and to say that $|x| < R$ is satisfied for no x. This terminology is so constructed that *each power series has a radius of convergence R and the series is convergent when $|x| < R$*.

The following theorem, of which the best proofs are to be found in books on complex variables, is so important and useful that one should know it even though one does not know how to prove it:

THEOREM 7.24.—*If $\Sigma c_n x^n$ converges when $|x| < R$ and*

(7.241) $f(x) = c_0 + c_1x + c_2x^2 + c_3x^3 + \cdots$ $|x| < R,$

then $f(x)$ is differentiable and integrable when $|x| < R$ and the derivative *and integral may be obtained by termwise differentiation and integration so that*

(7.242) $f'(x) = 0 + c_1 + 2c_2x + 3c_3x^2 + \cdots$ $|x| < R$

and

(7.243) $\int_0^x f(t)dt = c_0x + \frac{c_1}{2}x^2 + \frac{c_2}{3}x^3 + \frac{c_3}{4}x^4 + \cdots$ $|x| < R.$

Another result which we need is given by the following:

THEOREM 7.25.—*If $R > 0$,*

(7.251) $f_1(x) = c_0 + c_1x + c_2x^2 + c_3x^3 + \cdots$ $|x| < R$

and

(7.252) $f_2(x) = d_0 + d_1x + d_2x^2 + d_3x^3 + \cdots,$ $|x| < R$

then $f_1(x) = f_2(x)$ when $|x| < R$ if and only if

(7.253) $c_0 = d_0; \quad c_1 = d_1; \quad c_2 = d_2; \quad \cdots .$

Problem 7.26

Starting with the formula obtained by setting $x = -t^2$ in (7.11), prove that for each real x,

$$\int_0^x e^{-t^2}\,dt = x - \frac{1}{3}\frac{x^3}{1!} + \frac{1}{5}\frac{x^5}{2!} - \frac{1}{7}\frac{x^7}{3!} + \frac{1}{9}\frac{x^9}{4!} - \cdots .$$

Problem 7.27

Show that

$$\frac{1}{1+x} = 1 - x + x^2 - x^3 + x^4 - x^5 + \cdots,$$

the series being convergent when $|x| < 1$ and divergent when $|x| > 1$. Use this result, Theorem 7.24, and the fact that log $1 = 0$ to prove that

$$\log(1+x) = x - \frac{x^2}{2} + \frac{x^3}{3} - \frac{x^4}{4} + \cdots,$$

the series being convergent when $|x| < 1$ and divergent when $|x| > 1$.

7.3. Power-series Solutions.—The best way to obtain an idea of the technique involved in solving differential equations by means of power series is to understand a simple example. Let us try to solve the equation

(7.31) $$\frac{dy}{dx} = ky,$$

k being a constant, by trying to find constants $c_0, c_1, c_2, \cdots$ and a constant $R > 0$ such that the series

(7.32) $y = c_0 + c_1x + c_2x^2 + c_3x^3 + \cdots$

will converge for $|x| < R$ to a solution $y = y(x)$ of (7.31). To attack the problem in an intelligent fashion, let us *assume* that $c_0, c_1, \cdots,$

and R represent constants for which (7.32) satisfies (7.31) when $|x| < R$. Then from (7.32) we obtain

$$\frac{dy}{dx} = c_1 + 2c_2 x + 3c_3 x^2 + 4c_4 x^3 + \cdots \qquad |x| < R$$

and

$$ky = kc_0 + kc_1 x + kc_2 x^2 + kc_3 x^3 + \cdots \qquad |x| < R.$$

Therefore

$$c_1 = kc_0; \qquad 2c_2 = kc_1; \qquad 3c_3 = kc_2; \qquad 4c_4 = kc_3; \qquad \cdots$$

so that

$$c_1 = c_0 k; \qquad c_2 = \frac{c_0 k^2}{2!}; \qquad c_3 = \frac{c_0 k^3}{3!}; \qquad \cdots .$$

Putting these expressions for the c's in (7.32) gives, when $|x| < R$,

$$(7.33) \quad y = c_0 \left[1 + \frac{kx}{1} + \frac{(kx)^2}{2!} + \frac{(kx)^3}{3!} + \frac{(kx)^4}{4!} + \cdots \right].$$

What we have shown so far is that, *if* (7.31) has a solution of the form (7.32), then $y(x)$ must have the form (7.33). The next step is to examine (7.33) to see whether it really does furnish a solution of (7.31). It can be shown (by the ratio test, for example) that the series in (7.33) converges for all x; we may take $R = \infty$ and show that (7.33) satisfies (7.31) for all x.

Thus we have obtained a solution of the differential equation in the form of a series. It happens that the series in (7.33) is the power-series expansion of $c_0 e^{kx}$, and we may therefore present our solutions in the familiar form $y = c_0 e^{kx}$. It is important to emphasize the fact that (7.33) would still be a solution of (7.31) if we were unable to see that the series in (7.33) converges to a familiar elementary function. Frequently one is unable to see that series solutions converge to familiar elementary functions for the simple reason that functions defined by power series are frequently not elementary functions.

Problems

Find the solutions of the following equations representable in the form $y = c_0 + c_1 x + c_2 x^2 + \cdots$:

(7.34)	$\dfrac{dy}{dx} = 2xy$	*Ans.:* $y = ce^{x^2}$
(7.35)	$x \dfrac{dy}{dx} = y$	*Ans.:* $y = cx$
(7.36)	$x^2 \dfrac{dy}{dx} = y$	*Ans.:* $y = 0$
(7.37)	$\dfrac{dy}{dx} = x + y$	*Ans.:* $y = ce^x - 1 - x$

Problem 7.38

Find the solutions of (7.36) which are representable in the form

$$y = c_0 + c_1 x^{-1} + c_2 x^{-2} + c_3 x^{-3} + \cdots . \qquad Ans.: y = ce^{-1/x}.$$

7.4. Some Equations of Second Order.—The equations solved in Section 7.3 were of the first order. In this section, we apply the method to the second-order equation

$$(7.41) \qquad\qquad y'' = xy.$$

Assuming that

$$y = c_0 + c_1 x + c_2 x^2 + c_3 x^3 + \cdots$$

is a solution of (7.41) we can compare coefficients in the series

$$y'' = 2c_2 + 3 \cdot 2c_3 x + 4 \cdot 3c_4 x^2 + \cdots$$
$$xy = \quad 0 + \quad c_0 x + \quad c_1 x^2 + \cdots$$

to see that

$$2c_2 = 0; \qquad 3 \cdot 2c_3 = c_0; \qquad 4 \cdot 3c_4 = c_1; \qquad 5 \cdot 4c_5 = c_2; \qquad \cdots .$$

Hence $c_2 = c_5 = c_8 = \cdots = 0$, and we can express the remaining c's in terms of c_0 and c_1 to obtain

$$(7.42) \quad y = c_0 \left(1 + \frac{x^3}{2 \cdot 3} + \frac{x^6}{2 \cdot 3 \cdot 5 \cdot 6} + \frac{x^9}{2 \cdot 3 \cdot 5 \cdot 6 \cdot 8 \cdot 9} + \cdots \right)$$
$$+ c_1 \left(x + \frac{x^4}{3 \cdot 4} + \frac{x^7}{3 \cdot 4 \cdot 6 \cdot 7} + \frac{x^{10}}{3 \cdot 4 \cdot 6 \cdot 7 \cdot 9 \cdot 10} + \cdots \right).$$

Each series converges for all values of x, and (7.42) is the general solution* of (7.41).

Problem 7.43

Prove that the functions in the parentheses in (7.42) are linearly independent and hence that (7.42) really is the general solution of (7.41).

Problem 7.44

Use the method of this section to solve the equation $y'' + y = 0$.

Problem 7.45

Find the first few terms of the expansion in powers of x of the function $y(x)$ for which $y(0) = 1$, $y'(0) = 0$, and $(1 - x)y'' = xy$.

---

* It is no disgrace to fail to know whether the series in parentheses are elementary functions of x. But it is a disgrace to fail to see that they are nevertheless impeccable functions of x whose values can be computed just as values of $\cos x$ and $\sin x$ can be computed from their series expansions. If the functions were named, respectively, jos x and jin x, the general solution of (7.41) would then be

$$y = c_0 \text{ jos } x + c_1 \text{ jin } x.$$

Problem 7.46

Find the first few terms of the expansion in powers of x of the function $y(x)$ for which $y(0) = 0$, $y'(0) = 1$, and $y'' - xy' - x^2 y = 0$.

7.5. A Nonlinear Example.—We shall not give much space here to the important and difficult problems involved in solving nonlinear differential equations, but we consider briefly the example

(7.51) $$y'' = x^2 + y^2.$$

Assuming that

(7.52) $$y = c_0 + c_1 x + c_2 x^2 + c_3 x^3 + \cdots$$

is a solution of (7.51) for some range of values of x, we find

$$y'' = 1 \cdot 2c_2 + 2 \cdot 3c_3 x + 3 \cdot 4c_4 x^2 + 4 \cdot 5c_5 x^3 + \cdots$$

and

$$x^2 + y^2 = c_0^2 + (c_0 c_1 + c_1 c_0)x + (1 + c_0 c_2 + c_1 c_1 + c_2 c_0)x^2$$
$$+ (c_0 c_3 + c_1 c_2 + c_2 c_1 + c_3 c_0)x^3 + (c_0 c_4 + c_1 c_3 + c_2 c_2 + c_3 c_1 + c_4 c_0)x^4 + \cdots.$$

Equating coefficients of like powers of x, we obtain equations that determine $c_2, c_3, c_4, \cdots$ in terms of c_0 and c_1. Substituting these values in (7.52) gives

(7.53) $$y = c_0 + c_1 x + \tfrac{1}{2}c_0^2 x^2 + \tfrac{1}{3}c_0 c_1 x^3 + \tfrac{1}{12}(1 + c_0^3 + c_1^2)x^4 + \tfrac{1}{12}c_0^2 c_1 x^5$$
$$+ \tfrac{1}{360}(2c_0 + 5c_0^4 + 10c_0 c_1^2)x^6 + \cdots.$$

We do not enter into the question of convergence of (7.53). A student who wishes to pursue a study of (7.53) may well pay attention firstly to the case in which $c_0 = c_1 = 0$ and accordingly $y(0) = y'(0) = 0$. In this case, many of the coefficients in (7.53) vanish.

Problem 7.54

We saw in Section 5.9 that $y(x) = \tan x$ is the unique function which satisfies the condition $y(0) = 0$ and

(7.541) $$\frac{dy}{dx} = 1 + y^2 \qquad\qquad -\frac{\pi}{2} < x < \frac{\pi}{2}.$$

Let us use also the fact (which we do not prove here) that $\tan x$ can be represented in the form

(7.542) $$\tan x = c_1 x + c_3 x^3 + c_5 x^5 + c_7 x^7 + \cdots,$$

the series being convergent when $|x| < \pi/2$. By determining the c's so that the right member of (7.542) satisfies (7.541), show that when $|x| < \pi/2$

(7.55) $$\tan x = x + \frac{1}{3}x^3 + \frac{2}{15}x^5 + \frac{17}{315}x^7 + \frac{62}{2,835}x^9 + \frac{1,382}{155,925}x^{11} + \cdots.$$

Problem 7.56

Use the result of the previous problem to obtain several terms of the power-series expansions of $\sec^2 x$ and $\log \cos x$.

Remark 7.57

It is often possible to use power series in a purely formal way to discover solutions of equations. Suppose functions $u(x, y)$ are sought for which the partial differential equation

$$(7.571) \qquad x \frac{\partial u}{\partial x} + y \frac{\partial u}{\partial y} = 2u$$

holds. A function of the form

$$u = \sum a_{j,k} x^i y^k,$$

for which formal differentiation gives

$$x \frac{\partial u}{\partial x} = \sum j a_{j,k} x^i y^k; \qquad y \frac{\partial u}{\partial y} = \sum k a_{j,k} x^i y^k,$$

should satisfy (7.571) if

$$\sum (j + k - 2) a_{j,k} x^i y^k = 0$$

and hence if $a_{j,k} = 0$ when $j + k - 2 \neq 0$ or $j \neq 2 - k$. Thus functions of the form

$$u = \sum A_k x^{2-k} y^k = x^2 \sum A_\kappa \left(\frac{y}{x}\right)^k$$

should satisfy (7.571). But since $\Sigma A_k (y/x)^k$ can, for different choices of the A's, represent many different functions of y/x, one may suspect that the function

$$(7.572) \qquad u = x^2 \phi \left(\frac{y}{x}\right)$$

will satisfy (7.571) for many different functions ϕ. Actually, it is easy to show that if ϕ is differentiable, then (7.572) satisfies (7.571) when $x \neq 0$. Do this. [According to Section 5.6 a function $f(x, y)$ which is homogeneous in x and y of degree 2 can be written in the form $x^2 \phi(y/x)$.]

Problem 7.58

Use the formal method of Remark 7.57 to discover solutions of the equation

$$x \frac{\partial u}{\partial x} + y \frac{\partial u}{\partial y} = ku$$

where k is a constant. You may check your results by differentiation and substitution. For the case in which $k = 0$, the results may be compared with those of Problem 2.256; for the case $k = 2$, with Problem 7.57.

7.6. An Important Special Case.—Three famous linear differential equations with nonconstant coefficients are

$$(7.61) \quad (x^2 - x) \frac{d^2 y}{dx^2} + [(\alpha + \beta + 1)x - \gamma] \frac{dy}{dx} + \alpha \beta y = 0$$

(hypergeometric)

$$(7.62) \qquad x^2 \frac{d^2y}{dx^2} + x \frac{dy}{dx} + (x^2 - \alpha^2)y = 0 \qquad \text{(Bessel)}$$

$$(7.63) \qquad (1 - x^2) \frac{d^2y}{dx^2} - 2x \frac{dy}{dx} + \alpha(\alpha + 1)y = 0 \qquad \text{(Legendre)}$$

where the Greek letters represent constants. These equations are, as indicated by the names at the right, known as the *hypergeometric differential equation, Bessel's differential equation,* and *Legendre's differential equation.* Each is important because of its applications. Each is a linear differential equation of the second order with coefficients which are polynomials in the independent variable. Thus each equation has the form

$$(7.64) \qquad Py'' + Qy' + Ry = 0$$

where P, Q, and R are polynomials in x. As in Chapter 6, let

$$(7.65) \qquad Ly = Py'' + Qy' + Ry$$

so that L is a linear operator and (7.64) may be written $Ly = 0$.

A standard method of seeking solutions of $Ly = 0$ is to seek to determine an exponent m (which may or may not be an integer) and a set of coefficients $c_0, c_1, c_2, \cdots$ such that

$$(7.66) \qquad y = x^m(c_0 + c_1x + c_2x^2 + \cdots)$$

will converge and be a solution of $Ly = 0$ for some range of values of x. This method is known as the *method of Frobenius.* In any case in which $m < 0$, let x be restricted to a range over which $x \neq 0$. If r has one of the values $m, m + 1, m + 2, \cdots$, then

$$(7.661) \qquad \begin{aligned} Lx^r &= Pr(r - 1)x^{r-2} + Qrx^{r-1} + Rx^r \\ &= [r(r - 1)P + rxQ + x^2R]x^{r-2}. \end{aligned}$$

If y is defined by (7.66), then

$$(7.662) \qquad y = \sum_{n=0}^{\infty} c_n x^{m+n}$$

and

$$(7.663) \qquad Ly = \sum_{n=0}^{\infty} c_n Lx^{m+n}$$

$$= \sum_{n=0}^{\infty} c_n[(m + n)(m + n - 1)P + (m + n)xQ + x^2R]x^{m+n-2}.$$

When the last series is expanded and coefficients of like powers of x are collected, we obtain

$$(7.664) \qquad Ly = A_0x^q + A_1x^{q+1} + A_2x^{q+2} + \cdots$$

where q is one of the exponents $m - 2$, $m - 1$, m, $m + 1$, $\cdots$; where the coefficients A_0, A_1, A_2, $\cdots$ are determined in terms of m and c_0, c_1, c_2, $\cdots$; and where $A_0 \neq 0$ unless special values are given to m or to the c's. The next step is to try to determine m so that the *indicial equation* $A_0 = 0$ is satisfied, and then to try to determine the c's so that $A_1 = 0$, $A_2 = 0$, $A_3 = 0$, $\cdots$. If one succeeds in making these determinations of m and c_0, c_1, c_2, $\cdots$, then

$$(7.665) \qquad y = x^m(c_0 + c_1 x + c_2 x^2 + \cdots)$$

is a solution of $Ly = 0$ for the range (if any) of values of x for which the series converges and $x \neq 0$ if $m < 0$.

We illustrate the method of this section by finding solutions of the three equations (7.61), (7.62), and (7.63) in the following sections.

7.7. The Hypergeometric Equation.—When

$$(7.71) \qquad Ly = (x^2 - x)\frac{d^2y}{dx^2} + [(\alpha + \beta + 1)x - \gamma]\frac{dy}{dx} + \alpha\beta y,$$

the hypergeometric equation becomes $Ly = 0$. We find that

$$(7.72) \qquad Lx^r = r(1 - \gamma - r)x^{r-1} + (\alpha + r)(\beta + r)x^r.$$

Hence, if

$$(7.73) \qquad y = x^m \sum_{n=0}^{\infty} c_n x^n = \sum_{n=0}^{\infty} c_n x^{m+n}$$

for some range of values of x, then*

$$
\begin{aligned}
(7.74) \quad Ly &= \sum_{n=0}^{\infty} c_n L x^{m+n} \\
&= \sum_{n=0}^{\infty} c_n[(m + n)(1 - \gamma - m - n)x^{m+n-1} \\
&\qquad\qquad + (\alpha + m + n)(\beta + m + n)x^{m+n}] \\
&= c_0 m(1 - \gamma - m)x^{m-1} \\
&\quad + \sum_{n=1}^{\infty} c_n(m + n)(1 - \gamma - m - n)x^{m+n-1} \\
&\quad + \sum_{n=0}^{\infty} c_n(\alpha + m + n)(\beta + m + n)x^{m+n} \\
&= c_0 m(1 - \gamma - m)x^{m-1} \\
&\quad + \sum_{n=0}^{\infty} [-c_{n+1}(m + n + 1)(\gamma + m + n) \\
&\qquad\qquad + c_n(\alpha + m + n)(\beta + m + n)]x^{m+n}.
\end{aligned}
$$

*Students unaccustomed to use of the symbol Σ should not be dismayed by the appearance of such formulas as (7.74). They should on the one hand write the first few terms of the series followed by the traditional 3 dots and should on the other hand become familiar with use of the symbol.

The next step is to try to determine m such that the *indicial equation*

(7.741) $$c_0 m(1 - \gamma - m) = 0$$

holds and then to determine the c's such that

(7.742) $\quad (m + n + 1)(\gamma + m + n)c_{n+1}$
$$= (\alpha + m + n)(\beta + m + n)c_n \qquad n = 0, 1, 2, \cdots.$$

If $\gamma \neq 0, -1, -2, -3, \cdots$, we can satisfy (7.741) by setting $m = 0$, let $c_0 = 1$, and determine $c_1, c_2, c_3, \cdots$ from (7.742) to obtain the series in the right member of the equation

(7.75) $\quad F(\alpha, \beta, \gamma; x) = 1 + \dfrac{\alpha \cdot \beta}{\gamma \cdot 1} x + \dfrac{\alpha(\alpha + 1)\beta(\beta + 1)}{\gamma(\gamma + 1)1 \cdot 2} x^2 + \cdots$

$\quad + \dfrac{\alpha(\alpha + 1) \cdots (\alpha + n - 1)\beta(\beta + 1) \cdots (\beta + n - 1)}{\gamma(\gamma + 1) \cdots (\gamma + n - 1)1 \cdot 2 \cdots n} x^n$

$\quad + \cdots.$

This series is known as the *hypergeometric series*. The function to which it converges is known as the *hypergeometric function*, and it is denoted by $F(\alpha, \beta, \gamma; x)$ as indicated in (7.75). If α or β is 0 or a negative integer, the function is a polynomial; otherwise the series is a power series with radius of convergence 1, as may be shown by the ratio test. Thus, if $\gamma \neq 0, -1, -2, \cdots$, then (7.75) defines a function satisfying the hypergeometric equation when[*] $|x| < 1$.

Returning to (7.741) and (7.742) we see that if $\gamma \neq 1, 2, 3, \cdots$ we can satisfy (7.741) by setting $m = 1 - \gamma$, let $c_0 = 1$, and determine $c_1, c_2, c_3, \cdots$ from (7.742) to obtain

(7.77) $$x^{1-\gamma}F(\alpha - \gamma + 1, \beta - \gamma + 1, 2 - \gamma; x)$$

as a solution of the hypergeometric equation over the interval

$$0 < x < 1$$

and over the interval $-1 < x < 0$.

[*] Anyone who happens to know the theory of *analytic extension*, which is best known as a part of the theory of analytic functions of a complex variable, should see that analytic extension furnishes a solution for wider ranges of x. Anyone not so fortunate can form an idea of the meaning of this remark from the following example: For the equation

(7.76) $$(x^2 - x)y'' + (3x - 1)y' + y = 0$$

we have $\alpha = \beta = \gamma = 1$. From (7.75) we see that

(7.761) $\qquad F(1, 1, 1; x) = 1 + x + x^2 + \cdots = \dfrac{1}{1 - x} \qquad |x| < 1.$

Therefore $1/(1 - x)$ satisfies (7.76) when $|x| < 1$, and one may guess that the same is true for other values of $x \neq 1$. Substitution shows that the guess is correct.

Thus, if γ is not an integer, we have two linearly independent functions, say $y_1(x)$ and $y_2(x)$, satisfying the hypergeometric equation $Ly = 0$ over the interval $0 < x < 1$; and accordingly each function satisfying $Ly = 0$ over the interval $0 < x < 1$ must (Theorem 6.04) be a linear combination of $y_1(x)$ and $y_2(x)$. Since $x = 0$ is a singular point of $Ly = 0$, Theorem 6.04 does not apply to the whole interval $-1 \leq x \leq 1$.

Whether γ is an integer or not, at least one of the two functions in (7.75) and (7.77) must be solution of $Ly = 0$ over the interval $0 < x < 1$; let one be denoted by $y_1(x)$. It is easy to show that, for each sufficiently small positive number x_0, $y_1(x) \neq 0$ when $0 < x \leq x_0$. Then, using the method of Section 6.8, we find that each solution of $Ly = 0$ may be represented over the interval $0 < x \leq x_0$ by the formula

$$(7.78) \quad y(x) = cy_1(x) + c_2 y_1(x) \int_{x_0}^{x} \frac{1}{s^{\gamma}(1 - s)^{\alpha+\beta-\gamma+1}[y_1(s)]^2}\, ds.$$

This formula is useful for obtaining properties of $y(x)$ when x is near 0, but we do not press this matter here.

Problem 7.79

If A, B, C, D, E, and F are constants for which $A \neq 0$ and $B^2 - 4AC \neq 0$, the equation

$$(7.791) \qquad (At^2 + Bt + C)\frac{d^2y}{dt^2} + (Dt + E)\frac{dy}{dt} + Fy = 0$$

can be transformed into a hypergeometric equation by a simple change of variable. Show that constants p and q can be determined such that $p \neq 0$ and that, when $t = px + q$, (7.791) holds if and only if

$$(7.792) \qquad (x^2 - x)\frac{d^2y}{dx^2} + (Gx + H)\frac{dy}{dx} + Iy = 0$$

where G, H, and I are appropriate constants. Then show that constants α, β, and γ can be determined so that (7.792) takes the form

$$(x^2 - x)\frac{d^2y}{dx^2} + [(\alpha + \beta + 1)x - \gamma]\frac{dy}{dx} + \alpha\beta y = 0$$

of a hypergeometric equation. What conclusion can be drawn from this work?

7.8. Bessel's Equation.—When

$$(7.81) \qquad Ly = x^2\frac{d^2y}{dx^2} + x\frac{dy}{dx} + (x^2 - \alpha^2)y,$$

Bessel's equation becomes $Ly = 0$. We find in this case

$$(7.82) \qquad Lx^r = (r^2 - \alpha^2)x^r + x^{r+2}.$$

Hence, if

$$(7.83) \qquad y = x^m \sum_{n=0}^{\infty} c_n x^n = \sum_{n=0}^{\infty} c_n x^{m+n}$$

for some range of values of x, then

$$(7.831) \quad Ly = \sum_{n=0}^{\infty} c_n L x^{m+n} = \sum_{n=0}^{\infty} c_n [\{(m+n)^2 - \alpha^2\} x^{m+n} + x^{m+n+2}]$$
$$= c_0 \{m^2 - \alpha^2\} x^m + c_1 \{(m+1)^2 - \alpha^2\} x^{m+1}$$
$$+ \sum_{n=0}^{\infty} [\{(m+n+2)^2 - \alpha^2\} c_{n+2} + c_n] x^{m+n+2}.$$

The next step is to try to determine m such that the *indicial equation*

$$(7.832) \qquad c_0 \{m^2 - \alpha^2\} = 0$$

holds and then to determine the c's such that

$$(7.833) \qquad c_1 \{(m+1)^2 - \alpha^2\} = 0$$

and

$$(7.834) \qquad \{(m+n+2)^2 - \alpha^2\} c_{n+2} = -c_n \qquad n = 0, 1, 2, \cdots .$$

If α is not a negative integer, we can set $m = \alpha$, set* $c_0 = 1/2^\alpha \alpha!$, set $c_1 = 0$, and then determine $c_2, c_3, \cdots$ from (7.834) to obtain the series in the right member of the equation

---

* Many students of differential equations are unacquainted with the definition and properties of the factorial function $\alpha!$ except in the cases in which $\alpha = 0, 1, 2, \cdots$. The values of $\alpha!$ and the reasons for setting $c_0 = 1/2^\alpha \alpha!$ need not concern us here. The *factorial function* $\alpha!$, which is the same as the *gamma function* $\Gamma(\alpha + 1)$, is defined for $\alpha \neq -1, -2, -3, \cdots$ by the formula

$$\alpha! = \lim_{n \to \infty} \frac{n^\alpha}{\left(1 + \frac{\alpha}{1}\right)\left(1 + \frac{\alpha}{2}\right)\left(1 + \frac{\alpha}{3}\right) \cdots \left(1 + \frac{\alpha}{n}\right)}.$$

By use of this formula, it is easy to prove that $(\alpha + 1)! = \alpha!(\alpha + 1)$ when $\alpha \neq -1, -2, -3, \cdots$; this is called the *functional equation of the factorial function*. The formulas

$$\left(-\frac{1}{2}\right)! = \sqrt{\pi}, \qquad \left(\frac{1}{2}\right)! = \frac{\sqrt{\pi}}{2}, \qquad \int_0^1 t^\alpha (1-t)^\beta \, dt = \frac{\alpha! \beta!}{(\alpha + \beta + 1)!}$$

are more esoteric. The factorial function is a nonelementary function for which graphs, tables, and references to literature may be found in the Jahnke-Emde book cited in Section 2.6.

$$(7.84) \quad J_\alpha(x) = \frac{x^\alpha}{2^\alpha \alpha!}\left[1 - \frac{1}{1(\alpha+1)}\left(\frac{x}{2}\right)^2 + \frac{1}{1\cdot 2(\alpha+1)(\alpha+2)}\left(\frac{x}{2}\right)^4\right.$$

$$- \cdots + (-1)^n \frac{1}{1\cdot 2 \cdots n(\alpha+1)(\alpha+2)\cdots(\alpha+n)}\left(\frac{x}{2}\right)^{2n}$$

$$\left. + \cdots \right].$$

The series in brackets converges for all values of x; the function on the right is called *Bessel's function of the first kind of order* α and is denoted by $J_\alpha(x)$ as in (7.84). Using the fundamental formula $\alpha!(\alpha+1) = (\alpha+1)!$, we can write (7.84) in the form

$$(7.85) \quad J_\alpha(x) = \left(\frac{x}{2}\right)^\alpha \left[\frac{1}{0!\alpha!} - \frac{1}{1!(\alpha+1)!}\left(\frac{x}{2}\right)^2 + \frac{1}{2!(\alpha+2)!}\left(\frac{x}{2}\right)^4\right.$$

$$\left. + \cdots + (-1)^n \frac{1}{n!(\alpha+n)!}\left(\frac{x}{2}\right)^{2n} + \cdots \right]$$

$$\alpha \neq -1, -2, -3, \cdots .$$

In particular,

$$(7.851) \quad J_0(x) = 1 - \frac{x^2}{2^2} + \frac{x^4}{2^2 4^2} - \frac{x^6}{2^2 4^2 6^2} + \frac{x^8}{2^2 4^2 6^2 8^2} - \cdots .$$

If $\alpha \geq 0$, the function $J_\alpha(x)$ is a solution of Bessel's equation $Ly = 0$ over the entire infinite interval $-\infty < x < \infty$.

If $\alpha < 0$ but $\alpha \neq -1, -2, -3, \cdots$, $J_\alpha(x)$ is a solution of Bessel's equation $Ly = 0$ over the infinite interval $x > 0$; but

$$(7.852) \qquad\qquad \lim_{x \to 0+} J_\alpha(x) = +\infty .$$

When α is not a positive integer, we can set $m = -\alpha$ and proceed exactly as above to show that $J_{-\alpha}(x)$ is a solution of $Ly = 0$ at least over the infinite interval $x > 0$.

When α is not an integer, the functions $J_\alpha(x)$ and $J_{-\alpha}(x)$ are linearly independent, and accordingly we obtain the following result which we formulate as a theorem:

THEOREM 7.86.—*If* α *is not an integer, then each function* $y(x)$ *satisfying Bessel's equation*

$$(7.861) \qquad\qquad x^2 \frac{d^2y}{dx^2} + x\frac{dy}{dx} + (x^2 - \alpha^2)y = 0$$

over the interval $x > 0$ *must have the form*

$$(7.862) \qquad\qquad y(x) = c_1 J_\alpha(x) + c_2 J_{-\alpha}(x)$$

where c_1 *and* c_2 *are constants.*

If $\alpha \geqq 0$ and α is not an integer, then the statement involving (7.852) implies that $J_{-\alpha}(x)$ is not bounded over the interval $0 < x \leqq 1$. Since $J_\alpha(x)$ is bounded over the interval $0 < x \leqq 1$, this fact and Theorem 7.86 imply the conclusion of the following theorem for the case in which α is not an integer.

THEOREM 7.87.—*If $\alpha \geqq 0$, then each function $y(x)$ which satisfies Bessel's equation over the interval $x > 0$ and which is bounded over the interval $0 < x \leqq 1$ must have the form*

$$(7.871) \qquad\qquad y(x) = cJ_\alpha(x)$$

where c is a constant.

When α is 0 or a positive integer, $J_\alpha(x)$ is a solution of Bessel's equation over the infinite interval; a function $y_\alpha(x)$ such that $J_\alpha(x)$ and $y_\alpha(x)$ are linearly independent solutions of Bessel's equation over the interval $x > 0$ is called a *Bessel function of the second kind.* For each α, it is easy to show that, if x_0 is a sufficiently small positive number, then

$$J_\alpha(t) \neq 0 \qquad\qquad 0 < t \leqq x_0.$$

Hence (see Section 6.8) each solution $y(x)$ of Bessel's equation can be represented over the interval $0 < x \leqq x_0$ by the formula

$$(7.88) \qquad\qquad y(x) = c_1 J_\alpha(x) + c_2 J_\alpha(x) \int_{x_0}^x \frac{1}{s[J_\alpha(s)]^2}\, ds.$$

Therefore each Bessel function of the second kind must be representable in the form (7.88) where c_2 is a constant not 0. There are better formulas for Bessel functions of the second kind; but (7.88) can be used to obtain the conclusion of Theorem 7.87 for the cases in which $\alpha = 0, 1, 2, 3, \cdots$. We do not enter into the details; they seem complicated to one not accustomed to "estimating" functions.

Bessel functions are often called *cylindrical harmonics;* they are used in problems in which there is radial symmetry about an axis. In many cases the axis is a wire or the axis of a cylinder or pipe. Scientific libraries contain books on Bessel functions and their applications. The Jahnke-Emde tables cited in Section 2.6 devote 127 pages to Bessel functions, giving many graphs and tables.

Problem 7.89

Let $y(x)$ be a solution, for $x > 0$, of Bessel's equation

$$(7.891) \qquad\qquad x^2 y'' + xy' + (x^2 - \alpha^2)y = 0.$$

Show that if $y = uv$ where $u(x)$ and $v(x)$ have two derivatives each, then

$$x^2 uv'' + (2x^2 u' + xu)v' + [x^2 u'' + xu' + (x^2 - \alpha^2)u]v = 0.$$

Determine $u(x)$ so that the coefficient of v' is 0, and continue your work to show that the function $v(x)$ defined by

$$(7.892) \qquad\qquad v(x) = \sqrt{x}\, y(x)$$

is a solution of the differential equation

$$(7.893) \qquad\qquad v'' + \left[1 + \frac{\frac{1}{4} - \alpha^2}{x^2}\right] v = 0.$$

[This result can be used to determine properties of Bessel functions $y(x)$. If α and h are fixed, then when A is a large positive number the coefficients in (7.893) differ very little over the interval $A \leq x \leq A + h$ from the coefficients in the equation

$$(7.894) \qquad\qquad w'' + w = 0.$$

A solution of (7.894) over the interval $A \leq x \leq A + h$ must have the form

$$w = C \sin (x - x_0)$$

where C and x_0 are constants. Hence it is not surprising (we give no proof here) that, if $y(x)$ is a Bessel function, then the graph of $\sqrt{x}\, y(x)$ over the interval $A \leq x \leq A + h$ looks very much like a piece of a sine curve. The positive zeros of $\sqrt{x}\, y(x)$ and $y(x)$ are the same; each has an infinite set $z_1 < z_2 < z_3 < \cdots$ of them, and the distance $z_{n+1} - z_n$ between two consecutive zeros converges to π as $n \to \infty$.]

Problem 7.895

When $x > 0$, Bessel's equation of order α can be written in the form

$$(7.8951) \qquad\qquad \frac{d^2y}{dx^2} + \frac{1}{x}\frac{dy}{dx} + \left(1 - \frac{\alpha^2}{x^2}\right) y = 0.$$

Show that if k is a constant not 0, then each solution $z(x)$ of the equation

$$(7.8952) \qquad\qquad \frac{d^2z}{dx^2} + \frac{1}{x}\frac{dz}{dx} + \left(k^2 - \frac{\alpha^2}{x^2}\right) z = 0$$

has the form $z = y(kx)$ where $y(x)$ satisfies (7.8951). [This means that each solution of (7.8952) has the form $z = y_\alpha(kx)$ where $y_\alpha(x)$ is a linear combination of Bessel functions.]

Problem 7.896

Considering positive values of x, show that if

$$(7.8961) \qquad\qquad \frac{d^2w}{dx^2} + \frac{a}{x}\frac{dw}{dx} + k^2w = 0,$$

then an exponent α can be determined such that the function $z(x)$ defined by $z(x) = x^{-\alpha}w(x)$ satisfies (7.8952). [The value of α is $(1 - a)/2$. This means that each solution $w(x)$ of (7.8961) has, when $k \neq 0$, the form $w = x^\alpha y_\alpha(kx)$ where $y_\alpha(x)$ is a linear combination of Bessel functions.] By examining the case in which $a = 0$, $k = 1$, show that each linear combination of $\sin x$ and $\cos x$ must be a linear combination of $\sqrt{x}\, J_{\frac{1}{2}}(x)$ and $\sqrt{x}\, J_{-\frac{1}{2}}(x)$.

7.9. Legendre's Equation.—When

$$(7.91) \qquad Ly = (1 - x^2)\frac{d^2y}{dx^2} - 2x\frac{dy}{dx} + \alpha(\alpha + 1)y,$$

Legendre's equation becomes $Ly = 0$. In this case we find

$$(7.911) \qquad Lx^r = r(r - 1)x^{r-2} + (\alpha - r)(\alpha + r + 1)x^r.$$

Hence, if

$$(7.912) \qquad y = x^m \sum_{n=0}^{\infty} c_n x^n = \sum_{n=0}^{\infty} c_n x^{m+n}$$

for some range of values of x, then

$$(7.913) \quad Ly = \sum_{n=0}^{\infty} c_n Lx^{m+n}$$

$$= \sum_{n=0}^{\infty} c_n[(m + n)(m + n - 1)x^{m+n-2}$$

$$+ (\alpha - m - n)(\alpha + m + n + 1)x^{m+n}]$$

$$= c_0 m(m - 1)x^{m-2} + c_1(m + 1)mx^{m-1}$$

$$+ \sum_{n=0}^{\infty} [(m + n + 2)(m + n + 1)c_{n+2}$$

$$+ (\alpha - m - n)(\alpha + m + n + 1)c_n]x^{m+n}.$$

Putting $m = 0$ and letting c_0 and c_1 be constants different from 0 to which values may be assigned later, we find two linearly independent solutions

$$(7.92) \quad y_1 = c_0 \left[1 - \frac{(\alpha + 1)\alpha}{2!} x^2 + \frac{(\alpha + 1)(\alpha + 3)\alpha(\alpha - 2)}{4!} x^4 \right.$$

$$\left. - \frac{(\alpha + 1)(\alpha + 3)(\alpha + 5)\alpha(\alpha - 2)(\alpha - 4)}{6!} x^6 + \cdots \right]$$

and

$$(7.93) \quad y_2 = c_1 \left[x - \frac{(\alpha + 2)(\alpha - 1)}{3!} x^3 \right.$$

$$+ \frac{(\alpha + 2)(\alpha + 4)(\alpha - 1)(\alpha - 3)}{5!} x^5$$

$$\left. - \frac{(\alpha + 2)(\alpha + 4)(\alpha + 6)(\alpha - 1)(\alpha - 3)(\alpha - 5)}{7!} x^7 + \cdots \right].$$

If α is not an integer, each of the series is an infinite series with radius of convergence equal to 1. The functions are called *Legendre functions*. The solution $y_1(x)$ is a polynomial if α is 0, an even positive integer, or an odd negative integer; and $y_2(x)$ is a polynomial if α is an odd positive integer or an even negative integer.

When α is 0 or a positive integer, one of the two functions in (7.92) and (7.93) is not a polynomial; the other is a polynomial of degree α which, when the constant is assigned a certain particular value, is called the *Legendre polynomial* of degree α and is denoted by $P_\alpha(x)$. The constants are so adjusted that, for each $\alpha = 0, 1, 2, \cdots$,

$$(7.94) \quad P_\alpha(x) = \frac{(2\alpha)!}{2^\alpha \alpha! \alpha!} \left[x^\alpha - \frac{\alpha(\alpha-1)}{2(2\alpha-1)} x^{\alpha-2} \right.$$
$$+ \frac{\alpha(\alpha-1)(\alpha-2)(\alpha-3)}{2\cdot 4(2\alpha-1)(2\alpha-3)} x^{\alpha-4}$$
$$\left. - \frac{\alpha(\alpha-1)(\alpha-2)(\alpha-3)(\alpha-4)(\alpha-5)}{2\cdot 4\cdot 6(2\alpha-1)(2\alpha-3)(2\alpha-5)} x^{\alpha-6} + \cdots \right].$$

It is easy to see that

$$(7.941) \qquad \frac{(2\alpha)!}{2^\alpha \alpha! \alpha!} = \frac{1\cdot 3\cdot 5 \cdots (2\alpha-1)}{\alpha!} \qquad \alpha = 1, 2, 3, \cdots .$$

Any adjustment of the constants different from the above would necessitate insertion of constant factors in the terms of the right member of the identity

$$(7.95) \quad (1 - 2xt + t^2)^{-\frac{1}{2}} = P_0(x) + P_1(x)t + P_2(x)t^2 + \cdots$$

which holds when $|x|$ and $|t|$ are sufficiently small. It is a good exercise in the use of series to prove (7.95); the trick is to expand

$$\{1 + [t(t - 2x)]\}^{-\frac{1}{2}}$$

by the binomial formula, to pick out the coefficients of the various powers of t, and to see that they are the Legendre polynomials. The manipulations are easily justified when $|x| \leq 1$ and $|t| \leq \frac{4}{10}$, for in this case

$$|t^2 - 2xt| \leq |t|^2 + |2xt| \leq .16 + .8 = .96 < 1.$$

Legendre functions and polynomials are often called *zonal functions* and *zonal harmonics*. They enter into many problems, in particular into many problems in which it is convenient to use spherical coordinates. The identity (7.95) is used with x defined by $x = \cos\theta$, θ being a spherical coordinate.

Problem 7.96

Show that $P_0(x) = 1$; $P_1(x) = x$; $P_2(x) = (3x^2 - 1)/2$; $P_3(x) = (5x^3 - 3x)/2$; $P_4(x) = (35x^4 - 30x^2 + 3)/8$; $P_5(x) = (63x^5 - 70x^3 + 15x)/8$.

Problem 7.961

Show by means of formula (7.95) that for each $n = 0, 1, 2, \cdots$

$$(7.962) \qquad\qquad P_n(1) = 1; \qquad P_n(-1) = (-1)^n.$$

Problem 7.97

Verify the *formula of Rodrigues*

(7.971) $$P_n(x) = \frac{1}{2^n n!} \frac{d^n}{dx^n} (x^2 - 1)^n$$

for a few values of n; if curiosity impels and ability permits, prove the formula.

Problem 7.98

Verify the formulas*

(7.981) $$\int_{-1}^{1} P_m(x)P_n(x)dx = 0 \qquad\qquad m \neq n$$

(7.982) $$\int_{-1}^{1} [P_n(x)]^2 dx = \frac{2}{2n+1} \qquad n = 0, 1, 2, \cdots$$

for a few values of m and n.

Problem 7.99

Show that, if $Q_0(x)$ and $Q_1(x)$ denote, respectively, the functions in (7.93) and (7.92) when $\alpha = 0$, $c_1 = 1$ and when $\alpha = 1$, $c_0 = -1$, then

(7.991) $$Q_0(x) = \frac{1}{2} \log \frac{1+x}{1-x} \qquad\qquad |x| < 1$$

and

(7.992) $$Q_1(x) = \frac{x}{2} \log \frac{1+x}{1-x} - 1 \qquad\qquad |x| < 1.$$

Hint: In evaluating the series, use the fact that

$$x + \frac{x^3}{3} + \frac{x^5}{5} + \cdots = \int_0^x (1 + t^2 + t^4 + \cdots)dt,$$

and notice that the integrand is a geometric series.

* The reason why (7.981) holds and an indication of reasons why the result is important are set forth in Chapter 12. When (7.981) has been established, we can obtain (7.982) by the following use of (7.95): From (7.95) we obtain

(7.983) $$\frac{1}{1 - 2xt + t^2} = \sum_{m=0}^{\infty} \sum_{n=0}^{\infty} P_m(x)P_n(x)t^{m+n}.$$

Integrating (7.983) over the interval $-1 \leq x \leq 1$ and using (7.981) give, after some reductions that are justified by rules for operating with series,

$$\sum_{n=0}^{\infty} \frac{2}{2n+1} t^{2n} = \sum_{n=0}^{\infty} \left\{ \int_{-1}^{1} [P_n(x)]^2 dx \right\} t^{2n};$$

and comparing the coefficients of the powers of t then gives (7.982). Another proof of (7.981) and (7.982) involves use of the formula of Rodrigues and integration by parts.

CHAPTER 8

LINEAR DIFFERENTIAL EQUATIONS
WITH CONSTANT COEFFICIENTS

8.0. Notation.—Throughout this chapter we let L_a denote the linear operator

$$(8.01) \qquad L_a = a_0 D^n + a_1 D^{n-1} + \cdots + a_{n-1} D + a_n$$

where the a's are constants and $a_0 \neq 0$; let

$$(8.02) \qquad L_a(m) = a_0 m^n + a_1 m^{n-1} + \cdots + a_{n-1} m + a_n$$

so that $L_a(m) = 0$ is the characteristic equation of the operator L_a; and let $m_1, m_2, \cdots, m_n$ denote the roots of $L_a(m) = 0$ so that, as in Section 6.4,

$$(8.03) \qquad L_a = a_0 (D - m_1)(D - m_2) \cdots (D - m_n).$$

8.1. Solution of the Homogeneous Equation $L_a y = 0$.—The simplest way to form preliminary ideas about solutions of $L_a y = 0$ is to solve some simple problems.

To solve the equation

$$(8.101) \qquad (D - m_1)y = 0$$

we introduce the integrating factor $e^{-m_1 x}$ and obtain the general solution

$$(8.102) \qquad y = c_1 e^{m_1 x}.$$

To solve the second-order differential equation

$$(8.111) \qquad (D - m_1)(D - m_2)y = 0$$

we may set $(D - m_2)y = u$ and solve the equation $(D - m_1)u = 0$ for u (by use of the previous paragraph or otherwise) to obtain

$$(8.112) \qquad (D - m_2)y = c_1' e^{m_1 x}.$$

Introducing the integrating factor $e^{-m_2 x}$, we obtain

$$(8.113) \qquad \frac{d}{dx} e^{-m_2 x} y = c_1' e^{(m_1 - m_2)x}.$$

The formula obtained by integrating (8.113) is of one type when $m_1 \neq m_2$ and of a different type when $m_1 = m_2$; we shall have more to

144

say about this point later, but meanwhile a student should note it carefully. If $m_1 \neq m_2$, integration of (8.113) gives

(8.114) $$e^{-m_2x}y = c_1 e^{(m_1-m_2)x} + c_2,$$

where $c_1 = c_1'/(m_1 - m_2)$, and the general solution of (8.111) is

(8.115) $$y = c_1 e^{m_1x} + c_2 e^{m_2x}.$$

If $m_1 = m_2$, the right member of (8.113) is the constant c_1'; integration of (8.113) gives

$$e^{-m_2x}y = c_1 x + c_2$$

where $c_1 = c_1'$, and the general solution of (8.111) is

(8.116) $$y = (c_1 x + c_2)e^{m_2x}.$$

For the third-order equation

(8.121) $$(D - m_1)(D - m_2)(D - m_3)y = 0$$

there are three different situations, as follows: (i) The m's are distinct, that is, $m_1 \neq m_2$, $m_1 \neq m_3$, $m_2 \neq m_3$. (ii) Two m's are equal but different from the other, say $m_1 \neq m_2 = m_3$. (iii) The m's are all equal, that is, $m_1 = m_2 = m_3$. In each of the first two cases we can set $(D - m_3)y = u$ and use the previous paragraph to obtain the solutions of the equation $(D - m_1)(D - m_2)u = 0$. This gives

$$(D - m_3)y = c_1' e^{m_1x} + c_2' e^{m_2x},$$

and we multiply by e^{-m_3x} to obtain

(8.122) $$\frac{d}{dx} e^{-m_3x}y = c_1' e^{(m_1-m_3)x} + c_2' e^{(m_2-m_3)x}.$$

Thus, in case (i) where the m's are distinct, we obtain

(8.123) $$y = c_1 e^{m_1x} + c_2 e^{m_2x} + c_3 e^{m_3x}$$

as the general solution of (8.121). In case (ii) where $m_1 \neq m_2 = m_3$, we find from (8.122) that

(8.124) $$y = c_1 e^{m_1x} + (c_2 x + c_3)e^{m_2x}$$

is the general solution of (8.121). Finally, in case (iii) where

$$m_1 = m_2 = m_3,$$

we can set $(D - m_3)y = u$ and use the previous paragraph to obtain

$$(D - m_3)y = (c_1' x + c_2')e^{m_1x}$$

so that, since $m_3 = m_1$,

$$\frac{d}{dx}\, e^{-m_1 x} y = c_1' x + c_2'$$

and

(8.125) $$y = (c_1 x^2 + c_2 x + c_3)e^{m_1 x}$$

is the general solution of (8.121).

It is clear that the methods used in the three previous paragraphs enable us first to guess and then to prove by induction the following theorem:

Theorem 8.13.—*If*

(8.131) $$L_a = a_0 D^n + a_1 D^{n-1} + \cdots + a_{n-1} D + a_n$$

where the a's are constants and $a_0 \neq 0$ and if $m_1, m_2, \cdots, m_n$ are the n roots of the characteristic equation

(8.132) $$L_a(m) = a_0 m^n + a_1 m^{n-1} + \cdots + a_{n-1} m + a_n = 0,$$

then the general solution of $L_a(y) = 0$ is

(8.133) $$y = c_1 e^{m_1 x} + c_2 e^{m_2 x} + \cdots + c_n e^{m_n x}$$

if the m's are distinct; is

(8.134) $$y = (c_0 + c_1 x + c_2 x^2 + \cdots + c_{n-1} x^{n-1})e^{m_1 x}$$

if the m's are all equal to m_1; and is

(8.135) $$y = [c_0^{(1)} + c_1^{(1)} x + \cdots + c_{\alpha_1 - 1}^{(1)} x^{\alpha_1 - 1}]e^{m_1 x} + \cdots$$
$$+ [c_0^{(k)} + c_1^{(k)} x + \cdots + c_{\alpha_k - 1}^{(k)} x^{\alpha_k - 1}]e^{m_k x}$$

if α_1 of the m's are equal to m_1, α_2 of the m's are equal to m_2, and so on, until finally α_k of the m's are equal to m_k, where the numbers $m_1, m_2, \cdots, m_k$ are distinct.

The third case is the "general case" which reduces to the first case when the m's are distinct and to the second case when the m's are all equal. This theorem is of such importance that it should be remembered. In particular, it should always be remembered that *each solution of a homogeneous linear differential equation of order n with constant coefficients is a linear combination of n terms of the form $x^p e^{qx}$ where p is 0 or a positive integer and q is a constant.* When the characteristic equation has been solved, Theorem 8.13 tells exactly what terms $x^p e^{qx}$ are to be used. It may be observed that Theorem 8.13 reduces the amount of work involved in finding solutions of $L_a y = 0$ to an irreducible minimum. Obviously one cannot write down the solutions until the exponents are found; and as soon as the exponents are found, one simply writes down the solutions.

It must not be forgotten that the m's may be complex.   In fact, in most applications they are complex numbers with real part 0 or negative.   For the equation

$$(8.14) \qquad \frac{d^2y}{dx^2} + k^2 y = 0$$

of the harmonic oscillator, in which k is a positive constant, the characteristic equation $m^2 + k^2 = 0$ has roots ik and $-ik$; and accordingly, by Theorem 8.13, the general solution of (8.14) is

$$(8.141) \qquad y = c_1 e^{ikx} + c_2 e^{-ikx}.$$

Problems

Using Theorem 8.13, write the general solutions of the following equations:

(8.151) $(D + 1)(D + 2)y = 0$
(8.152) $(D - 1)^2 (D + 1)^2 y = 0$
(8.153) $(D + 1)(D - 1)(D + i)(D - i)y = 0$
(8.154) $D^3 y = 0$
(8.155) $(D^2 + 4D + 4)y = 0$
(8.156) $(D^4 + 5D^3 + 5D^2 - 5D - 6)y = 0$*
(8.157) $(2D^2 + 3D + 4)y = 0$

Problem 8.16

Show that each function which is equal to its first derivative must have the form $y = c_1 e^x$; that each function which is equal to its second derivative must have the form $y = c_1 e^x + c_2 e^{-x}$; that each function which is equal to its third derivative must have the form

$$y = c_1 e^x + c_2 e^{-x/2} \cos \tfrac{1}{2} \sqrt{3}\, x + c_3 e^{-x/2} \sin \tfrac{1}{2} \sqrt{3}\, x;$$

and that each function which is equal to its fourth derivative must have the form

$$y = c_1 e^x + c_2 e^{-x} + c_3 \cos x + c_4 \sin x.$$

Problem 8.161

According to Theorem 6.03, the equation

$$(8.1611) \qquad (D^4 - 1)y = 0$$

has four solutions y_1, y_2, y_3, y_4 such that

$$
\begin{array}{llll}
y_1(0) = 1, & y_1'(0) = 0, & y_1''(0) = 0, & y_1'''(0) = 0 \\
y_2(0) = 0, & y_2'(0) = 1, & y_2''(0) = 0, & y_2'''(0) = 0 \\
y_3(0) = 0, & y_3'(0) = 0, & y_3''(0) = 1, & y_3'''(0) = 0 \\
y_4(0) = 0, & y_4'(0) = 0, & y_4''(0) = 0, & y_4'''(0) = 1.
\end{array}
$$

* This equation should remind students of algebra problems so adjusted that the answers are simple and easily found.

Find the solutions.   *Ans.:*

$$y_1 = \tfrac{1}{4}e^x + \tfrac{1}{4}e^{-x} \qquad\qquad + \tfrac{1}{2}\cos x.$$
$$y_2 = \tfrac{1}{4}e^x - \tfrac{1}{4}e^{-x} + \tfrac{1}{2}\sin x.$$
$$y_3 = \tfrac{1}{4}e^x + \tfrac{1}{4}e^{-x} \qquad\qquad - \tfrac{1}{2}\cos x.$$
$$y_4 = \tfrac{1}{4}e^x - \tfrac{1}{4}e^{-x} - \tfrac{1}{2}\sin x.$$

Problem 8.162

Using the results of the preceding problem, find the solution $y(x)$ of (8.1611) for which

$$y(0) = b_1, \qquad y'(0) = b_2, \qquad y''(0) = b_3, \qquad y'''(0) = b_4.$$

Ans.: $y(x) = \tfrac{1}{4}(b_1 + b_2 + b_3 + b_4)e^x + \tfrac{1}{4}(b_1 - b_2 + b_3 - b_4)e^{-x}$
$$+ \tfrac{1}{2}(b_2 - b_4)\sin x + \tfrac{1}{2}(b_1 - b_3)\cos x.$$

Problem 8.17

Show that, if a, b, and c are constants for which $a \neq 0$ and $b^2 \neq ac$, then the general solution of

$$(8.171) \qquad\qquad a\frac{d^2y}{dx^2} + 2b\frac{dy}{dx} + cy = 0$$

is

$$(8.172) \qquad\qquad y = c_1 e^{m_1 x} + c_2 e^{m_2 x}$$

where $m_1 = (-b - \sqrt{b^2 - ac})/a$ and $m_2 = (-b + \sqrt{b^2 - ac})/a$.   Show that, if $b^2 - ac = -\delta^2$ where $\delta > 0$, the general solution can be written in the form

$$y = e^{-(b/a)x}\left[A\cos\frac{\delta}{a}x + B\sin\frac{\delta}{a}x \right]$$

and in the form

$$y = Ce^{-(b/a)x}\cos\frac{\delta}{a}(x - x_0).$$

Consider the case in which $b^2 = ac$.

We obtained Theorem 8.13 by a straightforward method using only fundamental concepts of mathematics; it did not depend on knowing in advance what the solutions are or even on any clever guesses as to what form the solutions might have.   It is of course possible that a brilliant individual may hit upon the solutions of $L_a y = 0$ by the following method: Since the successive x derivatives of e^{mx} are merely products of constants by e^{mx}, it is reasonable to guess that e^{mx} will be a solution of

$$(8.18) \qquad L_a y \equiv (a_0 D^n + a_1 D^{n-1} + \cdots + a_{n-1}D + a_n)y = 0$$

if m is shrewdly chosen.   It is easy to see that e^{mx} will satisfy (8.18) if and only if

$$(8.181) \qquad (a_0 m^n + a_1 m^{n-1} + \cdots + a_{n-1}m + a_n)e^{mx} = 0$$

and hence, since e^{mx} never vanishes, if and only if

$$(8.182) \qquad a_0 m^n + a_1 m^{n-1} + \cdots + a_{n-1}m + a_n = 0.$$

If $m_1, m_2, \cdots, m_n$ are the roots of (8.182), it then becomes clear that

$$(8.183) \qquad y = c_1 e^{m_1 x} + c_2 e^{m_2 x} + \cdots + c_n e^{m_n x}$$

is a solution of $L_a y = 0$. If the m's are distinct and if one knows that in this case the n functions $e^{m_1 x}, e^{m_2 x}, \cdots, e^{m_n x}$ form a linearly independent set, then Theorem 6.04 can be applied to show that (8.183) is the general solution of $L_a y = 0$. If the m's are not distinct, the functions $e^{m_1 x}, e^{m_2 x}, \cdots, e^{m_n x}$ are obviously not linearly independent and one who depends upon brilliant guessing to furnish his solutions must put his intellect to work to produce the results set forth in the second and third cases in Theorem 8.13.

Problem 8.19

If $f(x)$ has n derivatives and a is a constant, then

$$(8.191) \qquad (D - a)^n f(x) = e^{ax} D^n e^{-ax} f(x);$$

to prove (8.191) we show easily that it holds when $n = 1$; and if it holds for a given n, then the computation

$$(D - a)^{n+1} f(x) = (D - a) e^{ax} D^n e^{-ax} f(x)$$
$$= e^{ax} D^{n+1} e^{-ax} f(x) + a e^{ax} D^n e^{-ax} f(x) - a e^{ax} D^n e^{-ax} f(x) = e^{ax} D^{n+1} e^{-ax} f(x)$$

shows that it holds for the next greater value of n. Use formula (8.191) to show that

$$(8.192) \qquad (D - a)^n (c_1 x^{n-1} + c_2 x^{n-2} + \cdots + c_n) e^{ax} = 0.$$

What is the connection, if any, between (8.192) and Theorem 8.13?

Problem 8.193

Making use of Theorems 6.04 and 8.13, show that the set of n functions

$$e^{m_1 x}, e^{m_2 x}, e^{m_3 x}, \cdots, e^{m_n x}$$

is linearly independent if and only if the m's are distinct (that is, if no two of the m's are equal).

8.2. Particular Solutions of the Nonhomogeneous Equation $L_a y = f$.

—In Section 6.5 we gave a method by which $L_a y = f$ can be completely solved when L_a is a linear operator with constant coefficients. In Section 8.1 we showed how one can write down the general solution of the homogeneous equation $L_a y = 0$ when the roots of the characteristic equation $L_a(m) = 0$ have been found.

Since the general solution of $L_a y = f$ can be obtained by adding a particular solution $Y(x)$ of $L_a y = f$ to the general solution of $L_a y = 0$, it is worth while to know some special methods by which in important cases a particular solution of $L_a y = f$ may be obtained quickly and easily.

Many useful purposes are served by solving the equation $L_a y = f$ where f is a function of the form $f = x^p e^{qx}$ where p is 0 or a positive integer and q is a constant. By setting $q = 0$, we obtain simply x^p. By setting $p = 0$ and $q = \alpha + i\beta$, where α and β are real constants, we obtain the function

$$e^{(\alpha + i\beta)x} = e^{\alpha x} e^{i\beta x}$$

which is called a *damped harmonic* when $\alpha < 0$ and a *pure harmonic* (or simply *harmonic*) when $\alpha = 0$. We shall have much more to say about these points later.

8.3. A Special Method of Solving $L_a y = x^p e^{qx}$.—The method considered in this section may be illustrated by solving the equation

$$(8.301) \qquad (D - 1)(D - 2)y = e^{3x}.$$

If $y(x)$ is a solution of (8.301), then the fact that

$$(D - 3)e^{3x} = 0$$

implies that

$$(D - 3)(D - 1)(D - 2)y = 0$$

and hence (Theorem 8.13) that y must have the form

$$(8.302) \qquad y = Ae^{3x} + c_1 e^x + c_2 e^{2x}$$

where A, c_1, and c_2 are constants. The statement that each solution of (8.301) must have the form (8.302) is naturally noncommittal with respect to the question whether or not functions of the form (8.302) satisfy (8.301). Since (Theorem 8.13)

$$(D - 1)(D - 2)(c_1 e^x + c_2 e^{2x}) = 0,$$

the question whether or not (8.302) satisfies (8.301) is equivalent to the question whether or not the function Ae^{3x} satisfies (8.301). Since

$$(D - 1)(D - 2)Ae^{3x} = 2Ae^{3x},$$

we see that Ae^{3x} satisfies (8.301) if and only if $A = \frac{1}{2}$. Thus the general solution of (8.301) is

$$(8.303) \qquad y = \tfrac{1}{2} e^{3x} + c_1 e^x + c_2 e^{2x}.$$

We now consider the general problem of solving

$$(8.311) \qquad (D - m_1)(D - m_2) \cdots (D - m_n)y = x^p e^{qx}$$

where p is 0 or a positive integer and q is a constant. The homogeneous equation

$$(8.312) \qquad (D - m_1)(D - m_2) \cdots (D - m_n)y = 0$$

has the general solution

$$(8.313) \qquad Y_1(x) = c_1 y_1(x) + c_2 y_2(x) + \cdots + c_n y_n(x)$$

in which the character of the y's depends upon the m's as stated in Theorem 8.13. Since* (Theorem 8.13)

---

* No one should fail to note that (8.314) is implied by the fact that $y = x^p e^{qx}$ is a solution of $(D - q)^{p+1}y = 0$.

(8.314) $$(D - q)^{p+1}x^p e^{qx} = 0,$$

we can apply the operator $(D - q)^{p+1}$ to (8.311) to see that each solution of (8.311) must satisfy the equation

(8.315) $$(D - q)^{p+1}(D - m_1)(D - m_2) \cdots (D - m_n)y = 0.$$

This is a homogeneous equation to which we can apply Theorem 8.13. If q is a k-fold root of the characteristic equation, that is, if k of the m's are equal to q and the others are different from q, then by Theorem 8.13 the general solution of (8.315) must have the form

(8.316) $$y = Y(x) + Y_1(x)$$

where $Y_1(x)$ is given by (8.313) and

(8.317) $$Y(x) = (A_1 x^k + A_2 x^{k+1} + \cdots + A_{p+1} x^{k+p})e^{qx}.$$

In the special case in which q is not a root of the characteristic equation and accordingly $k = 0$, (8.317) reduces to

(8.318) $$Y(x) = (A_1 + A_2 x + \cdots + A_{p+1} x^p)e^{qx};$$

if $p = 0$, (8.317) reduces to

(8.319) $$Y(x) = A_1 x^k e^{qx};$$

and if $k = p = 0$, (8.317) reduces to

(8.320) $$Y(x) = A_1 e^{qx}.$$

We continue to consider the general case in which k and p may be 0 or positive integers. Since $Y_1(x)$ is a solution of the homogeneous equation (8.312), it follows that $Y(x) + Y_1(x)$ is a solution of (8.311) if and only if $Y(x)$ is a solution of (8.311). Since (8.311) has solutions by Theorem 6.03 and each solution of (8.311) must have the form $Y(x) + Y_1(x)$, it follows that $Y(x)$ *must be a solution of* (8.311) *for at least one set of constants* $A_1, A_2, \cdots, A_{p+1}$. The method of determining the A's for which $Y(x)$ is a particular solution consists in computing

(8.321) $$(D - m_1)(D - m_2) \cdots (D - m_n)Y$$

in terms of the A's and then determining the A's so that the result will be $x^p e^{qx}$.

A mathematician may say that this process, by which we start with (8.311) and arrive at the conclusion that (8.317) must be a particular solution of (8.311) provided that the A's are properly determined, is so easy to remember and to execute that there is no need to remember (8.317). This expresses the attitude of one who must know how to solve equations and must be able to tell others how to solve them but who is seldom required to solve one himself. Many applied mathematicians, in particular mechanical, electrical, and chemical engineers, must solve so many equations that their attitude is different. They may say that there is no need to work out (8.317) every time one wants to use it and that the result should be remembered. It should be remembered that *the equation*

$$(8.33) \qquad (D^n + a_1 D^{n-1} + \cdots + a_{n-1} D + a_n)y = e^{qx}$$

has a solution of the form $A e^{qx}$ provided that q is not a root of the characteristic equation; it should be remembered that (8.33) *has a solution of the form $A x e^{qx}$ provided that q is a simple root of the characteristic equation;* in fact, the more one remembers about (8.317) the quicker one is able to produce solutions of his problems. Section 8.5 bears upon this point.

The fact that the form of the solutions of the equation $L_a y = x^p e^{qx}$ depends on whether q is a root of the characteristic equation $L_a(m) = 0$ cannot be too strongly emphasized. In many applications, the question whether or not q is a root of $L_a(m) = 0$ is equivalent to the question whether or not the frequency of an impressed mechanical or electrical force is the same as a *natural frequency* of a system under discussion, and this in turn is equivalent to the question whether or not the impressed forces produce *resonance* in the system. Sometimes resonance is desirable; one seeks it as he turns a knob on a radio to tune in KDKA. Sometimes resonance is undesirable; it is frequently responsible for destruction of expensive mechanical and electrical equipment.

Example 8.34

To solve the equation

$$(8.341) \qquad (D - 1)(D - 2)y = x$$

by the method of this section, we see that, if (8.341) holds, then

$$D^2(D - 1)(D - 2)y = 0$$

and hence

$$y = Y(x) + Y_1(x)$$

where $Y_1 = c_1 e^x + c_2 e^{2x}$ is a solution of the homogeneous equation and $Y = A + Bx$. Since

$$(D - 1)(D - 2)Y = (2A - 3B) + 2Bx,$$

we see that Y satisfies (8.341) if and only if $B = \frac{1}{2}$, $A = \frac{3}{4}$. Hence the general solution of (8.341) is

$$(8.342) \qquad y = \tfrac{3}{4} + \tfrac{1}{2}x + c_1 e^x + c_2 e^{2x}.$$

Example 8.35

For the equation

(8.351)
$$(D - 2)(D - 3)y = x^3 e^{2x}$$

the tentative particular solution formed in accordance with the above discussion has the form

$$Y = (A_1 x + A_2 x^2 + A_3 x^3 + A_4 x^4)e^{2x}.$$

Computation of $(D - 2)(D - 3)Y$ may be systematized as follows: For each $n = 1, 2, 3, 4,$

$$(D - 3)x^n e^{2x} = (nx^{n-1} - x^n)e^{2x}$$

so that

$$(D - 3)Y = [A_1 + (2A_2 - A_1)x + (3A_3 - A_2)x^2 + (4A_4 - A_3)x^3 - A_4 x^4]e^{2x}.$$

For each $n = 0, 1, 2, 3, 4,$

$$(D - 2)x^n e^{2x} = nx^{n-1}e^{2x}$$

so that

$$(D - 2)(D - 3)Y = [(2A_2 - A_1) + 2(3A_3 - A_2)x + 3(4A_4 - A_3)x^2 - 4A_4 x^3]e^{2x}.$$

This will be $x^3 e^{2x}$ if and only if $A_4 = -\frac{1}{4}$, $A_3 = -1$, $A_2 = -3$, and $A_1 = -6$; and accordingly

$$Y = -\tfrac{1}{4}(24x + 12x^2 + 4x^3 + x^4)e^{2x}.$$

The general solution of the homogeneous equation corresponding to (8.351) is

$$c_1 e^{2x} + c_2 e^{3x},$$

and accordingly the general solution of (8.351) is

$$y = -\tfrac{1}{4}(24x + 12x^2 + 4x^3 + x^4)e^{2x} + c_1 e^{2x} + c_2 e^{3x}.$$

The result is in agreement with that of Example 6.58 where (8.351) was solved by another method.

Problem 8.36

Apply the method of this section to the equation

(8.361)
$$(D^2 + 1)y = e^{ix}$$

to obtain the particular solution

$$Y = -\frac{i}{2}xe^{ix}.$$

Problem 8.37

Find a particular solution of the equation

(8.371)
$$(D^2 + 1)y = \cos x$$

by taking the real part of a solution of (8.361). Check the accuracy of your result by substitution in (8.371).

Problems

Find particular solutions of the following equations; if you are not sure your answers are correct, check them.

(8.381) ✓　　　　　　　　　　　$(D^2 + 1)y = e^{ax}$

(8.382)　　　　　　　　　　　　$(D^2 + 1)y = xe^{ax}$

(8.383) ✓　　　　　　　　　　　$(D^2 + 1)y = x^2 e^{ax}$

(8.384)　　 *N*　　　　　　　　　$(D^2 + 1)y = x$

(8.385) ? *tried*　　　　　　　$(D^2 + 1)y = x \sin x$

(8.386)　　　　　　　　　　　　$(D^2 + 1)y = e^{-x} \sin x$

(8.387) ? *no try*　　　　　　$(D^2 + 1)y = xe^{-x} \sin x$

(8.388)　 ? ?????　　　　$(D^2 + 4D + 4)y = e^{-x}$

(8.389) ? ?????　　　　$(D^2 + 4D + 4)y = e^{-2x}$ *had it and didn't know i*

(8.390)　　　　　　　　　　　　$Dy = x$

(8.391) ✓　　　　　　　　　　　$Dy = e^{ax} \sin bx$

(8.392)　　　　　　　　　　　　$Dy = x^2 e^{ax} \cos bx$

Problem 8.393

Considering the case in which m_1, m_2, E, and ω are real, $m_1 \neq 0$, $m_2 \neq 0$, and $m_1 \neq m_2$, find the solution $y(x)$ of the equation

$$(D - m_1)(D - m_2)y = E \cos \omega x$$

for which $y(0) = y'(0) = 0$.　*Ans.:*

$$y(x) = E \frac{m_1}{(m_1 - m_2)(m_1^2 + \omega^2)} e^{m_1 x} + E \frac{m_2}{(m_2 - m_1)(m_2^2 + \omega^2)} e^{m_2 x}$$

$$+ \frac{E(m_1 m_2 - \omega^2) \cos \omega x}{(m_1^2 + \omega^2)(m_2^2 + \omega^2)} - \frac{E(m_1 + m_2)\omega \sin \omega x}{(m_1^2 + \omega^2)(m_2^2 + \omega^2)}.$$

Problem 8.394

Considering the case in which m_1, E, and ω are real and $m_1 \neq 0$, find the solution $Y(x)$ of the equation

$$(D - m_1)^2 Y = E \cos \omega x$$

for which $Y(0) = Y'(0) = 0$.　*Ans.:*

$$Y = \frac{E(\omega^2 - m_1^2)}{(m_1^2 + \omega^2)^2} e^{m_1 x} + \frac{Em_1}{m_1^2 + \omega^2} xe^{m_1 x} + \frac{E(m_1^2 - \omega^2) \cos \omega x}{(m_1^2 + \omega^2)^2} - \frac{2Em_1\omega \sin \omega x}{(m_1^2 + \omega^2)^2}.$$

Problem 8.395

Do you believe that the answers $y(x)$ and $Y(x)$ of the two previous problems should be nearly the same when m_2 is nearly m_1? The question can be settled by proving that, when m_1, E, ω, and x are fixed, $y(x)$ converges to $Y(x)$ as $m_2 \to m_1$.

8.4. Transients.—In many problems involving oscillations in mechanical and electrical systems, the roots of the characteristic equation $L_a(m) = 0$ of an operator

(8.41)　　　　$L_a = a_0 D^n + a_1 D^{n-1} + \cdots + a_{n-1}D + a_n$

are all either negative real numbers or complex numbers with negative real parts. Thus, if the roots of the characteristic equation are $m_1, m_2, \cdots, m_n$, then

(8.42)　　　　　　　$m_k = -\alpha_k + i\beta_k$　　　　　$k = 1, 2, \cdots, n$

where

(8.421) $$\alpha_k > 0 \qquad\qquad k = 1, 2, \cdots, n$$

and β_k is real but may be 0, positive, or negative. According to Theorem 8.13, each solution of $L_a y = 0$ must have the form

$$y = c_1 e^{m_1 x} + c_2 e^{m_2 x} + \cdots + c_n e^{m_n x}$$

in case the m's are distinct; and in any case each solution of $L_a y = 0$ must be a linear combination of n terms of the form

(8.43) $$y_k(x) = x^p e^{m_k x}$$

in which p is 0 or a positive integer. Using (8.42), we can write (8.43) in the form

(8.431) $$y_k(x) = x^p e^{-\alpha_k x} e^{i\beta_k x} \qquad k = 1, 2, \cdots, n.$$

In mechanical and electrical problems, x often represents time (measured, perhaps, in seconds) and y represents a displacement, current, etc. In these and other problems it is of interest to know what happens to $y_k(x)$ as x increases. The form of the function $y_k(x)$ naturally depends upon p, α_k, and β_k. Nevertheless, since $\alpha_k > 0$, $y_k(x)$ approaches 0 as x increases; in other words, $y_k(x)$ is a *transient*. To prove this, we observe first that $|e^{i\beta_n x}| = 1$ and hence that

(8.44) $$|y_k(x)| = x^p e^{-\alpha_k x} \qquad\qquad x > 0.$$

Since $\alpha_k > 0$, the factor $e^{-\alpha_k x}$ approaches 0 as x increases; but we must face the fact that, if $p > 0$, then x^p becomes infinite as x increases. One way to throw (8.44) into such a form that one can estimate it when x is large is to use the formula $x^p = e^{p \log x}$ to obtain

(8.45) $$|y_k(x)| = e^{-\alpha_k x [1 - (p/\alpha_k)(\log x)/x]}$$

We can now see that, if x is large so that $(\log x)/x$ is near 0, then the exponent in (8.45) is of the order of magnitude of $-\alpha_k x$; therefore, in spite of the disturbing factor x^p, $|y_k(x)|$ and $y_k(x)$ approach 0 at an exponential rate as x increases.

Since a linear combination of transients is a transient, it follows that, if the roots of the characteristic equation of L_a all have negative real parts, then all solutions of the homogeneous equation $L_a y = 0$ are transients.

If some one of the roots of the characteristic equation has a non-negative real part, say $m_j = \alpha_j + i\beta_j$ where $\alpha_j \geq 0$, then the equation $L_a y = 0$ will have a solution of the form

(8.46) $$y_j(x) = e^{\alpha_j x} e^{i\beta_j x}$$

and this is not a transient.   In fact, $|\, y_j(x)\,| = 1$ for all x if $\alpha_j = 0$, and $|\, y_j(x)\,| \to \infty$ as $x \to \infty$ if $\alpha_j > 0$.

The results obtained in this section may be summed up in the following theorem:

Theorem 8.47.—*The solutions of a homogeneous equation $L_a y = 0$ are all transients if and only if the roots of the characteristic equation $L_a(m) = 0$ all have negative real parts.*

Problem 8.48

Show that, if a, b, and c are positive constants, then all solutions of the equation

$$(8.481)\qquad a\frac{d^2 y}{dx^2} + b\frac{dy}{dx} + cy = 0$$

are transients.   Are there any other conditions under which all solutions of (8.481) are transients?

8.5. Impedance.—As throughout this chapter, let L_a denote the operator

$$(8.51)\qquad L_a = a_0 D^n + a_1 D^{n-1} + \cdots + a_{n-1}D + a_n$$

where the a's are constants.   In this section, we make a special study of the equation

$$(8.52)\qquad L_a y = E_0 e^{mx}$$

in which E_0 is a constant not 0 and m is a real or complex constant; in important cases, m is a pure imaginary number which is often denoted by $i\omega$.   For each m let the number $L_a(m)$, defined in Section 6.43 by the equation

$$(8.53)\qquad L_a(m) = a_0 m^n + a_1 m^{n-1} + \cdots + a_{n-1}m + a_n,$$

be called the *impedance** of the differential equation (8.52).   Thus the impedance is a function of the operator and the constant m in (8.52). Definitions of Section 6.43 imply that *the roots of the characteristic equation of the operator L_a are the values of m for which the impedance is 0.*

As was shown in Section 8.3, the character of the solutions of the equation $L_a y = e^{mx}$ depends upon the question whether or not m is a root of the characteristic equation, that is, whether or not m is a zero of the impedance.   If m is a zero of the impedance, we have nothing to add to the discussion of Section 8.3.

---

* This term is appropriated from the theory of electric circuits.   It is customary to think of the electric circuit rather than of the differential equation as *having* the impedance.   The question whether the impedance belongs to the differential equation or to the electric circuit is as trivial as the question whether a shoelace belongs to a shoe or to the person who owns the shoe.

If m is not a zero of the impedance, we recall from Section 8.3 that the equation $L_a y = E_0 e^{mx}$ must have a solution of the form $y = A e^{mx}$ where A is a properly chosen constant. It is very easy to give an expression for the constant; in fact,

$$L_a(A e^{mx}) = A L_a(m) e^{mx},$$

and this is equal to $E_0 e^{mx}$ if and only if $A = E_0/L_a(m)$. Thus a solution of $L_a y = e^{mx}$ is

(8.54) $$y = \frac{E_0}{L_a(m)} e^{mx}.$$

This solution is of particular interest in cases in which all solutions of the homogeneous equation $L_a y = 0$ are transients, since in this case each solution of $L_a(y) = E_0 e^{mx}$ can differ from (8.54) by at most a transient. In this case, (8.54) is called the *steady-state* solution of $L_a y = E_0 e^{mx}$.

We now consider the following situation which occurs in many mechanical and electrical problems. Let all solutions of the homogeneous equation $L_a y = 0$ be transients, and let $m = i\omega$ where ω is real so that the equation to be solved is

(8.55) $$L_a y = E_0 e^{i\omega x}.$$

Very often one knows before setting up the differential equations that the solutions of $L_a y = 0$ are transients, and one is not interested in them. All one wants is the steady-state solution of (8.55), and one can get it simply by dividing the right member of (8.55) by the impedance; the result is

(8.551) $$y = \frac{E_0}{L_a(i\omega)} e^{i\omega x}.$$

There is no danger that $L_a(i\omega)$ is 0 since, under our hypotheses, the zeros of $L_a(m)$ must all have negative real parts. The number $L_a(i\omega)$ is a complex number which is real only in special cases.

If $L_a(i\omega) = u + iv$ where u and v are real and we set $Z_0 = (u^2 + v^2)^{\frac{1}{2}}$ and let ϕ be the angle such that $-\pi < \phi \leq \pi$ and

$$\cos \phi = \frac{u}{Z_0}, \qquad \sin \phi = \frac{v}{Z_0},$$

then

$$L_a(i\omega) = Z_0(\cos \phi + i \sin \phi)$$

so that, by an Euler formula,

(8.552) $$L_a(i\omega) = Z_0 e^{i\phi}.$$

The angle ϕ is called the *phase angle* of the impedance, and the number Z_0 is called the *absolute value* or *modulus* of the impedance. Using (8.552) in (8.551) gives the steady-state solution in the form

$$(8.553) \qquad y = \frac{E_0}{Z_0} e^{i(\omega x - \phi)}.$$

Finding the steady-state solutions of equations of the form

$$(8.56) \qquad L_a y = E_0 e^{i\omega x}$$

is now a simple matter. One simply finds the absolute value Z_0 and phase angle ϕ of the impedance $L_a(i\omega)$ and, by dividing and subtracting in the proper places, comes out with (8.553) as the solution of the problem.

If E_0 and the operator L_a are real (that is, if the coefficients are real), solutions of the equations

$$(8.561) \qquad L_a y = E_0 \cos \omega t, \qquad L_a y = E_0 \sin \omega t$$

are obtained by taking real and imaginary parts of solutions of (8.56).

In many applications of linear differential equations, each solution is the sum of a steady-state solution and a transient. In some problems, for example, some problems in telegraphy, only the transients are of interest. In some problems, for example, problems in electrical-power transmission, only the steady-state solutions are of interest. Finally, in some problems, both transients and steady-state solutions are significant. The following problems involve only steady-state solutions:

Problem 8.57

Find the steady-state solutions of the equation

$$(8.571) \qquad a\frac{d^4 y}{dx^4} + b\frac{d^3 y}{dx^3} + c\frac{d^2 y}{dx^2} + d\frac{dy}{dx} + ky = E_0 \cos \omega t$$

in which a, b, c, d, and k are real constants not all zero. *Solution:* Let

$$(8.572) \qquad L_a = aD^4 + bD^3 + cD^2 + dD + k.$$

The impedance is

$$L_a(i\omega) = a(i\omega)^4 + b(i\omega)^3 + c(i\omega)^2 + d(i\omega) + k = (a\omega^4 - c\omega^2 + k) + i(d\omega - b\omega^3);$$

the absolute value of the impedance is

$$Z_0 = \sqrt{(a\omega^4 - c\omega^2 + k)^2 + (d\omega - b\omega^3)^2},$$

and the phase angle ϕ of the impedance is determined by the equations

$$\cos \phi = \frac{a\omega^4 - c\omega^2 + k}{Z_0}, \qquad \sin \phi = \frac{d\omega - b\omega^3}{Z_0}.$$

The steady-state solution of the equation

$$(8.573) \qquad\qquad L_a y = E_0 e^{i\omega x}$$

is

$$(8.574) \qquad\qquad y = \frac{E_0}{Z_0} e^{i(\omega x - \phi)},$$

and the steady-state solution of (8.571) is

$$(8.575) \qquad\qquad y = \frac{E_0}{Z_0} \cos (\omega x - \phi).$$

Problem 8.58

Suppose that a and k are positive in (8.571). Show that, in the "low-frequency" case in which ω is near 0, the "amplitude" E_0/Z_0 in (8.575) is near E_0/k and that the phase angle ϕ is near 0.

Problem 8.581

Suppose a is positive in (8.571). Show that, in the "high-frequency" case in which ω is very great, the "amplitude" E_0/Z_0 in (8.575) is near $E_0/(a\omega^4)$ in the sense that the ratio $[E_0/Z_0]/[E_0/(a\omega^4)]$ is near 1. Show also that the phase angle ϕ is near 0. In fact, it is not difficult to show that $\phi \to 0$ in such a way that $\omega\phi \to -b/a$ as $\omega \to \infty$.

Problem 8.582

To what extent would the work of the last three problems have to be changed to cover the equation

$$\alpha \frac{d^2y}{dx^2} + \beta \frac{dy}{dx} + \gamma y = E_0 \cos \omega t$$

in which α, β, and γ are real constants not all 0? What can be said about a similar equation of order 16?

Problem 8.59

Assuming that a and b are positive constants and that the E's are given constants, show that the steady-state solution of the equation

$$(8.591) \qquad\qquad \frac{d^2y}{dx^2} + 2a \frac{dy}{dx} + by = \sum_{n=-N}^{N} E_n e^{inx}$$

is

$$(8.592) \qquad Y_N(x) = \sum_{n=-N}^{N} \frac{E_n}{\sqrt{(b - n^2)^2 + 4a^2n^2}} \, e^{i(nx - \phi_n)}$$

where the phase angles ϕ_n are given by the formulas

$$(8.593) \quad \cos \phi_n = \frac{b - n^2}{\sqrt{(b - n^2)^2 + 4a^2n^2}}; \quad \sin \phi_n = \frac{2an}{\sqrt{(b - n^2)^2 + 4a^2n^2}}.$$

Show that, if $|n|$ is large, then ϕ_n is near $-\pi$. Show that if $\cdots E_{-2}$, E_{-1}, E_0, E_1, E_2, $\cdots$ is an infinite set of E's which is bounded, that is, if there is a constant B for which

$$(8.594) \qquad\qquad |E_n| \leqq B \qquad\qquad n = 0, \pm 1, \pm 2, \cdots,$$

then

(8.595) $$\lim_{N \to \infty} Y_N(x)$$

must exist.

8.6. Use of Fourier Series.—It should be mentioned at this point that applied mathematicians have very good reasons for wanting to use Fourier series when solving equations of the form $L_a y = f(x)$ in which $f(x)$ is a given periodic function of x.

Let $2h$ be a positive period of $f(x)$; by this we mean that $2h > 0$ and that $f(x + 2h) = f(x)$ for all x. The formulas we obtain look simplest when $h = \pi$; very often one makes the period 2π by making a change in the scale of the independent variable. Suppose further that, in each finite interval $a \leq x \leq b$, $f(x)$ is continuous except perhaps at a finite set of points and that the integral

(8.601) $$\int_a^b |f(x)|^2 \, dx$$

exists, the integral being a Cauchy integral (Section 2.4) if $f(x)$ is unbounded.*

The constants E_n, defined by the formulas

(8.61) $$E_n = \frac{1}{2h} \int_{-h}^{h} f(s) e^{-in(\pi/h)s} \, ds \quad n = 0, \pm 1, \pm 2, \cdots ,$$

are called the *Fourier coefficients* of $f(x)$. [The constants $\sqrt{2h}\, E_n$ are also called the Fourier coefficients of $f(x)$; see Chapter 12.] The series to the right of the [$\sim$] in

(8.62) $f(x) \sim E_0 + [E_{-1} e^{-i(\pi/h)x} + E_1 e^{i(\pi/h)x}] + \cdots$
$$+ [E_{-n} e^{-in(\pi/h)x} + E_n e^{in(\pi/h)x}] + \cdots$$

is called the *Fourier series* of $f(x)$; the [$\sim$] means merely that the series opposite $f(x)$ is the Fourier series of $f(x)$. It is customary to abbreviate (8.62) in the form

(8.621) $$f(x) \sim \sum_{n=-\infty}^{\infty} E_n e^{in(\pi/h)x}.$$

The functions $f_N(x)$ defined by

(8.622) $$f_N(x) = \sum_{n=-N}^{N} E_n e^{in(\pi/h)x}. \qquad N = 0, 1, 2, \cdots$$

are the *partial sums* of the Fourier series.

* We could obtain results with less severe restrictions on $f(x)$; but it is very gratifying to engineers that we do not need *more* restrictions.

The terms of the Fourier series of $f(x)$ are called *harmonics* of $f(x)$. Since the functions $f(x)$ and $e^{-in(\pi/h)x}$ both have period $2h$, any interval of integration of length $2h$ can be used instead of the interval

$$-h \leqq s \leqq h$$

in (8.61). For example, the same Fourier coefficients would be obtained by using the interval $0 \leqq s \leqq 2h$.

The following theorem justifies a procedure much used by applied mathematicians. The theorem is so phrased as to give all the information about Fourier series required for solution of many problems.* For one whose mathematical training has not advanced beyond the material heretofore presented in this book, a proof of the theorem must be decidedly long and difficult. One reason why we do not require $f(x)$ to be continuous is set forth in Section 3.9. The idea of the theorem is as follows: *To get a solution of $L_a y = f$, add solutions of the equations $L_a y = E_n e^{in(\pi/h)x}$.*

THEOREM 8.63.—*Let*

$$(8.631) \qquad a_0 \frac{d^k y}{dx^k} + a_1 \frac{d^{k-1}y}{dx^{k-1}} + \cdots + a_{k-1}\frac{dy}{dx} + a_k y = f(x)$$

be a linear differential equation, of order $k \geqq 1$, with constant coefficients and $a_0 \neq 0$. Let $f(x)$ have period $2h$, and let $f(x)$ be bounded† *and have at most a finite set of discontinuities in each finite interval. For each $n = 0, \pm 1, \pm 2, \cdots$, let E_n denote the Fourier coefficient*

$$(8.632) \qquad E_n = \frac{1}{2h}\int_{-h}^{h} f(s)e^{-in(\pi/h)s}\,ds$$

of $f(x)$. Let

$$(8.633) \quad L_a\left(\frac{in\pi}{h}\right) = a_0\left(\frac{in\pi}{h}\right)^k + a_1\left(\frac{in\pi}{h}\right)^{k-1} + \cdots + a_{k-1}\left(\frac{in\pi}{h}\right) + a_k$$

denote the impedance of the equation

$$(8.634) \qquad a_0 \frac{d^k y}{dx^k} + a_1 \frac{d^{k-1}y}{dx^{k-1}} + \cdots + a_{k-1}\frac{dy}{dx} + a_k y = E_n e^{in(\pi/h)x}.$$

If $L_a(in\pi/h) \neq 0$, let

$$(8.635) \qquad y_n(x) = \frac{E_n}{L_a(in\pi/h)}\, e^{in(\pi/h)x}$$

---

* A general theorem which implies this theorem was proved by A. Hammerstein, *Ein Existenzbeweis für Systeme von Differentialgleichungen mit Hilfe der Methode von unendlichvielen Veranderlichen*, Deutsche Mathematiker Vereinigung Jahresbericht, Vol. 38 (1929), pp. 238–243.

† The hypothesis that $f(x)$ is bounded may be replaced by the hypothesis that the integral in (8.601) exists.

denote the solution of (8.634) *formed in accordance with Section* 8.5; *and if* $L_a(in\pi/h) = 0$, *let* $y_n(x)$ *be any solution of* (8.634) *formed in accordance with Section* 8.3. *Let*

$$Y_N(x) = y_0(x) + [y_{-1}(x) + y_1(x)] + \cdots + [y_{-N}(x) + y_N(x)].$$

Then, as N *becomes infinite,* $Y_N(x)$ *converges uniformly over the infinite interval to a continuous function* $y(x)$ *which has* $k - 1$ *continuous derivatives and satisfies* (8.631) *wherever* $f(x)$ *is continuous. If* $L_a(in\pi/h) \neq 0$ *for each* $n = 0, \pm1, \pm2, \cdots$, *then* $y(x)$ *has period* $2h$.

The meaning of the uniform convergence is this: However a positive number ϵ may be assigned, there is an integer N_ϵ, depending on ϵ but not on x, such that

$$| y(x) - Y_N(x) | < \epsilon$$

for all values of x *in the whole infinite interval when* N *is greater than* N_ϵ. Students who may previously have regarded uniform convergence as an unnecessary elaboration of mathematicians should now see that it is a very good idea. Engineers often find that $Y_N(x)$ is sufficiently good approximation to $y(x)$ to suit their purposes even when N is small, in some cases as small as 1 or 2 or 3. There are occasions on which N is taken to be 20 or even greater.

The functions $E_n e^{in(\pi/h)x}$ are harmonics of the given function $f(x)$, and the functions $y_n(x)$ are harmonics of the solution $y(x)$. The equations (8.635) are obtained from (8.631) by replacing $f(x)$ by its harmonics. The solution of (8.633) is obtained in the form most desired by engineers, namely, in the form of a sum of harmonics.

When the Fourier coefficients are defined by (8.61), the *Parseval equality* (see Section 12.7), which gives a relation between $f(x)$ and the amplitudes of its harmonics, becomes

$$\int_{-h}^{h} | f(x) |^2 \, dx = 2h \sum_{n=-\infty}^{\infty} | E_n |^2.$$

This formula holds whether the Fourier series of $f(x)$ converges or not; its proof is too complicated to be given here. The formula has many diverse applications. For example, when x represents time and $f(x)$ is an electric current, it says that the amount of heat produced by the current in a period is equal to the "sum" of the individual amounts of heat produced by its individual harmonics. This is a special property of harmonics.

It is true that the hypotheses which we have placed upon $f(x)$ are not sufficient to ensure convergence of the Fourier series of $f(x)$; but this fact is, as the lawyers say, incompetent, irrelevant, and immaterial. Insofar as use of Fourier series in the solution of (8.631) is concerned, applied mathematicians may ignore all the interesting theory relating to convergence of Fourier series.*

The method described in Theorem 8.63 for solving (8.631) is used even when $f(x)$ is not periodic. Let $a \leqq x \leqq b$ be an interval in which $f(x)$ has at most a finite set of discontinuities and $f(x)$ is bounded or at least

$$\int_a^b |f(x)|^2 \, dx$$

exists. Let

$$E_n = \frac{1}{b-a} \int_a^b f(s)e^{-in\pi s/(b-a)} \, ds,$$

and let $y_n(x)$ and $Y_N(x)$ be defined as in Theorem 8.63. Then the conclusion of Theorem 8.63 holds insofar as the interval $a \leqq x \leqq b$ is concerned. It is only when $f(x)$ has period $b - a$ that the formulas for the solution are ordinarily useful outside the interval $a \leqq x \leqq b$.

That Fourier coefficients are really used in the solution of problems is attested by the fact that very expensive machines (harmonic analyzers) have been constructed to compute them.

Problem 8.64

By making suitable changes in notation and by evaluating expressions when this is possible, use Theorem 8.63 to obtain a special theorem which covers the Fourier series method of solving the special equation

$$\frac{d^2x}{dt^2} + \omega^2 x = f(t).$$

8.7. Variation of Parameters.—A special method of obtaining solutions of a nonhomogeneous equation $L_a y = f$, after the homogeneous equation $L_a y = 0$ has been solved, is known as the method of *variation of parameters*. This method is used in cases where the coefficients in the operator L_a are nonconstant functions of x as well as when they are constant.

---

* No one has ever been able to find out whether the following is a true or a false statement: "If $f(x)$ is a continuous function having period 2π, then there is at least one value of x for which the Fourier series of $f(x)$ converges." On the one hand, it is well known that there are continuous functions, having period 2π, whose Fourier series are divergent for some values of x. On the other hand, there are many known sufficient conditions for convergence of Fourier series. If $f(x)$ has period $2h$, if the interval $-h \leqq x \leqq h$ can be divided into a finite set of subintervals in each of which $f(x)$ is nondecreasing or nonincreasing, and if

$$\int_{-h}^h |f(x)| \, dx$$

exists as a Cauchy integral (Section 2.4), then the Fourier series of $f(x)$ converges to

$$\lim_{h \to 0} \frac{f(x+h) + f(x-h)}{2}$$

for each x in the neighborhood of which $f(x)$ is bounded and therefore converges to $f(x)$ wherever $f(x)$ is continuous.

Let the equation to be solved have the form

$$(8.71) \qquad L_a y = (a_0 D^n + a_1 D^{n-1} + \cdots + a_{n-1} D + a_n) y = f$$

where the a's are continuous and $a_0 \neq 0$, and let the general solution of the homogeneous equation $L_a y = 0$ be

$$(8.72) \qquad y = c_1 y_1(x) + c_2 y_2(x) + \cdots + c_n y_n(x) \equiv \Sigma c_k y_k.$$

The stratagem of the method under discussion is that of replacing the constants (or parameters) $c_1, c_2, \cdots, c_n$ by functions $\gamma_1, \gamma_2 \cdots, \gamma_n$ of x and determining these functions in such a way that

$$(8.73) \qquad y = \gamma_1 y_1(x) + \gamma_2 y_2(x) + \cdots + \gamma_n y_n(x) = \Sigma \gamma_k y_k$$

will be a solution of $L_a y = f$. The procedure is motivated by the optimistic principles that one should make one's work as simple as possible and that a set of n functions can be found which satisfies n conditions.

With the γ's as yet undetermined but assumed to have all the derivatives we want to use, let y be defined by (8.73). Then for each x

$$Dy = \Sigma \gamma_k y_k' + \Sigma \gamma_k' y_k$$

where primes denote derivatives with respect to x. To simplify further work, let the γ's be required to satisfy the condition $\Sigma \gamma_k' y_k = 0$. Then

$$D^2 y = \Sigma \gamma_k y_k'' + \Sigma \gamma_k' y_k'.$$

If $n > 2$, we simplify further work by demanding that $\Sigma \gamma_k' y_k' = 0$ and then obtain

$$D^3 y = \Sigma \gamma_k y_k''' + \Sigma \gamma_k' y_k''.$$

This procedure is continued until we have required

$$(8.731) \qquad\qquad \Sigma \gamma_k' y_k^{(\nu)} = 0 \qquad\qquad \nu = 0, 1, \cdots, n-2$$

and have obtained

$$(8.732) \qquad\qquad D^\nu y = \Sigma \gamma_k y_k^{(\nu)} \qquad\qquad \nu = 0, 1, 2, \cdots, n-1$$
$$(8.733) \qquad\qquad D^n y = \Sigma \gamma_k y_k^{(n)} + \Sigma \gamma_k' y_k^{(n-1)}.$$

We then find that

$$L_a y = \sum_{\nu=0}^{n} a_{n-\nu} D^\nu y = \sum_{\nu=0}^{n} a_{n-\nu} \sum_{k=1}^{n} \gamma_k y_k^{(\nu)} + a_0 \sum_{k=1}^{n} \gamma_k' y_k^{(n-1)}$$

$$= \sum_{k=1}^{n} \gamma_k \sum_{\nu=0}^{n} a_{n-\nu} y_k^{(\nu)} + a_0 \sum_{k=1}^{n} \gamma_k' y_k^{(n-1)}$$

$$= \sum_{k=1}^{n} \gamma_k L_a y_k + a_0 \sum_{k=1}^{n} \gamma_k' y_k^{(n-1)} = a_0 \sum_{k=1}^{n} \gamma_k' y_k^{(n-1)},$$

the last step being justified by the fact that $L_a y_k = 0$ for each k. It thus appears that if the γ's satisfy the $n - 1$ equations (8.731) and the additional equation

$$(8.734) \qquad\qquad \sum_{k=1}^{n} \gamma_k' y_k^{(n-1)} = \frac{f}{a_0},$$

then $L_a y$ will be f; *i.e.*, the function y defined by (8.733) will be a solution of $L_a y = f$. Persons who have not become accustomed to use of the convenient summation symbol Σ may wish to write all the above formulas without use of the symbol and the n equations (8.731) and (8.734) in the form

$$(8.735) \quad \begin{cases} y_1\,\gamma_1' + y_2\,\gamma_2' + \cdots + y_n\,\gamma_n' = 0 \\ y_1'\,\gamma_1' + y_2'\,\gamma_2' + \cdots + y_n'\,\gamma_n' = 0 \\ \cdots \cdots \cdots \cdots \cdots \cdots \cdots \cdots \cdots \cdots \cdots \\ y_1^{(n-2)}\gamma_1' + y_2^{(n-2)}\gamma_2' + \cdots + y_n^{(n-2)}\gamma_n' = 0 \\ y_1^{(n-1)}\gamma_1' + y_2^{(n-1)}\gamma_2' + \cdots + y_n^{(n-1)}\gamma_n' = \dfrac{f}{a}. \end{cases}$$

It is always possible* to solve the equations (8.735) for $\gamma_1', \gamma_2', \cdots, \gamma_n'$; and integration furnishes functions $\gamma_1, \cdots, \gamma_n$ for which (8.73) is a solution of $L_a y = f$.

Since the preceding theory may appear to be somewhat formidable, we supplement it by careful consideration of an example on which we have twice previously tested the power of our methods.   (See Test example in the index.)

Example 8.74

To solve the equation

$$(8.741) \qquad (D - 2)(D - 3)y = x^3 e^{2x}$$

by the method of variation of parameters, we observe that the general solution of the homogeneous equation is

$$(8.742) \qquad Y_1 = c_1 e^{2x} + c_2 e^{3x}.$$

The stratagem is to determine functions γ_1 and γ_2 such that

$$(8.743) \qquad y = \gamma_1 e^{2x} + \gamma_2 e^{3x}$$

will be a solution of (8.741).   We find

$$(8.744) \qquad Dy = 2\gamma_1 e^{2x} + 3\gamma_2 e^{3x} + (\gamma_1' e^{2x} + \gamma_2' e^{3x}).$$

Imposing the condition

$$(8.745) \qquad \gamma_1' e^{2x} + \gamma_2' e^{3x} = 0$$

on the γ's we find

$$(8.746) \qquad D^2 y = 4\gamma_1 e^{2x} + 9\gamma_2 e^{3x} + 2\gamma_1' e^{2x} + 3\gamma_2' e^{3x}.$$

Since $(D - 2)(D - 3) = D^2 - 5D + 6$, we can multiply (8.743), (8.744), and (8.746), respectively, by 6, -5, and 1 and then add to obtain

$$(D - 2)(D - 3)y = 2\gamma_1' e^{2x} + 3\gamma_2' e^{3x}.$$

Therefore (8.743) will be a solution of (8.741) if (8.745) holds and

$$(8.747) \qquad 2\gamma_1' e^{2x} + 3\gamma_2' e^{3x} = x^3 e^{2x}.$$

* For proof of this, we must refer to Chapter 16.   The determinant W of the coefficients in (8.735) is the Wronskian of n linearly independent functions and hence is not 0.   Since $W \neq 0$, equations (8.735) determine functions $\gamma_1'(x), \cdots,$ $\gamma_n'(x)$ uniquely, and it can be shown that they are continuous functions of x.   It is possible to solve equations (8.735) by means of determinants and to get very pretty formulas for solutions of $L_a y = f$.

Solving (8.745) and (8.747) for γ_1' and γ_2', we obtain

(8.748) $\gamma_1' = -x^3, \qquad \gamma_2' = x^3 e^{-x}.$

Integration [by use of (6.583)] gives

$$\gamma_1 = -\tfrac{1}{4}x^4 + c', \qquad \gamma_2 = -(x^3 + 3x^2 + 6x + 6)e^{-x} + c'',$$

and substitution in (8.743) gives

$$y = -\tfrac{1}{4}(x^4 + 4x^3 + 12x^2 + 24x)e^{2x} + c_1 e^{2x} + c_2 e^{3x}$$

as the general solution of (8.741) [see Example 8.35].

Problem 8.751

Solve, by the method of variation of parameters, $y'' + y = \sec x$. *Ans.:* $y = (c_1 + \log \cos x) \cos x + (c_2 + x) \sin x$.

Problem 8.752

Obtain formula (6.872) by the method of variation of parameters.

8.76. Cauchy's Linear Equations.—Some linear equations with nonconstant coefficients can be transformed into equations with constant coefficients by a change of variable.   The *Cauchy equation**

(8.761) $b_0 x^2 \dfrac{d^2 y}{dx^2} + b_1 x \dfrac{dy}{dx} + b_2 y = f(x),$

in which b_0, b_1, and b_2 are constants, is an example.   When $x > 0$, we may set

$$t = \log x, \qquad x = e^t, \qquad y(x) = y(e^t) = Y(t)$$

to obtain

$$\frac{dy}{dx} = \frac{dY}{dt}\frac{dt}{dx} = \frac{1}{x}\frac{dY}{dt}, \qquad \frac{d^2 y}{dx^2} = \frac{1}{x^2}\frac{d^2 Y}{dt^2} - \frac{1}{x^2}\frac{dY}{dt}$$

so that

$$x\frac{dy}{dx} = \frac{dY}{dt}, \qquad x^2\frac{d^2 y}{dx^2} = \frac{d^2 Y}{dt^2} - \frac{dY}{dt}$$

and (8.761) may be written

(8.762) $b_0 \dfrac{d^2 Y}{dt^2} + (b_1 - b_0) \dfrac{dY}{dt} + b_2 Y = f(e^t).$

This is one of our friends, a linear differential equation with constant coefficients.

Problem 8.77

Give a complete discussion of the equation

(8.771) $x^2 \dfrac{d^2 y}{dx^2} + ax \dfrac{dy}{dx} + by = 0,$

considering only positive values of x.   If some pairs of values of the constants a and b are in any way peculiar, make the facts clear.

* Named after the French mathematician A. L. Cauchy (1789–1857).

Problem 8.78

Find what, if anything, can be accomplished by seeking solutions of (8.771) having the form $y = x^m$.

8.8. Systems of Equations.—It often happens in algebra that the easiest way to find a number y is to find two or more equations connecting y and other numbers and then to find y by solving the system of equations. Similarly it often happens that the easiest way to find a function $y(x)$ is to find two or more differential equations connecting $y(x)$ and its derivatives with other functions and their derivatives and then to find $y(x)$ by solving the system of equations. Sometimes one is required to find all the functions involved in the system of equations.

A system of two linear differential equations of the first order in two unknown functions $y(x)$ and $z(x)$ has the form

$$(8.81) \qquad \begin{cases} a_1 \dfrac{dy}{dx} + a_2 \dfrac{dz}{dx} + a_3 y + a_4 z = f_1 \\[2mm] b_1 \dfrac{dy}{dx} + b_2 \dfrac{dz}{dx} + b_3 y + b_4 z = f_2 \end{cases}$$

where the a's and b's and f's are given functions of x. The problem is that of finding functions $y = y(x)$ and $z = z(x)$ for which the equations hold. We consider in this section only the case in which the a's are constants.

A standard method of solving systems of linear differential equations with constant coefficients may be illustrated by solving the above system (8.81). Assuming that y and z are functions of x for which (8.81) holds and that x is restricted to an interval in which $f_1(x)$ and $f_2(x)$ have continuous derivatives, we begin by writing the equations (8.81) in the form

$$(8.811) \qquad (a_1 D + a_3)y + (a_2 D + a_4)z = f_1$$
$$(8.812) \qquad (b_1 D + b_3)y + (b_2 D + b_4)z = f_2.$$

Applying the operator $b_2 D + b_4$ to (8.811) and the operator $-(a_2 D + a_4)$ to (8.812) and adding the results, we obtain

$$(8.813) \qquad (A_1 D^2 + A_2 D + A_3)y = F$$

where

$$(8.814) \quad A_1 = a_1 b_2 - a_2 b_1, \qquad A_2 = a_1 b_4 + a_3 b_2 - a_2 b_3 - a_4 b_1$$
$$(8.815) \quad A_3 = a_3 b_4 - a_4 b_3, \qquad F = (b_2 D + b_4)f_1 - (a_2 D + a_4)f_2.$$

If $A_1 = A_2 = A_3 = 0$ while $F \neq 0$, then (8.813) has no solutions and accordingly the system (8.81) has no solutions. If $A_1 = A_2 = A_3 = 0$

and $F = 0$, then (8.813) places no restriction on y. If $A_1 = A_2 = 0$ while $A_3 \neq 0$, then (8.813) determines y uniquely. If $A_1 = 0$ while $A_2 \neq 0$, then (8.813) is a linear differential equation of first order with constant coefficients and y must have the form

$$y = Y(x) + c_1 y_1(x).$$

If $A \neq 0$, then (8.813) is of the second order and y must have the form

$$y = Y(x) + c_1 y_1(x) + c_2 y_2(x)$$

where $Y(x)$ is a solution of (8.813) and $y_1(x)$ and $y_2(x)$ are linearly independent solutions of the corresponding homogeneous equation. It is possible to eliminate y from (8.811) and (8.812) to obtain an equation in z similar to (8.813) which, except in trivial cases, implies that $z(x)$ must have some special form. However, it is simpler to substitute in one of the equations (8.811) and (8.812) the functions $y(x)$ already found and to use the resulting equation to determine the possible forms of $z(x)$. It must be emphasized that there is nothing in the above argument to show that all (or indeed any) of the functions $y(x)$ and $z(x)$ of the forms determined above really satisfy the system (8.81); in the absence of a theory covering the subject one must substitute the forms in (8.81) to see which (if any) of them do satisfy (8.81). Another method of treating systems of equations which is, in this and certain other respects, more satisfactory is given later in this chapter.

Problem 8.816

Solve the system of differential equations appearing in Problem 1.39.

Problem 8.82

Solve the system of equations

$$(8.821) \quad \begin{cases} \dfrac{dy}{dx} = a_{11}y + a_{12}z + a_{13}w \\[2mm] \dfrac{dz}{dx} = a_{21}y + a_{22}z + a_{23}w \\[2mm] \dfrac{dw}{dx} = a_{31}y + a_{32}z + a_{33}w \end{cases}$$

for the case in which the matrix of the a's is

$$\begin{pmatrix} 0 & 1 & 1 \\ 1 & 0 & 1 \\ 1 & 1 & 0 \end{pmatrix},$$

i.e., $a_{11} = 0$, $a_{12} = 1$, $a_{13} = 1$, $a_{21} = 1$, $a_{22} = 0$, etc. *Ans.:* $y = c_1 e^{2x} + c_2 e^{-x}$, $z = c_1 e^{2x} + c_3 e^{-x}$, $w = c_1 e^{2x} - (c_2 + c_3)e^{-x}$.

Problem 8.83

Solve the above system (8.821) for the cases in which the matrices of the a's are, respectively,

$$\begin{pmatrix} 1 & 0 & 0 \\ 0 & 2 & 0 \\ 0 & 0 & 3 \end{pmatrix}; \quad \begin{pmatrix} 1 & 0 & 0 \\ 2 & 0 & 0 \\ 3 & 0 & 0 \end{pmatrix}; \quad \begin{pmatrix} 1 & 2 & 3 \\ 0 & 0 & 0 \\ 0 & 0 & 0 \end{pmatrix}.$$

Check your answers in each case.

Problem 8.84

Prove that, if y, z, and w satisfy the system (8.821), then $y(x)$ must satisfy a linear homogeneous differential equation with constant coefficients and with order 3 or less.

Problem 8.85

Prove that, if $y_1(x)$, $y_2(x)$, $\cdots$, $y_n(x)$ constitute a set of n functions such that the derivative of each one of them is a linear combination of functions in the set, then each of the n functions must be a linear combination of terms of the form $x^p e^{qx}$ where p is 0 or a positive integer and q is a constant. Is the result in agreement with the fact that $\sin x$ and $\cos x$ constitute such a set?

Problem 8.86

A system of four linear differential equations of second order in four unknown functions $y_1(x)$, $y_2(x)$, $y_3(x)$, and $y_4(x)$ has the form

$$(a_{j,1}D^2 + a_{j,2}D + a_{j,3})y_1 + (a_{j,4}D^2 + a_{j,5}D + a_{j,6})y_2$$
$$+ (a_{j,7}D^2 + a_{j,8}D + a_{j,9})y_3 + (a_{j,10}D^2 + a_{j,11}D + a_{j,12})y_4 = f_j(x)$$

where j takes values 1, 2, 3, and 4. Assume that the a's are given constants and that the f's have all the derivatives you want to use. Show that, if $y_1(x)$, $\cdots$, $y_4(x)$ constitute a solution of the system, then $y_1(x)$ must satisfy a linear differential equation in y_1 alone with constant coefficients which is of order 16 unless a certain relation among the a's happens to be satisfied. [One who contemplates the labor involved in solving the system even when the a's are relatively small nonnegative integers given by the matrix

$$\begin{pmatrix} 7 & 0 & 8 & 6 & 6 & 9 & 8 & 5 & 5 & 0 & 1 & 3 \\ 4 & 9 & 4 & 0 & 7 & 7 & 1 & 3 & 4 & 7 & 7 & 6 \\ 2 & 2 & 1 & 7 & 7 & 8 & 8 & 5 & 0 & 1 & 0 & 3 \\ 3 & 1 & 4 & 1 & 5 & 9 & 2 & 6 & 5 & 8 & 9 & 7 \end{pmatrix}$$

should understand how it is possible that skilled workers may be occupied for some time when an important system of differential equations is encountered.]

8.9. Inverse Operators.

—The remainder of this chapter is devoted to inverse operators. They are used extensively in some phases of applied mathematics.

Let L denote an operator of the form

$$L = a_0 D^n + a_1 D^{n-1} + \cdots + a_{n-1}D + a_n$$

in which the a's are constants* and $a_0 \neq 0$. We have hitherto regarded n as a positive integer; but now we include also the case in which $n = 0$ and accordingly $L = a_0$.

If $f(x)$ is continuous and $n > 0$, then the equation $Ly = f$ has (Theorem 6.04) a general solution of the form

$$(8.901) \quad y(x) = Y(x) + c_1 y_1(x) + c_2 y_2(x) + \cdots + c_n y_n(x)$$

where $Y(x)$ is a particular solution of $Ly = f$, where the c's are constants, and where $y_1, y_2, \cdots, y_n$ are n linearly independent solutions of $Ly = 0$. There are times when the symbol $L^{-1}f$ is used to represent an "indefinite" one of the solutions $y(x)$ of $Ly = f$ in much the same way that the symbol $\int f(x)dx$ is used to denote an "indefinite" one of the functions $y(x)$ for which $y'(x) = f(x)$. With this interpretation, $L^{-1}f$ means some one of the functions in (8.901).

When the symbols $\sqrt{2}$ and $2^{\frac{1}{2}}$ appear in calculations, it would be decidedly inconvenient to be uncertain as to whether the number involved is 1.4142 or -1.4142. Likewise, when the symbol $L^{-1}f$ appears in calculations, it is decidedly inconvenient to be unable to say what function it represents. When serious use is made of the symbol $L^{-1}f$, it is nearly always defined in the unambiguous fashion which we now describe.

Let x_0 represent a fixed value of the independent variable; in many applications, x_0 is 0. When $f(x)$ is continuous and $n > 0$, there is (Theorem 6.03) a unique function $y(x)$ such that $Ly = f$ and

$$(8.902) \quad y(x_0) = y'(x_0) = y''(x_0) = \cdots = y^{(n-1)}(x_0) = 0;$$

this function is denoted by $L^{-1}f$. If $n = 0$, the equation $Ly = f$ becomes simply $a_0 y = f$; this is an algebraic equation with unique solution $y = a_0^{-1}f$ which we denote by $L^{-1}f$.

For many applications, the requirement that $f(x)$ be continuous is too severe. Anyone who wishes to do so may assume merely that $f(x)$ has at most a finite set of discontinuities in each finite interval and that the Cauchy integral (Section 2.4) $\int_a^b |f(x)|\, dx$ exists for some interval $a \leq x \leq b$ containing x_0; but we always assume that $f(x)$ satisfies these conditions. When $n > 0$ there is (although the proof of Theorem 6.03 must be slightly modified to prove it) a unique continuous function $y(x)$, $a \leq x \leq b$, having $(n - 1)$ continuous derivatives such that (8.902) holds and $Ly = f$ for each x in $a \leq x \leq b$ for which $f(x)$ is continuous. This function is denoted by $L^{-1}f$.

---

* The reader will see that some of the discussion applies to the case in which the a's are functions of x not necessarily constant, but we simplify matters by assuming the a's to be constants.

Thus with each operator L we associate an operator L^{-1} which is called the *inverse* or *reciprocal* of L. We use the notations L^{-1} and $1/L$ interchangeably; in other words, $1/L = L^{-1}$. It is merely repeating the definition of L^{-1} to say that the equality $y = L^{-1}f$ means that $Ly = f$ and, moreover, that $y(x)$ and its first $n - 1$ derivatives vanish when $x = x_0$. *The formula*

$$LL^{-1}f = f$$

is always correct (when we restrict f as stated above). However, even when $y(x)$ has $n(n > 0)$ continuous derivatives, *the formula $L^{-1}Ly = y$ is correct only when y and its first $(n - 1)$ derivatives vanish at x_0.* The fact that $y = L^{-1}f$ always implies $Ly = f$ and that $Ly = f$ implies $y = L^{-1}f$ only in special circumstances cannot be too strongly emphasized; these points must be kept continually in mind when one works with operators.

Products of operators are defined as in Section 6.1, and the product $L^{-1}L^{-1} \cdots L^{-1}$ with n factors is denoted by L^{-n}. It is convenient to define L^0 as the *identity*, that is, the operator which carries each function into itself. Thus $L^0f = f$ for each function f. Now L^α is defined for each integer α. The product LL^{-1} is the identity. When the order of L is positive $(n > 0)$, $L^{-1}Lf = f$ only for special functions and accordingly $L^{-1}L$ is not the identity. These facts show that, if L is an operator of positive order, then $LL^{-1} \neq L^{-1}L$ so that L does not commute with its own inverse.*

The inverse of the operator D itself is of particular interest. For each f,

$$(8.903) \qquad\qquad D^{-1}f = \int_{x_0}^{x} f(t)dt$$

since (Chapter 2) the right member of (8.903) is the unique function $y(x)$ such that $Dy = f$ and $y(x_0) = 0$. The fact that

$$DD^{-1}f = f$$

wherever $f(x)$ is continuous is essentially the fundamental theorem of the calculus as embodied in Theorem 2.36. The fact that, even when $f(x)$ has a continuous derivative, the formula $D^{-1}Df = f$ holds only in special circumstances is shown by the equality

$$(8.904) \qquad D^{-1}Df(x) = \int_{x_0}^{x} f'(t)dt = f(x) - f(x_0);$$

it is only when $f(x_0) = 0$ that $D^{-1}Df = f$. The operator D^{-1} is called an *integral operator* because the result of applying D^{-1} to f is an

---

* This means that L^{-1} is not the inverse of L in the sense in which the term *inverse* is ordinarily used in mathematical theory of groups.

integral of f. The operator D, which should be called a *derivative operator* because the result of applying D to f is the derivative of f, is commonly called a *differential operator*.

When m is a constant, a formula for $(D - m)^{-1}f$ is quickly obtained by use of an integrating factor.   If $y = (D - m)^{-1}f$, then

$$(D - m)y = f$$

and $y(x_0) = 0$.   Hence, also, $e^{-mx}y(x)$ vanishes when $x = x_0$; and accordingly the formula

$$\frac{d}{dx} e^{-mx}y = e^{-mx}f(x)$$

implies that

$$e^{-mx}y = \int_{x_0}^{x} e^{-mt}f(t)dt$$

and

$$y = e^{mx} \int_{x_0}^{x} e^{-mt}f(t)dt = \int_{x_0}^{x} e^{m(x-t)}f(t)dt.$$

Thus

(8.905) $$\frac{1}{D - m} f = \int_{x_0}^{x} e^{m(x-t)}f(t)dt.$$

Observe that (8.905) reduces to (8.903) when $m = 0$.

Our next task is to become acquainted with some of the rules for manipulating operators.   Each operator L of order n can be factored (Section 6.43) in the form

$$L = a_0(D - m_1)(D - m_2) \cdots (D - m_n),$$

the m's being the roots of the characteristic equation $L(m) = 0$. The order of the factors on the right is immaterial since (Section 6.43) the factors commute.   *If L_1 and L_2 are two operators of the form L, then L_1 and L_2 commute;* for L_1L_2 and L_2L_1 can be represented as products of constants and factors of the form $D - m$.

We are going to prove that

(8.906) $$\frac{1}{L_1L_2} = \frac{1}{L_1}\frac{1}{L_2} = \frac{1}{L_2}\frac{1}{L_1}$$

or, what amounts to the same thing,

(8.9061) $$(L_1L_2)^{-1} = L_1^{-1}L_2^{-1} = L_2^{-1}L_1^{-1}.$$

Let L_1 and L_2 have orders $n_1 \geqq 0$ and $n_2 \geqq 0$, respectively; and let $y = (L_1L_2)^{-1}f$.   Then y and its first $(n_1 + n_2 - 1)$ derivatives vanish at x_0 and $L_1L_2y = f$ so that $L_1Y = f$ where $Y = L_2y$.   Now Y involves derivatives of $y(x)$ only up to n_2, and accordingly Y and its first

$n_1 - 1$ derivatives vanish at x_0; therefore, $Y = L_1^{-1}f$, and $L_2 y = L_1^{-1}f$. Since y and its first $n_2 - 1$ derivatives vanish at x_0, we obtain

$$y = L_2^{-1}L_1^{-1}f.$$

Therefore, $(L_1L_2)^{-1} = L_2^{-1}L_1^{-1}$. Likewise, $(L_2L_1)^{-1} = L_1^{-1}L_2^{-1}$. But L_1 and L_2 commute so that $L_1L_2 = L_2L_1$ and therefore $(L_1L_2)^{-1} = (L_2L_1)^{-1}$. Combining equalities gives (8.9061). If $L_1, L_2, \cdots, L_k$ are k operators of the form L, repeated use of (8.9061) gives

$$(L_1L_2 \cdots L_k)^{-1} = L_1^{-1}L_2^{-1} \cdots L_k^{-1};$$

in particular,

$$(L^k)^{-1} = (L^{-1})^k = L^{-k}.$$

In this formula, we have an excellent example of the fact that the notation for the inverse makes results look very simple. In proving (8.9061), we proved the following important fact: *If L_1 and L_2 are operators of the form considered above, then L_1^{-1} and L_2^{-1} commute.* The facts relating to commuting may be summed up as follows: *The operators of the form L commute among themselves; the operators of the form L^{-1} commute among themselves; but L_1 and L_2^{-1} do not commute when the orders of L_1 and L_2 are positive.*

The fact that the reciprocals, as well as the operators L themselves, are linear is so important that we prove it. Where c_1 and c_2 are constants and f_1 and f_2 are continuous functions, let

$$L^{-1}f_1 = y_1, \qquad L^{-1}f_2 = y_2.$$

Then $Ly_1 = f_1$, $Ly_2 = f_2$, and

$$y_1^{(k)}(x_0) = y_2^{(k)}(x_0) = 0 \qquad k = 0, 1, \cdots, n - 1,$$

n being the order of the operator L. Setting $y = c_1 y_1 + c_2 y_2$, we see that

$$Ly = c_1 Ly_1 + c_2 Ly_2 = c_1 f_1 + c_2 f_2$$

and

$$y^{(k)}(x_0) = c_1 y_1^{(k)}(x_0) + c_2 y_2^{(k)}(x_0) = 0 \qquad k = 0, 1, \cdots, n - 1$$

so that $y = L^{-1}(c_1 f_1 + c_2 f_2)$. Thus

(8.907) $L^{-1}(c_1 f_1 + c_2 f_2) = y = c_1 y_1 + c_2 y_2 = c_1 L^{-1}f_1 + c_2 L^{-1}f_2,$

and *linearity of L^{-1} is established.*

Our next step is to obtain formulas for $(D - m)^{-k}f$ when k is a positive integer. The formulas involve integrals which may seem complicated, but the formulas are important and useful. Letting $f_1(x)$ denote the right member of (8.905), we obtain

$$(D - m)^{-2}f = (D - m)^{-1}[(D - m)^{-1}f] = (D - m)^{-1}f_1(x)$$
$$= \int_{x_0}^{x} e^{m(x-u)}f_1(u)du = \int_{x_0}^{x} e^{m(x-u)} \, du \int_{x_0}^{u} e^{m(u-t)}f(t)dt,$$

and simplifying the last member gives

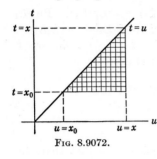

$$(8.9071) \quad (D - m)^{-2}f$$
$$= \int_{x_0}^{x} du \int_{x_0}^{u} e^{m(x-t)}f(t)dt.$$

Figure 8.9072 indicates the region in a (u, t) plane over which $e^{m(x-t)}f(t)$ is integrated; and inspection of the figure shows what the new limits of integration will be when the order of integration is changed. Changing the order of integration and simplifying the

Fig. 8.9072.

result give

$$(D - m)^{-2}f = \int_{x_0}^{x} dt \int_{t}^{x} e^{m(x-t)}f(t)du$$
$$= \int_{x_0}^{x} e^{m(x-t)}f(t)dt \int_{t}^{x} du = \int_{x_0}^{x} (x - t)e^{m(x-t)}f(t)dt.$$

Using a repetition of the method, we can show that

$$(D - m)^{-3}f = \int_{x_0}^{x} e^{m(x-u)} \, du \int_{x_0}^{u} (u - t)e^{m(u-t)}f(t)dt$$
$$= \int_{x_0}^{x} e^{m(x-t)}f(t)dt \int_{t}^{x} (u - t)du$$

and hence

$$(D - m)^{-3}f = \int_{x_0}^{x} \frac{(x - t)^2}{2!} e^{m(x-t)}f(t)dt.$$

When the method is understood, it is easy to repeat it and to prove by induction the important formula

$$(8.908) \quad \frac{1}{(D - m)^k} f = \int_{x_0}^{x} \frac{(x - t)^{k-1}}{(k - 1)!} e^{m(x-t)}f(t)dt \quad k = 1, 2, 3, \cdots.$$

For each k, the right member is a formula involving a single integral for the unique solution $y(x)$ of the equation $(D - m)^k y = f$ for which $y(x)$ and its first $(k - 1)$ derivatives vanish at x_0.

Setting $m = 0$ in (8.908) gives the formula

$$(8.909) \quad \frac{1}{D^k} f = \int_{x_0}^{x} \frac{(x - t)^{k-1}}{(k - 1)!} f(t)dt \quad k = 1, 2, 3, \cdots$$

which is often used.

Problem 8.9091

Use the formula (8.908) to show that

$$(8.9092) \qquad \frac{1}{(D-m)^k} f(x) = e^{\alpha x} \frac{1}{(D+\alpha-m)^k} e^{-\alpha x} f(x)$$

when m and α are constants and k is a positive integer.

Problem 8.9092

Show that if $m \neq i\omega$

$$\frac{1}{D-m} e^{i\omega x} = \frac{1}{i\omega-m} e^{i\omega x} - \frac{e^{(i\omega-m)x_0}}{i\omega-m} e^{mx}.$$

Show that, if ω is real and the real part of m is negative, then the second term on the right is a transient and the first term is the steady-state solution of

$$(D-m)y = e^{i\omega x}.$$

8.91. Quotients and Partial Fractions.—Our next step is to see what, if anything, the members of the formula

$$(8.911) \qquad \frac{L_1}{L_2} + \frac{L_3}{L_4} = \frac{L_1 L_4 + L_3 L_2}{L_2 L_4}$$

mean and to see whether the equality is correct. In the first place there may be some doubt as to whether the first quotient in (8.911) is to be defined to be $L_1 L_2^{-1}$ or $L_2^{-1} L_1$. The question whether or not it makes any difference which definition is used is the same as the question whether or not $L_1 L_2^{-1} = L_2^{-1} L_1$. Thus the two definitions are the same if and only if L_1 and L_2^{-1} commute. For definiteness, let us *define* the first quotient in (8.911) to be $L_1 L_2^{-1}$. Thus $L_1/L_2 = L_1 L_2^{-1}$, and quotients of other operators are to defined in the same way.

Meaning has now been attached to the members of (8.911), and we may write the formula in question in the form

$$(8.912) \qquad L_1 L_2^{-1} + L_3 L_4^{-1} = (L_1 L_4 + L_3 L_2)(L_2 L_4)^{-1}.$$

Using the fact that $(L_2 L_4)^{-1} = L_4^{-1} L_2^{-1} = L_2^{-1} L_4^{-1}$ we see that (8.912) holds if and only if

$$L_1 L_2^{-1} + L_3 L_4^{-1} = L_1 L_4 L_4^{-1} L_2^{-1} + L_3 L_2 L_2^{-1} L_4^{-1}$$

Since $L_4 L_4^{-1}$ is the identity, the first term on the right is $L_1 L_2^{-1}$; and since $L_2 L_2^{-1}$ is the identity, the last term is $L_3 L_4^{-1}$. Thus the formulas (8.911) and (8.912) are correct. The operators L_2 and L_4, being operators expressible as products of constants and factors of the form $(D-m)$, may have common factors; in this case the formula (8.911) does not make use of the least common denominator of arithmetic. The method of proof of (8.911) gives the better formula

(8.913) $$\frac{L_1}{L_2 L_5} + \frac{L_3}{L_4 L_5} = \frac{L_1 L_4 + L_3 L_2}{L_2 L_4 L_5}.$$

When we want to add two fractions whose denominators have a "greatest common factor" L_5, we can let the denominators be $L_2 L_5$ and $L_4 L_5$ and obtain a sum with "least common denominator" $L_2 L_4 L_5$ exactly as in arithmetic. The sum of any finite number of fractions of the form L_1/L_2 can be obtained by adding the first two, then adding the sum to the third, adding the new sum to the fourth, and so on, until the final sum with least common denominator is obtained. The essential point is that the algebraic manipulations are made exactly as they would be if the L's were numbers rather than operators.

We shall need rules for multiplying fractions in which the numerators are not 1 as in (8.906), and accordingly we prove that, *if the order n_3 of L_3 is less than or equal to the order n_4 of L_4, then*

(8.914) $$\left(\frac{L_1}{L_2}\right)\left(\frac{L_3}{L_4}\right) = \frac{L_1 L_3}{L_2 L_4}.$$

It is sufficient to prove that

$$L_1 L_2^{-1} L_3 L_4^{-1} f = L_1 L_3 L_2^{-1} L_4^{-1} f.$$

Since $L_4^{-1} f$ and its first $(n_4 - 1)$ derivatives vanish at x_0 and moreover since $n_3 \leqq n_4$,

$$L_3^{-1} L_3 L_4^{-1} f = L_4^{-1} f.$$

Therefore,

$$L_1 L_3 L_2^{-1} L_4^{-1} f = L_1 L_3 L_2^{-1} L_3^{-1} L_3 L_4^{-1} f = L_1 L_3 L_3^{-1} L_2^{-1} L_3 L_4^{-1} f = L_1 L_2^{-1} L_3 L_4^{-1} f,$$

and the result is established. The restriction $n_3 \leqq n_4$ must not be overlooked; in fact,

$$\left(\frac{1}{D}\right)\left(\frac{D}{1}\right) \neq \frac{D}{D} = DD^{-1}.$$

The idea of using identities, which express quotients of polynomials as sums of simpler *partial fractions*, is very much simplified when complex numbers are used. This eliminates the necessity of considering quadratic factors and their powers and accordingly eliminates the "difficult cases" sometimes presented in algebra and calculus books. Let Λ_1 denote an operator of the form L which we assume to be factored in the form

$$\Lambda_1 = (D - m_1)^{\sigma_1} (D - m_2)^{\sigma_2} \cdots (D - m_k)^{\sigma_k}$$

in which the m's are real or complex constants and $\sigma_1, \sigma_2, \cdots, \sigma_k$ are positive integers. Let Λ_2 be an operator of the form L (which is a constant in important cases) having order less than that of Λ_1; and let constants $A_k^{(p)}$ be determined as in the theory of partial fractions, such that

$$(8.915) \quad \frac{\Lambda_2}{(D - m)^{\sigma_1}(D - m_2)^{\sigma_2} \cdots (D - m_k)^{\sigma_k}}$$

$$= \frac{A_1^{(1)}}{(D - m_1)} + \frac{A_1^{(2)}}{(D - m_1)^2} + \cdots + \frac{A_1^{(\sigma_1)}}{(D - m_1)^{\sigma_1}}$$

$$+ \frac{A_2^{(1)}}{(D - m_2)} + \frac{A_2^{(2)}}{(D - m_2)^2} + \cdots + \frac{A_2^{(\sigma_2)}}{(D - m_2)^{\sigma_2}}$$

$$+ \cdots + \frac{A_k^{(1)}}{(D - m_k)} + \frac{A_k^{(2)}}{(D - m_k)^2} + \cdots + \frac{A_k^{(\sigma_k)}}{(D - m_k)^{\sigma_k}}$$

would be an identity in a variable m if D were everywhere replaced by m. *Then (8.915) is an identity in operators;* to see that this is so, we need merely observe that the algebraic manipulations by which one adds the fractions on the right to obtain the sum on the left when D is a real or complex variable can be duplicated when D is an operator to obtain the operational identity. The equation (8.915) gives the ordinary *partial-fraction expansion* of the operator Λ_2/Λ_1. Another partial-fraction expansion, always valid when none of the m's is 0, is that in which the numerator of each fraction in the right member of (8.915) contains D with an exponent one less than the exponent in the denominator. In this case, also, the equality in operators follows from the equality in real or complex numbers.

If Λ_4 is a polynomial in D of degree greater than or equal to that of Λ_1, then the formula

$$(8.916) \qquad \frac{\Lambda_4}{\Lambda_1} = \Lambda_3 + \frac{\Lambda_2}{\Lambda_1}$$

holds, Λ_3 and Λ_2 being, respectively, the quotient and remainder obtained by dividing exactly as though D were a number instead of an operator. For if $\Lambda_4 = \Lambda_3\Lambda_1 + \Lambda_2$ is an algebraic identity in D, then it is an operational identity and multiplication* on the right by Λ_1^{-1} gives (8.916).

The problem of finding the function $y(x)$ for which

$$(a_0D^n + a_1D^{n-1} + \cdots + a_{n-1}D + a_n)y = f$$

and

$$y(x_0) = y'(x_0) = \cdots = y^{(n-1)}(x_0) = 0$$

---

* We use here the obvious fact that, if $L_1 = L_2$, then $L_1 \Lambda_1^{-1} = L_2\Lambda_1^{-1}$; it is likewise true that, if $L_1 = L_2$, then $\Lambda_1^{-1}L_1 = \Lambda_1^{-1}L_2$. Thus an equality in operators may be multiplied *on the right* (or *on the left*) by an operator.

has now been made largely a matter of algebra. One divides by the coefficient of y exactly as though it were a number to obtain

$$y = \frac{1}{a_0 D^n + a_1 D^{n-1} + \cdots + a_n} f$$

and then expands the quotient into partial fractions to obtain the solution in the form

$$y = \sum \frac{A}{(D - m)^\sigma} f.$$

There are n terms in this sum. If the m's are distinct (that is, if no two are equal), each σ is 1; otherwise at least one σ must be greater than 1. The terms in the sum are to be evaluated by use of (8.908) or equivalent formulas. For example, the solution of

$$(D^2 + a^2)y = f$$

for which $y(x_0) = y'(x_0) = 0$ may, when $a \neq 0$, be found as follows:

$$y = \frac{1}{D^2 + a^2} f = \frac{1}{2ia} \left[\frac{1}{D - ia} f - \frac{1}{D + ia} f \right]$$

$$= \frac{1}{2ia} \left[\int_{x_0}^{x} e^{ia(x-t)} f(t)dt - \int_{x_0}^{x} e^{-ia(x-t)} f(t)dt \right]$$

$$= \frac{1}{a} \int_{x_0}^{x} \sin a(x - t)f(x)dt.$$

For many purposes, one does not want to combine terms of the form $(D - m)^{-1}f$ as we did in this example; the individual terms often have important interpretations.

The idea of juggling with operators as though they were numbers is very old; the greatest development of the idea is due to Oliver Heaviside (1850–1925) who used it extensively to solve problems involving electric circuits. It has been said that Heaviside disliked derivatives and integrals and always preferred to solve his problems by algebraic methods. It was a part of Heaviside's technique to use the *unit function* which we describe in presenting the next problem. Heaviside used the letter p to represent an operator "which can do everything that D does, and more." For our present purposes, this cryptic phrase merely indicates that there is a difference between the operator p of Heaviside and the differential operator D. The operator p is used in such a way that each correct formula involving the operators D and D^{-1} is correct when p and p^{-1} are substituted for D and D^{-1}; but some correct formulas involving p and p^{-1} are not correct when D and D^{-1} are substituted for p and p^{-1}. Hence p may be substituted for D in the results of the following problems.

Problems

Let $H(x)$ be the function defined by

(8.9161) $$H(x) = 0 \qquad\qquad x \leqq 0$$
$$= 1 \qquad\qquad x > 0.$$

This function was called the *unit function* by Heaviside and is now called the *Heaviside unit function* because Heaviside popularized its use. We have defined $H(0)$ to be 0, but we do not quarrel with anyone who wants to define $H(0)$ other-wise.* Let the number x_0, involved in the determination of inverses, be 0. If L is an operator of order n, then $L^{-1}H$ is the unique continuous function $y(x)$ such that $Ly = H(x)$ when $x \neq 0$ and $y(x)$ and its first $(n-1)$ derivatives vanish at $x = 0$. The nth derivative of $y(x)$ is undefined at $x = 0$ and has a finite jump at that point. The solution of problems by "Heaviside methods" involves use of formulas for functions $u(x)$ of the form $u(x) = L_1 L^{-1}H(x)$ for cases in which L_1 is an operator of order n_1 less than or equal to n. If $n_1 < n$, $u(x)$ is defined for all x. If $n_1 = n$, $u(x)$ is defined for $x \neq 0$; the fact that $u(x)$ is undefined when $x = 0$ is of no importance; a formula involving $H(x)$ is regarded as being correct if it is correct for all $x \neq 0$. Derive the following formulas in which a is a constant not 0:

(8.9162) $\quad D^{-1}H(x) = xH(x)$

(8.9163) $\quad \dfrac{1}{D + a} H(x) = \dfrac{1 - e^{-ax}}{a} H(x)$

(8.9164) $\quad \dfrac{D}{D + a} H(x) = e^{-ax}H(x)$

(8.9165) $\quad \dfrac{1}{D^2 + a^2} H(x) = \dfrac{1 - \cos ax}{a^2} H(x)$

(8.9166) $\quad \dfrac{D}{D^2 + a^2} H(x) = \dfrac{\sin ax}{a} H(x)$

(8.9167) $\quad \dfrac{D^2}{D^2 + a^2} H(x) = \cos ax H(x)$

(8.9168) $\quad D^{-k}H(x) = \dfrac{x^k}{k!} H(x) \qquad\qquad\qquad\qquad k = 1, 2, \cdots$

(8.9169) $\quad \dfrac{D}{(D + a)^k} H(x) = \dfrac{x^{k-1}}{(k - 1)!} e^{ax}H(x) \qquad\qquad k = 1, 2, \cdots$

Hint: For the last formula, use (8.908) and the fact that

$$\int_0^x \frac{(x - t)^{k-1}}{(k - 1)!} e^{-a(x-t)}\, dt = \int_0^x \frac{u^{k-1}}{(k - 1)!} e^{-au}\, du$$

* It makes no difference how $H(0)$ is defined and in fact it makes no difference whether it is defined at all; one can completely ignore the value $x = 0$ in formulas involving $H(x)$. Some writers claim that $H(x)$ is a peculiar function such that $H(x)$ has simultaneously all values from 0 to 1 when $x = 0$, and sometimes weird conclusions are drawn from this peculiarity. This claim serves no useful purpose, and it is sometimes harmful in that it creates an impression that $H(x)$ is not subject to precise mathematical analysis. If we define $H(0)$ to be $\frac{1}{2}$, then the formula $H(x) = \frac{1}{2}(1 + \operatorname{sgn} x)$ holds when $x = 0$ as well as when $x \neq 0$.

Problem 8.917

Verify each step in the following solution: If m_1 and m_2 are different constants, $f(x)$ is continuous, and $y(x)$ is the solution of

$$(D - m_1)(D - m_2)y = f(x)$$

for which $y(x_0) = y'(x_0) = 0$, then

$$y = \frac{1}{(D - m_1)(D - m_2)} f(x) = \frac{1}{m_1 - m_2} \left(\frac{1}{D - m_1} - \frac{1}{D - m_2} \right) f(x)$$

so that

$$y = \frac{1}{m_1 - m_2} e^{m_1 x} \int_{x_0}^{x} e^{-m_1 t} f(t)dt - \frac{1}{m_1 - m_2} e^{m_2 x} \int_{x_0}^{x} e^{-m_2 t} f(t)dt.$$

Remark: The solution of the above problem, obtained by the method of partial fractions, looks different from the solution of the same equation obtained in Problem 6.594. The solution in Problem 6.594 involves two *iterated* or *tandem* integrations whereas the solution in Problem 8.917 involves two entirely *separate* or *parallel* integrations. One who is curious about the relation between the two solutions may change the order of integration [as we did in arriving at (8.908)] in the iterated integral in Problem 6.594, integrate with respect to t_2, and find that the result is precisely the same as the solution given in Problem 8.917.

Problem 8.918

Use the formula (8.9092) to show that

$$\frac{1}{(D - 2)(D - 3)} x^n e^{2x} = e^{2x} \frac{1}{D(D - 1)} x^n.$$

Use this formula to find the particular solution of the equation

$$(D - 2)(D - 3)y = x^3 e^{2x}$$

for which $y(0) = y'(0) = 0$. *Ans.:* $y = -(\frac{1}{4}x^4 + x^3 + 3x^2 + 6x + 6)e^{2x} + 6e^{3x}$. (See Example 8.74.)

Problem 8.919

Assuming that $m_1, m_2, \cdots, m_n$ are n different numbers, use the method of partial fractions to find the solution of the equation

$$(D - m_1)(D - m_2) \cdots (D - m_n)y = f(x)$$

for which $y(x_0) = y'(x_0) = \cdots = y^{(n-1)}(x_0) = 0$. *Hint:* The easiest way to find constants $A_1, A_2, \cdots, A_n$ such that

$$\frac{1}{(D - m_1)(D - m_2) \cdots (D - m_n)} = \sum_{k=1}^{n} \frac{A_k}{(D - m_k)}$$

is to regard D temporarily as being a number rather than an operator, to multiply by the denominator on the left to obtain

$$\sum_{k=1}^{n} A_k \frac{(D - m_1)(D - m_2) \cdots (D - m_n)}{(D - m_k)} = 1,$$

and then, for each k, to let $D \to m_k$ to obtain

$$A_k = \left\{ \frac{D - m_k}{(D - m_1)(D - m_2) \cdots (D - m_n)} \right\}_k \qquad k = 1, 2, \cdots, n$$

where $\{\ \ \}_k$ means the result of canceling the factor $(D - m_k)$ from the numerator and denominator and setting $D = m_k$ in the result; for example,

$$A_3 = \frac{1}{(m_3 - m_1)(m_3 - m_2)(m_3 - m_4)(m_3 - m_5) \cdots (m_3 - m_n)}.$$

Ans.: $\quad y = \sum_{k=1}^{n} \left\{ \frac{D - m_k}{(D - m_1)(D - m_2) \cdots (D - m_n)} \right\}_k e^{m_k x} \int_{x_0}^{x} e^{-m_k t} f(t)\, dt.$

8.92. Series Expansions of Operators.—When operators commute, the algebra of the operators is so much like the algebra of real numbers that we may wonder whether we can do anything with series of operators. We begin with a simple question. By using the fact that

$$\frac{1}{1 - x} = 1 + x + x^2 + \cdots$$

if and only if $|\,x\,| < 1$ we see that, if m is a constant not 0, then the first of the two formulas

$$(8.921) \qquad \frac{1}{D - m} \overset{?}{=} -\frac{1}{m} \frac{1}{1 - D/m} \overset{?}{=} -\frac{1}{m} - \frac{D}{m^2} - \frac{D^2}{m^3} - \frac{D^3}{m^4} - \cdots$$

and

$$(8.922) \qquad \frac{1}{D - m} \overset{?}{=} \frac{1}{D} \frac{1}{1 - m/D} \overset{?}{=} \frac{1}{D} + \frac{m}{D^2} + \frac{m^2}{D^3} + \frac{m^3}{D^4} + \cdots$$

is valid when D is a constant for which $|\,D/m\,| < 1$, and the second is valid when D is a constant for which $|\,m/D\,| < 1$; the question is whether or not these are *operational identities*, that is, identities when D is an operator.*

We look first at (8.921) and the question whether or not

$$(8.923) \qquad \frac{1}{D - m} f \overset{?}{=} -\frac{f}{m} - \frac{Df}{m^2} - \frac{D^2 f}{m^3} - \frac{D^3 f}{m^4} - \cdots.$$

The operator on the left applies to a function $f(x)$ if it is continuous. The operator on the right applies to each function $f(x)$, having derivatives of all orders, for which the series converges. Let us try $f = x^3$. Assuming that (8.923) is correct when $f = x^3$, we obtain immediately

$$(8.9231) \qquad \frac{1}{D - m} x^3 = -\frac{x^3}{m} - \frac{3x^2}{m^2} - \frac{6x}{m^3} - \frac{6}{m^4}.$$

Letting $y(x)$ denote the right member of (8.9231) we can show easily that

$$(D - m)y = x^3.$$

However it is not true that $y(x_0) = 0$ unless by accident x_0 is one of the roots of the cubic equation $y(x) = 0$. It thus appears that the expansion in the last member of (8.921) serves in some cases to furnish quickly a solution of $(D - m)y = f$.

* There is, of course, the possibility of trying to replace D by a more general operator L or L^{-1}.

But (8.921) is not an operational identity since the last member does not ordinarily furnish the particular solution of $(D - m)y = f$ for which $y(x_0) = 0$. Hence, except for the following problem, we disregard (8.921).

Problem 8.9232

Determine whether or not the following steps, which purport to find the particular solution of the equation $(D - 2)(D - 3)y = x^3 e^{2x}$ for which

$$y(0) = y'(0) = 0,$$

are correct:

$$y = \frac{1}{(D - 2)(D - 3)} x^3 e^{2x} = \frac{1}{D - 3} x^3 e^{2x} - \frac{1}{D - 2} x^3 e^{2x} = e^{2x} \frac{1}{D - 1} x^3 - e^{2x} \frac{1}{D} x^3$$

$$= e^{2x}[-1 - D - D^2 - \cdots]x^3 - e^{2x}D^{-1}x^3 = e^{2x}[-x^3 - 3x^2 - 6x - 6] - \tfrac{1}{4}e^{2x}x^4$$

Is the result in agreement with the result of Problem 8.918?

Problem 8.9233

By use of algebraic manipulations such as those in (8.922) and the fact that the binomial formula

$$(1 + z)^r = 1 + \frac{r}{1} z + \frac{r(r - 1)}{1 \cdot 2} z^2 + \frac{r(r - 1)(r - 2)}{1 \cdot 2 \cdot 3} z^3 + \cdots$$

where z and r are numbers and $|z| < 1$, prove that

$$(8.9234) \qquad \frac{D^{\sigma-1}}{(D - m)^\sigma} = \frac{1}{D} + \frac{\sigma}{1} \frac{m}{D^2} + \frac{\sigma(\sigma + 1)}{1 \cdot 2} \frac{m^2}{D^3} + \frac{\sigma(\sigma + 1)(\sigma + 2)}{1 \cdot 2 \cdot 3} \frac{m^3}{D^4} + \cdots$$

and

$$(8.9235) \qquad \frac{1}{(D - m)^\sigma} = \frac{1}{D^\sigma} + \frac{\sigma}{1} \frac{m}{D^{\sigma+1}} + \frac{\sigma(\sigma + 1)}{1 \cdot 2} \frac{m^2}{D^{\sigma+2}}$$

$$+ \frac{\sigma(\sigma + 1)(\sigma + 2)}{1 \cdot 2 \cdot 3} \frac{m^3}{D^{\sigma+3}} + \cdots$$

are algebraic identities when σ is a positive integer, m and D are numbers, and $|D| > |m|$. To what do (8.9234) and (8.9235) reduce when $\sigma = 1$?

We now prove that

$$(8.924) \qquad \frac{1}{D - m} = \frac{1}{D} + \frac{m}{D^2} + \frac{m^2}{D^3} + \cdots$$

is an operational identity by evaluating the result of applying the operator on the right to a function f and observing that the result is $(D - m)^{-1}f$. Multiplying (8.909) by m^{k-1} gives, for each $k = 1, 2, 3, \cdots$,

$$\frac{m^{k-1}}{D^k} f = \int_{x_0}^x \frac{[m(x - t)]^{k-1}}{(k - 1)!} f(t)dt.$$

Addition gives

$$\sum_{k=1}^n \frac{m^{k-1}}{D^k} f = \int_{x_0}^x \left[\sum_{k=1}^n \frac{\{m(x - t)\}^{k-1}}{(k - 1)!} \right] f(t)dt.$$

We are now prepared to use the fact that

$$\lim_{n \to \infty} \sum_{k=1}^n \frac{\{m(x - t)\}^{k-1}}{(k - 1)!} = e^{m(x-t)}.$$

Whether we assume that $f(x)$ is continuous or that $f(x)$ merely satisfies the more general conditions set forth after (8.902), it follows* that

$$\lim_{n \to \infty} \int_{x_0}^x \sum_{k=1}^n \frac{[m(x-t)]^{k-1}}{(k-1)!} f(t)dt = \int_{x_0}^x e^{m(x-t)}f(t)dt.$$

Therefore,

(8.9241) $$\sum_{k=1}^\infty \frac{m^{k-1}}{D^k} f = \int_{x_0}^x e^{m(x-t)}f(t)dt.$$

The right side of (8.9241) is familiar; it is, by (8.905), simply $(D-m)^{-1}f$. Thus

$$(D-m)^{-1}f = \sum_{k=1}^\infty m^{k-1}D^{-k}f,$$

and the identity (8.924) is established.

There are many other ways of arriving at the identity (8.924). One method is that of *successive approximations* used in the proof of Picard's theorem in Chapter 15; in fact, the identity is a corollary of Picard's theorem.

Another interesting method is the method of *successive substitution*. To illustrate this method, let

(8.925) $$y = (D-m)^{-1}f.$$

Then $(D-m)y = f$ and $y(x_0) = 0$ so that $Dy = f + my$ and

(8.9251) $$y = D^{-1}f + mD^{-1}y.$$

Substituting the right member for the last y gives

(8.9252) $$y = D^{-1}f + mD^{-1}[D^{-1}f + mD^{-1}y] = D^{-1}f + mD^{-2}f + m^2D^{-2}y.$$

Substituting the right member of (8.9251) for the last y in (8.9252) gives

$$y = D^{-1}f + mD^{-2}f + m^2D^{-3}f + m^3D^{-3}y.$$

By continuing the process, we obtain for each $n = 1, 2, 3, \cdots$

$$y = D^{-1}f + mD^{-2}f + \cdots + m^{k-1}D^{-k}f + R_k(x)$$

where

$$R_k(x) = m^k D^{-k}y = m\int_{x_0}^x \frac{m^{k-1}(x-t)^{k-1}}{(k-1)!} y(t)dt.$$

It can be shown, by methods such as those used in Chapter 15, that $R_k(x)$ converges† to 0. Therefore,

$$y = D^{-1}f + mD^{-2}f + m^2D^{-3}f + \cdots.$$

Comparing this result with (8.925) we obtain again the identity (8.924).

---

* The fact that the limit of the integral is the integral of the limit is the crucial fact involved; this point is considered in the proof of Picard's theorem in Chapter 15.

† The convergence is uniform over each finite interval in which (8.925) holds.

Problem 8.926

Assuming that $y(x)$ is the function for which $y(0) = 1$ and

$$\frac{dy}{dx} = y$$

show that (when $x_0 = 0$)

$$y = 1 + D^{-1}y,$$

and use the method of successive substitution to find $y(x)$.

Problem 8.9261

Assuming that $y(x)$ is the function for which $y(0) = 1$, $y'(0) = 0$, and

$$\frac{d}{dx}\left(x\frac{dy}{dx}\right) + xy = 0$$

show that (when $x_0 = 0$)

$$x\,\frac{dy}{dx} = -D^{-1}(xy)$$
$$y = 1 - D^{-1}[x^{-1}D^{-1}(xy)],$$

and use the method of successive substitution to find $y(x)$. Show that your solution should be Bessel's function $J_0(x)$.

Problem 8.9262

Show that if $y(x)$ is a continuous function for which $y(0) = 0$ and

(8.9263) $$\frac{dy}{dx} - y = \log x \qquad\qquad x > 0$$

then use of the identity (8.924) gives

(8.9264) $$y(x) = (e^x - 1)\log x - \Phi(x)$$

where

$$\Phi(x) = x + \frac{x^2}{2!}\left(1 + \frac{1}{2}\right) + \frac{x^3}{3!}\left(1 + \frac{1}{2} + \frac{1}{3}\right) + \frac{x^4}{4!}\left(1 + \frac{1}{2} + \frac{1}{3} + \frac{1}{4}\right) + \cdots.$$

Tell why Cauchy rather than Riemann integrals must be used. Show, by direct methods not involving (8.924), that, if $y(x)$ is defined for $x > 0$ by (8.9264), then $y(x) \to 0$ as $x \to 0$ and $y(x)$ satisfies (8.9263). Solve (8.9263) by use of the integrating factor e^{-x}, and use your result with (8.9264) to obtain the formula

$$\int_0^x e^{-t}\log t\, dt = (1 - e^{-x})\log x - e^{-x}\,\Phi(x).$$

Hint: By use of the fact that $t^n \log t \to 0$ as $t \to 0$ when $n = 1, 2, 3, \cdots$, it can be shown by integration by parts that when $x > 0$

$$\int_0^x t^n \log t\, dt = \frac{x^{n+1}}{n+1}\log x - \frac{x^{n+1}}{(n+1)^2} \qquad n = 0, 1, 2, \cdots.$$

We now give a straightforward derivation of an expansion of $(D - m)^{-\sigma}$ when σ is a positive integer. Replacing k by σ in (8.908) gives

$$\frac{1}{(D-m)^\sigma}f = \int_{x_0}^x \frac{(x-t)^{\sigma-1}}{(\sigma-1)!}e^{m(x-t)}f(t)dt.$$

By use of the formula

$$e^{m(x-t)} = \sum_{k=0}^{\infty} \frac{m^k(x-t)^k}{k!}$$

and, as before, of the methods of Chapter 15, it can be shown that the integral of the series is the series of integrals; thus

$$(D-m)^{-\sigma}f = \sum_{k=0}^{\infty} \frac{(k+\sigma-1)!m^k}{k!(\sigma-1)!} \int_{x_0}^{x} \frac{(x-t)^{k+\sigma-1}}{(k+\sigma-1)!} f(t)dt,$$

and use of (8.909) gives

$$(D-m)^{-\sigma}f = \sum_{k=0}^{\infty} \frac{(k+\sigma-1)!}{k!(\sigma-1)!} \frac{m^k}{D^{k+\sigma}} f.$$

Therefore,

(8.927) $$\frac{1}{(D-m)^{\sigma}} = \frac{1}{D^{\sigma}} + \frac{\sigma}{1}\frac{m}{D^{\sigma+1}} + \frac{\sigma(\sigma+1)}{1\cdot 2}\frac{m^2}{D^{\sigma+2}} + \cdots .$$

Thus we have proved the operational identity that corresponds to the algebraic identity (8.9235). If $\sigma = 1$, (8.927) becomes (8.924).

When the operators in (8.927) are applied to a function $f(x)$ of the types we are considering, it is possible to use uniform convergence of all the series involved to justify differentiating $\sigma - 1$ times with respect to x; in this way we obtain the operational identity

(8.9271) $$\frac{D^{\sigma-1}}{(D-m)^{\sigma}} = \frac{1}{D} + \frac{\sigma}{1}\frac{m}{D^2} + \frac{\sigma(\sigma+1)}{1\cdot 2}\frac{m^2}{D^3} + \cdots ,$$

which corresponds to the algebraic identity (8.9234).

We are now able to expand the reciprocal L^{-1} of each operator of the form

$$L = a_0(D-m_1)^{\sigma_1}(D-m_2)^{\sigma_2} \cdots (D-m_k)^{\sigma_k},$$

in which $k > 0$ and the σ's are positive integers, into a power series in D^{-1}. In the first place, L^{-1} may be represented in either one of the two forms

$$\sum \frac{A}{(D-m)^{\sigma}}; \qquad \sum \frac{AD^{\sigma-1}}{(D-m)^{\sigma}};$$

these are finite sums representing the two kinds of partial-fraction expansions. In the next place, each individual fraction is given as a power series in D^{-1} by one of the formulas (8.927) and (8.9271). Therefore L^{-1} must be representable in the form

(8.928) $$\frac{1}{L} = \sum_{n=i}^{\infty} \frac{B_n}{D^n} = B_1\frac{1}{D} + B_2\frac{1}{D^2} + B_3\frac{1}{D^3} + \cdots .$$

Either one of the two partial-fraction expansions of L^{-1} may be used to obtain this expansion of L^{-1}. A contribution (which may be 0) to each B_n is made by the coefficient of D^{-k} in the expansion of each partial fraction.

Problem 8.9281

Use the formula

$$\frac{1}{1 + D^4} = \frac{1}{D^4} - \frac{1}{D^8} + \frac{1}{D^{12}} - \frac{1}{D^{16}} + \cdots,$$

to show that the solution of $(D^4 + 1)y = 1$, for which

$$y(1) = y'(1) = y''(1) = y'''(1) = 0,$$

is

$$y = \frac{(x-1)^4}{4!} - \frac{(x-1)^8}{8!} + \frac{(x-1)^{12}}{12!} - \frac{(x-1)^{16}}{16!} + \cdots$$

Remark: If you start trying to find the solution of $(D^4 + 1)y = 1$ for which

$$y(1) = 1, \qquad y'(1) = 2, \qquad y''(1) = 3, \qquad y'''(1) = 4,$$

you will probably want to stop and read the next section.

Problem 8.9282

Obtain the first few terms of the expansion in powers of D^{-1} of

$$[(D - m_1)^3(D - m_2)]^{-1}.$$

Remark 8.929

In concluding this section on series expansions of operators, it is interesting to look at operators *defined* by series.   For example, let the operator e^{hD} be defined by

$$e^{hD} = 1 + hD + \frac{h^2D^2}{2!} + \frac{h^3D^3}{3!} + \cdots$$

where h is a constant.   If $f(x)$ has derivatives of all orders, then

$$e^{hD}f = f(x) + \frac{h}{1} f'(x) + \frac{h^2}{2!} f''(x) + \frac{h^3}{3!} f'''(x) + \cdots,$$

provided that the series on the right converges.   The right member reminds one of the formula*

$$f(x + h) = f(x) + \frac{h}{1} f'(x) + \frac{h^2}{2!} f''(x) + \frac{h^3}{3!} f'''(x) + \cdots$$

which holds when $f(x)$ is an *analytic function,* that is, a function such that its Taylor series converges to it.   Thus, if $f(x)$ is an analytic function,

$$e^{hD}f(x) = f(x + h).$$

We can now point out an essential difference between the operator p of Heaviside and the operator D: A fundamental property of the operator p is that the equation

$$e^{hp}f(x) = f(x + h)$$

holds for *all* functions $f(x)$ and, in particular, for the discontinuous Heaviside unit function.

* Doubtless this formula would look more familiar if x and h were interchanged in the formula; but obviously the names of the numbers are not significant.

Problem 8.9291

Show that, when D and a are properly restricted numbers,

$$(D^2 + a^2)^{-\frac{1}{2}} = \frac{1}{D} - \frac{2!a^2}{2^2 1! 1!} \frac{1}{D^3} + \frac{4!a^4}{2^4 2! 2!} \frac{1}{D^5} - \frac{6!a^6}{2^6 3! 3!} \frac{1}{D^7} + \cdots$$

$$+ (-1)^n \frac{(2n)! a^{2n}}{2^{2n} n! n!} \frac{1}{D^{2n+1}} + \cdots,$$

is an algebraic identity.   Taking the equality as the definition of the operator on the left, show that

$$\frac{1}{\sqrt{D^2 + a^2}} f = \int_{x_0}^x J_0(ax - at) f(t) dt$$

where J_0 is Bessel's function of order 0 (see Section 7.8).   Using this result, show that

$$\frac{1}{\sqrt{D^2 + a^2}} \frac{1}{\sqrt{D^2 + a^2}} f = \int_{x_0}^x f(t) dt \int_t^x J_0(ax - au) J_0(au - at) du.$$

Is there any connection between this formula and the formula

$$\frac{1}{D^2 + a^2} f = \frac{1}{a} \int_{x_0}^x \sin a(x - t) f(t) dt$$

which was obtained in Section 8.91?

8.93. Equations of Order Greater than 1 and Systems of Equations.
We begin by showing how inverse operators are used to determine the solution of the equation

$$(8.931) \qquad (a_0 D^n + a_1 D^{n-1} + \cdots + a_{n-1}D + a_n)y = f$$

for which

$$(8.9311) \quad y(x_0) = b_1, \qquad y'(x_0) = b_2, \cdots, \qquad y^{(n-1)}(x_0) = b_n,$$

the a's, b's, and x_0 being given constants and f a given function, and $a_0 \neq 0$.   The first step complicates matters, but it is a very useful complication in that it enables us to solve problems; in fact, it enables us to find a simple method of solving problems.   Let $y_1(x), \cdots, y_n(x)$ be n functions defined by the formulas

$$y_1(x) = y(x), \quad y_2(x) = y_1'(x), \quad y_3(x) = y_2'(x), \cdots, \quad y_n(x) = y_{n-1}'(x).$$

Using (8.931) and (8.9311), we see that $y_1, y_2, \cdots, y_n$ form a system of functions satisfying the system

$$(8.932) \quad \begin{cases} y_r' - y_{r+1} = 0 & r = 1, 2, \cdots, n - 1 \\ a_0 y_n' + a_1 y_n + a_2 y_{n-1} + \cdots + a_n y_1 = f \end{cases}$$

of n differential equations and the n boundary conditions

$$(8.9321) \qquad\qquad y_r(x_0) = b_r \qquad\qquad r = 1, 2, \cdots, n.$$

When explaining how to deal with the system (8.932), we can just as well explain how to deal with more general systems of linear equations. For each $r = 1, 2, \cdots, n$ and $s = 1, 2, \cdots n$, let α_{rs} and β_{rs} be constants, let $f_1, f_2, \cdots, f_n$ be n given functions of x, and consider the system of n equations

$$(8.933) \qquad \sum_{s=1}^{n} (\alpha_{rs}D + \beta_{rs})y_s = f_r \qquad r = 1, 2, \cdots, n.$$

The problem is that of finding n functions $y_1(x), \cdots, y_n(x)$ satisfying (8.933) and the n boundary conditions

$$(8.9331) \qquad y_s(x_0) = b_s \qquad s = 1, 2, \cdots, n.$$

Electrical engineers and others who must solve many systems of the form (8.933) and (8.9331) have special methods for solving them. We give a method of attacking the system which is useful both for solving the systems and for justifying a very simple procedure due to Heaviside.

The procedure at this point depends upon the coefficients α_{rs}. If $\alpha_{rs} = 0$ for each pair of values of r and s, then the system (8.933) involves no derivatives at all. The system is then a purely algebraic system to be handled by methods of algebra. If the determinant

$$(8.9332) \qquad (\alpha_{rs}) \equiv \begin{vmatrix} \alpha_{11} & \alpha_{12} & \cdots & \alpha_{1n} \\ \alpha_{21} & \alpha_{22} & \cdots & \alpha_{2n} \\ \cdot & \cdot & \cdot & \cdot \\ \alpha_{n1} & \alpha_{n2} & \cdots & \alpha_{nn} \end{vmatrix}$$

of the α_{rs} is 0, while the α_{rs} are not all 0, then, as is shown in algebra, it is possible to multiply each of the equations in (8.933) by a shrewdly chosen multiplier and add the results to obtain an equation of the form

$$(8.9333) \qquad c_1y_1 + c_2y_2 + \cdots + c_ny_n = f$$

where the c's are constants not all 0. By solving (8.9333) for one of the y's and substituting in (8.933), we obtain a system of differential equations with only $n - 1$ unknown functions. This process can be continued until one obtains a system of differential equations in which the determinant of the coefficients of the D's is not 0. Accordingly, it is sufficient for us to consider the case in which the determinant (α_{rs}) in (8.9332) is not 0; henceforth, we assume $(\alpha_{rs}) \neq 0$.

Problem 8.934

Write out the determinant (α_{rs}) arising from the system (8.932), and show that $(\alpha_{rs}) = a_0$.

Problem 8.9341

Show how to replace the problem of finding functions $y(x)$ and $z(x)$ for which

$$(a_{11}D^2 + a_{12}D + a_{13})y + (a_{21}D^2 + a_{22}D + a_{23})z = f_1(x)$$
$$(a_{31}D^2 + a_{32}D + a_{33})y + (a_{41}D^2 + a_{42}D + a_{43})z = f_2(x)$$

and

$$y(x_0) = b_1, \qquad y'(x_0) = b_2, \qquad z(x_0) = b_3, \qquad z'(x_0) = b_4$$

by the problem of finding four functions $y_1(x)$, $y_2(x)$, $y_3(x)$, $y_4(x)$ satisfying a system of differential equations and boundary conditions of the forms (8.933) and (8.9331). Write the determinant (α_{rs}) for the system, and determine the conditions under which it is 0.

If $y_1(x)$, $\cdots$, $y_n(x)$ is a set of functions for which (8.933) and (8.9331) both hold, then

$$D^{-1}Dy_s(x) = \int_{x_0}^{x} y_s'(u)du = y_s(x) - y_s(x_0) = y_s - b_s \qquad s = 1, 2, \cdots, n$$

and hence application of the operator D^{-1} to (8.933) gives

$$\sum_{s=1}^{n} (\alpha_{rs}y_s - \alpha_{rs}b_s + \beta_{rs}D^{-1}y_s) = D^{-1}f_r \qquad r = 1, 2, \cdots, n.$$

Letting γ_1, $\cdots$, γ_n denote the constants defined by

$$(8.9342) \qquad\qquad \gamma_r = \sum_{s=1}^{n} \alpha_{rs}b_s \qquad\qquad r = 1, 2, \cdots, n$$

we obtain

$$(8.935) \qquad \sum_{s=1}^{n} (\alpha_{rs} + \beta_{rs}D^{-1})y_s = D^{-1}f_r + \gamma_r \qquad r = 1, 2, \cdots, n$$

Conversely, if y_1, y_2, $\cdots$, y_n satisfy (8.935), then *both* the system (8.933) of differential equations and the system (8.9331) of boundary conditions must be satisfied. In the first place, differentiating (8.935) gives (8.933); and, in the second place, setting $x = x_0$ in (8.935) gives

$$\sum_{s=1}^{n} \alpha_{rs}y_s(x_0) = \gamma_r = \sum_{s=1}^{n} \alpha_{rs}b_s \qquad r = 1, 2, \cdots, n$$

so that

$$\sum_{s=1}^{n} \alpha_{rs}[y_s(x_0) - b_s] = 0 \qquad r = 1, 2, \cdots, n$$

and the hypothesis that the determinant (α_{rs}) is not zero implies (8.9331). Thus the problem of finding functions y_s for which *both* (8.933) and (8.9331) hold is replaced by the problem of finding functions y_s for which the single system (8.935) holds. We find the functions $y_1(x)$, $\cdots$ $y_n(x)$ we are seeking by solving (8.935).

To simplify writing, let

$$(8.9351) \qquad Z_{rs} = \alpha_{rs} + \beta_{rs}D^{-1} \qquad r, s = 1, 2, \cdots, n$$

so that Z_{rs} is a linear operator, and the system (8.935) of equations becomes

$$(8.9352) \qquad \begin{cases} Z_{11}y_1 + Z_{12}y_2 + \cdots + Z_{1n}y_n = D^{-1}f_1 + \gamma_1 \\ Z_{21}y_1 + Z_{22}y_2 + \cdots + Z_{2n}y_n = D^{-1}f_2 + \gamma_2 \\ \quad \cdots \cdots \cdots \cdots \cdots \cdots \cdots \\ Z_{n1}y_1 + Z_{n2}y_2 + \cdots + Z_{nn}y_n = D^{-1}f_n + \gamma_n. \end{cases}$$

Let Δ be the operator defined by

$$(8.9353) \qquad \Delta = \begin{vmatrix} Z_{11} & Z_{12} & \cdots & Z_{1n} \\ Z_{21} & Z_{22} & \cdots & Z_{2n} \\ \cdot & \cdot & \cdots & \cdot \\ Z_{n1} & Z_{n2} & \cdots & Z_{nn} \end{vmatrix},$$

and let Δ_{rs} denote the *cofactor* of the element Z_{rs} in this determinant, that is, the product of $(-1)^{r+s}$ and the determinant obtained by omitting the row and column containing Z_{rs}. Thus Δ and each Δ_{rs} are polynomials in D^{-1} with constant coefficients obtained by expanding the determinants exactly as one would if D^{-1} were a number. If we apply to the equations in (8.9352) the operators $\Delta_{1r}, \Delta_{2r}, \cdots, \Delta_{nr}$ and add, we obtain exactly as in algebra

$$(8.936) \qquad \Delta y_r = \sum_{s=1}^{n} \Delta_{sr}(D^{-1}f_s + \gamma_s) \qquad r = 1, 2, \cdots, n;$$

and it follows exactly as in algebra that, if (8.936) holds, then (8.935) holds.* Thus our problem is reduced to the problem of solving the equations (8.936).

The system (8.936) is simpler than the system (8.935) because each of the equations in (8.936) involves just one of the functions $y_1(x)$, $\cdots$, $y_n(x)$. If Δ were a number rather than an operator and if $\Delta \neq 0$, we should find the y's immediately by dividing (8.936) by Δ. Since Δ is a polynomial in D^{-1}, the equations (8.936) are *integral equations* of a special kind, and a little juggling is necessary to put the equations in a form to which our theory of differential equations applies. Since D^nD^{-n} and $D^{n-1}D^{-(n-1)}$ both equal the identity oper-

---

* Many persons believe that the easiest way to get the equations (8.936) when one is solving a problem is not to write out and expand the determinants but to use the simplest algebraic manipulations involved in eliminating the y's one at a time from the system. In any case, use of the notation of determinants furnishes a convenient method of displaying the results of solving for $y_1, \cdots, y_n$.

ator, we can write (8.936) in the form

$$(8.9361) \quad \Delta D^n D^{-n} y_r = \sum_{s=1}^{n} \Delta_{sr} D^{n-1} D^{-(n-1)} (D^{-1} f_s + \gamma_s) \quad r = 1, 2, \cdots, n.$$

Upon expanding the determinant Δ in (8.9353), we obtain

$$\Delta = A_0 + A_1 D^{-1} + \cdots + A_n D^{-n}$$

where the A's are constants depending on the α's and β's and where $A_0 \neq 0$ since A_0 is the determinant (α_{rs}). Likewise, for each r and s

$$\Delta_{rs} = A_0^{(r,s)} + A_1^{(r,s)} D^{-1} + \cdots + A_{n-1}^{(r,s)} D^{-(n-1)}$$

where the A's depend upon the α's and β's and where the last exponent is $-(n-1)$ since the cofactors are determinants of order $n-1$. Let operators L and L_{rs} be defined by

$$L = A_0 D^n + A_1 D^{n-1} + \cdots + A_n$$
$$L_{rs} = A_0^{(r,s)} D^{n-1} + A_1^{(r,s)} D^{n-2} + \cdots + A_{n-1}^{(r,s)}.$$

By virtue of these definitions, the formulas $\Delta D^n = L$ and $\Delta_{rs} D^{n-1} = L_{rs}$ would be algebraic identities if D were a number. The formulas $\Delta D^n = L$ and $\Delta_{rs} D^{n-1} = L_{rs}$ are not operational identities; but if $g(x)$ is a function such that it and its first $n-1$ derivatives vanish when $x = x_0$, then $\Delta D^n g = Lg$; and if $h(x)$ is a function such that it and its first $n-2$ derivatives vanish when $x = x_0$, then $\Delta_{rs} D^{n-1} h = L_{rs} h$. It follows that if we set

$$g_s = D^{-n} y_s, \qquad h_s = D^{-(n-1)} (D^{-1} f_s + \gamma_s)$$

then

$$\Delta D^n g_s = Lg_s, \qquad \Delta_{sr} D^{-(n-1)} h_s = L_{sr} h_s.$$

Therefore we can write (8.9361) in the form

$$(8.937) \quad L D^{-n} y_r = \sum_{s=1}^{n} L_{sr} D^{-(n-1)} (D^{-1} f_s + \gamma_s) \qquad r = 1, 2, \cdots, n.$$

The operator L is a differential operator of the familiar type. Since $D^{-n} y_r$ and its first $n-1$ derivatives vanish when $x = x_0$, it follows that (8.937) holds if and only if

$$(8.9371) \quad D^{-n} y_r = \sum_{s=1}^{n} L^{-1} L_{sr} D^{-(n-1)} (D^{-1} f_s + \gamma_s) \quad r = 1, 2, \cdots, n.$$

By definition of D^{-n}, (8.9371) holds if and only if

$$(8.9372) \quad y_r = \sum_{s=1}^{n} D^n L^{-1} L_{sr} D^{-n+1} (D^{-1} f_s + \gamma_s) \qquad r = 1, 2, \cdots, n.$$

But

$$(8.9373) \qquad D^n L^{-1} L_{sr} D^{-n+1} = \frac{D^n}{L} \frac{L_{sr}}{D^{n-1}} = \frac{DL_{sr}}{L},$$

the last step being justified by (8.914) and the fact that the order of the operator L_{sr} is less than or equal to the order of the operator D^{n-1}. Since D and L_{sr} commute, the last member of (8.9373) is equal to $L_{sr}D/L$; therefore (8.9372) can be written in the forms

$$y_r = \sum_{s=1}^{n} \frac{L_{sr}D}{L} (D^{-1}f_s + \gamma_s) \qquad r = 1, 2, \cdots, n$$

and

$$(8.938) \qquad y_r = \sum_{s=1}^{n} \frac{L_{sr}}{L} f_s + \sum_{s=1}^{n} \frac{L_{sr}D}{L} \gamma_s \qquad r = 1, 2, \cdots, n.$$

Thus, under the hypothesis that the determinant (α_{rs}) *is not* 0, *there is a unique set of functions* $y_1(x), y_2(x), \cdots, y_n(x)$ *for which the equations* (8.933) *and* (8.9331) *hold; and these functions are given by the formulas* (8.938). The right side of (8.938) and various modifications of it obtained by replacing the quotients of operators by partial fraction expansions are known as *Heaviside expansions* of the solutions. More Heaviside expansions are obtained by expanding the quotients of operators into infinite series.

One who must solve problems should realize that the results which we have obtained are much simpler than the method by which they were obtained. The following fact, which was evident during the course of our work, will be used in the next section; for convenience of reference, we formulate it as a theorem.

Theorem 8.939. *The correct formulas* (8.938) *for the functions* $y_1(x), y_2(x), \cdots, y_n(x)$ *satisfying the differential equations*

$$(8.9391) \qquad \sum_{s=1}^{n} (\alpha_{rs}D + \beta_{rs})y_s = f_r \qquad r = 1, 2, \cdots, n$$

and the boundary conditions

$$(8.9392) \qquad y_s(x_0) = b_s \qquad s = 1, 2, \cdots, n$$

are obtained by solving the equations

$$(8.9393) \quad \sum_{s=1}^{n} (\alpha_{rs} + \beta_{rs}D^{-1})y_s = D^{-1}f_r + \sum_{s=1}^{n} \alpha_{rs}b_s \quad r = 1, 2, \cdots, n$$

for the y's exactly as one would if D *were a number not* 0.

8.94. Heaviside's Rule.—Theorem 8.939 leads at once to the famous *Heaviside rule* for finding the solution of the system of differential equations

$$(8.941) \qquad \sum_{s=1}^{n} (\alpha_{rs}D + \beta_{rs})y_s = f_r \qquad r = 1, 2, \cdots, n$$

satisfying the conditions

$$(8.942) \qquad\qquad y_s(x_0) = b_s \qquad\qquad s = 1, 2, \cdots, n.$$

It is the following: *Write the subsidiary equations*

$$(8.943) \qquad \sum_{s=1}^{n} (\alpha_{rs}D + \beta_{rs})y_s = f_r + \sum_{s=1}^{n} D\alpha_{rs}b_s \qquad r = 1, 2, \cdots, n$$

and solve them for the y's exactly as though D were a number not 0; the resulting equations are correct when D is interpreted as an operator.

This simple rule is correct because, when D is a number not 0, the result of solving the algebraic system (8.943) is naturally the same as the result of solving the algebraic system (8.9393). The result involves quotients of operators which are expanded into partial fractions as in Section 8.91 so that one obtains the y's as sums of terms of the forms

$$\frac{A}{(D-m)^\sigma} f_s; \qquad \frac{A}{(D-m)^\sigma} \sum_{s=1}^{n} \alpha_{rs}b_s$$

in which the A's and m's are constants and σ is a positive integer or 0. By use of a table giving values of $(D-m)^{-\sigma}f$, engineers are able to solve complicated systems of differential equations by pure algebraic methods; not a single derivative or integral appears in the whole process.

It is worthy of note that, in the simple case in which the b's are all 0, the system (8.943) is exactly the same as the system (8.941). In any case the system (8.943) can be obtained from the system (8.941) by the following simple procedure. Since

$$D^{-1}Dy_s = \int_{x_0}^{x} y_s'(t)dt = y_s(x) - y_s(x_0) = y_s - b_s,$$

application of the operator D^{-1} to (8.941) gives

$$\sum_{s=1}^{n} (\alpha_{rs} + D^{-1}\beta_{rs})y_s = D^{-1}f_r + \sum_{s=1}^{n} \alpha_{rs}b_s;$$

regarding D as a number and multiplying by D, we obtain (8.943).

Some persons apply a falacious argument to convince themselves that use of the Heaviside rule cannot produce correct solutions of problems. The argument is that if D is interpreted as an operator in (8.943), then $D\alpha_{rs}b_s$ is 0 for each r and s

so that the b's disappear from (8.943) and hence (8.943) cannot possibly produce solutions of (8.941) satisfying (8.942) for different sets of values of the b's. The answer to this falacious argument is the fact that if D is interpreted as a number in (8.943), then correct formulas for the required y's do result. We have proved this fact. A significant point in favor of the Heaviside rule is, in the words of Heaviside, "it works."

Problem 8.944

By replacing the differential equation

$$(8.9441) \qquad (a_0D^4 + a_1D^3 + a_2D^2 + a_3D + a_4)y = f$$

by a system of four equations in four unknown functions and then using the Heaviside rule, show that the solution of (8.9441) for which

$$(8.9442) \quad y(x_0) = b_1, \qquad y'(x_0) = b_2, \qquad y''(x_0) = b_3, \qquad y'''(x_0) = b_4$$

may be expressed in the form

$$(8.9443) \quad y = \frac{1}{a_0D^4 + a_1D^3 + a_2D^2 + a_3D + a_4}f$$

$$= \frac{a_0D^4 + a_1D^3 + a_2D^2 + a^3D}{a_0D^4 + a_1D^3 + a_2D^2 + a_3D + a_4}b_1 + \frac{a_0D^3 + a_1D^2 + a_2D}{a_0D^4 + a_1D^3 + a_2D^2 + a_3D + a_4}b_2$$

$$+ \frac{a_0D^2 + a_1D}{a_0D^4 + a_1D^3 + a_2D^2 + a_3D + a_4}b_3 + \frac{a_0D}{a_0D^4 + a_1D^3 + a_2D^2 + a_3D + a_4}b_4.$$

The next step of an applied mathematician who is solving a problem in which the a's have specific numerical values is to express the quotients of operators as sums of partial fractions; the results are then useful. It is amusing to look directly at (8.9443) to see how neatly it manages to furnish the solution of (8.9441) and (8.9442). Let the functions involving b_1, b_2, b_3, and b_4 be, respectively, $Y_1(x)$, $\cdots$, $Y_4(x)$. Show that

$$Y_1(x) = \left[1 - \frac{a_4}{a_0D^4 + a_1D^3 + a_2D^2 + a_3D + a_4}\right]b_1$$

$$Y_1'(x) = - \frac{a_4D}{a_0D^4 + a_1D^3 + a_2D^2 + a_3D + a_4}b_1,$$

$$Y_1''(x) = - \frac{a_4D^2}{a_0D^4 + a_1D^3 + a_2D^2 + a_3D + a_4}b_1$$

$$Y_1'''(x) = - \frac{a_4D^3}{a_0D^4 + a_1D^3 + a_2D^2 + a_3D + a_4}b_1,$$

$$Y_1^{iv}(x) = - \frac{a_4D^4}{a_0D^4 + a_1D^3 + a_2D^2 + a_3D + a_4}b_1$$

and hence that $Y_1(x)$ is the solution of the homogeneous equation corresponding to (8.9441) for which

$$Y_1(x_0) = b_1, \qquad Y_1'(x_0) = 0, \qquad Y_1''(x_0) = 0, \qquad Y_1'''(x_0) = 0.$$

What can be said about $Y_2(x)$, $Y_3(x)$, and $Y_4(x)$? If (8.9441) and (8.9442) were revised to involve an equation of order 6, could you guess how the equation corresponding to (8.9443) would look?

CHAPTER 9

MECHANICAL PROBLEMS

9.0. Introduction.—In this chapter we consider in detail the differential equations governing certain mechanical vibrations. With one exception, the differential equations obtained are all linear.*

9.01. A Weight on a Spring.—The problem considered in the next few sections is that of describing the motion of a mass which is bobbing up and down at the bottom of a spring. The spring may be an ordinary coil spring which resists compression as well as extension; or it may be a string or rod composed of rubber, steel, or some other elastic material. A force in the spring tends to pull the mass upward (at least when the weight is far enough down to keep the spring stretched), and gravitational force tends to pull it down. If the mass is moving in air (or in a partial vacuum or in water or in molasses or, in fact, in whatever the mass is moving), then there is an additional *damping force* pushing down on the weight when it is moving up and pushing up on the weight when it is moving down; the tendency of the damping force is to reduce, or *damp*, the motion of the weight. In addition to these fundamental forces, there may be an *impressed force* applied by some external mechanism; for example, one may push downward with a force of k units during the first 10 seconds of each minute, or one may make the weight of iron and supply equipment to produce a downward magnetic force of magnitude $f(t)$ at time t. The various forces acting on the mass engage in a tug of war to produce the bobbing of the mass. It will turn out that we attempt to determine the motion of the mass by means of a differential equation. We make no apology for the following tedious derivation of the differential equation; it is only by thoroughly understanding "easy" problems to see how "hard" they really are that one may reasonably hope to progress toward thoroughly understanding "harder" problems to see how "easy" they really are. Moreover, the method of obtaining the differential equation is important because many diverse problems lead in much the same way (but often with different physical interpretations of the constants and variables involved) to the same differential equation.

---

* A wide variety of mechanical problems solved by use of these equations may be found in an engineering textbook "Mechanical Vibrations," by J. P. Den Hartog, McGraw-Hill Book Company, Inc., New York, 1940.

9.02. Derivation of the Differential Equation.—Let a spring suspended from a fixed point have *natural length* l_0. Experiments show that there is a constant σ such that the upward force F_s exerted by the spring when it is stretched to length $u > l_0$ is

$$(9.022) \qquad\qquad F_s = \sigma \frac{u - l_0}{l_0}$$

provided that the stretching is within elastic limits. If the spring is a uniform straight string, the constant σ is the product of Young's

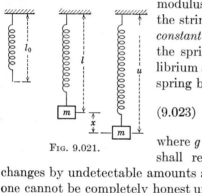

modulus and the area of a cross section of the string; in any case, σ is called the *spring constant* of the spring. If l is the length of the spring when it supports in static equilibrium a mass m which does not stretch the spring beyond elastic limits, then

$$(9.023) \qquad\qquad mg = \sigma \frac{l - l_0}{l_0}$$

FIG. 9.021.

where g is the acceleration of gravity. We shall regard g as a constant; actually g changes by undetectable amounts as the mass bobs up and down, and one cannot be completely honest unless one admits that we have made one of those convenient little mistakes which simplify work.

Let x represent the displacement of the mass from its equilibrium position, with x positive, 0, or negative according as the mass is below, at, or above the equilibrium position; then $x = u - l$. Let a force be represented by a positive or a negative number according as the force tends to pull the mass down or up. Putting $u = x + l$ in (9.022), we see that the force due to the spring is

$$(9.03) \qquad\qquad -F_s = -\frac{\sigma}{l_0} x - mg.$$

The force due to gravity is

$$(9.04) \qquad\qquad mg.$$

The damping force F_d is 0 when the mass m is not moving, and its magnitude increases as the magnitude of the velocity $x' = dx/dt$ increases. Experiments show that for relatively small velocities there is a *damping constant* $\delta > 0$ such that the formula

$$(9.05) \qquad\qquad F_d = -\delta x'$$

is at least approximately true. The negative sign is required since the force tends to pull the mass up when $x' > 0$ and down when

$x' < 0$. As in the above discussion, let

(9.06) $$f(t)$$

denote an impressed force applied to the mass by some external mechanism. The sum of the external forces acting on the mass m is then

(9.07) $$-\frac{\sigma}{l_0} x - \delta x' + f(t),$$

provided that x and x' lie within certain ranges and *the spring force* $-F_s$ *computed for static equilibrium with displacement* x *is equal to the spring force when the mass has displacement* x *but is in motion with velocity* x'. We assume that the statement in italics is true. Perhaps some readers feel that it is unnecessary to mention an assumption which is so obviously correct; perhaps others distrust an assumption which is so obviously incorrect. In any case, the assumption serves to simplify further work. It is important that the reader should learn to pay attention to the assumptions made in setting up differential equations and should learn that the problem of determining whether or not the assumptions are justifiable is often both important and difficult.

Using Newton's law as stated in Problem 2.394, we can equate $mx''(t)$ to the force in (9.07) to obtain

(9.08) $$x'' + \frac{\delta}{m} x' + \frac{\sigma}{ml_0} x = \frac{1}{m} f(t)$$

as the differential equation which "governs" the displacement of the mass bobbing up and down on a spring; by this we mean that $x(t)$ must have a continuous derivative and that $x(t)$ must satisfy (9.08) for each t for which $f(t)$ is continuous. The differential equation is a linear differential equation of the second order, with constant coefficients, in which the constants have definite physical meanings.

If the laws used and the assumptions made are correct and if the constants l_0, m, σ, and δ and the impressed force $f(t)$ are determined exactly, then the displacement $x(t)$ must satisfy (9.08). In this case,* the form of the function $x(t)$ may be determined by solving (9.08). In the following sections we obtain and discuss these solutions.

---

* If some or all of the laws, assumptions, and measurements are false but nevertheless involve only errors which are in some sense or other "small," there is still the possibility that a solution (9.08) will (at least for certain time intervals) furnish the displacement function $x(t)$ with sufficient accuracy to meet practical needs. In particular, if there is very little damping, it is very much worth while to see how the system would behave if there were no damping.

9.1. Free Undamped Motion.—If there is no external impressed force [that is, if $f(t) = 0$], the motion is said to be *free;* and if $\delta = 0$, the motion is said to be *undamped.* In this case the differential equation (9.08) becomes

$$(9.11) \qquad x'' + \frac{\sigma}{ml_0} x = 0.$$

This is the equation of the harmonic oscillator. Each real solution can be written in the form

$$(9.12) \qquad x = C \cos \sqrt{\frac{\sigma}{ml_0}} \, (t - t_0),$$

where C and t_0 are constants with $C \geqq 0$, and also in the form

$$(9.121) \qquad x = C \sin \sqrt{\frac{\sigma}{ml_0}} \, (t - t_1),$$

where C and t_1 are constants with $C \geqq 0$. If $C = 0$, the mass simply remains at rest in the equilibrium position. If $C > 0$, the mass oscillates between C and $-C$, the maximum value C being attained when and only when $\sqrt{\sigma/ml_0} \, (t - t_0)$ has one of the values 0, $\pm 2\pi$, $\pm 4\pi$, $\cdots$ and accordingly t has one of the values t_0, $t_0 + 2\pi \sqrt{ml_0/\sigma}$, $\cdots$. The difference between two such values of t is

$$(9.13) \qquad 2\pi \sqrt{\frac{ml_0}{\sigma}},$$

and this is the *period* of the motion which is called a *simple harmonic motion.* The constant C is called the *amplitude* and the constant t_0 is called the *phase constant* of the motion. This phase constant t_0 must not be confused with the phase angle ϕ. These constants and the graph of (9.12) are shown in Fig. 9.14.

The period $2\pi \sqrt{ml_0/\sigma}$ is the number of units of time required for one complete oscillation of the mass. The *frequency* ν of the motion is the number of complete oscillations per second; it is the reciprocal of the period and is therefore given by the formula

$$(9.15) \qquad \nu = \frac{1}{2\pi} \sqrt{\frac{\sigma}{ml_0}}.$$

That the period and frequency are independent of the phase constant t_0 is shown by the formulas; it is also obvious from physical considerations, since they would not be expected to depend upon the particular instant chosen to be represented by $t = 0$. The formulas show that the period and frequency are also independent of the amplitude; it is not quite so clear whether or not this is obvious from nonmathematical considerations.　It appears that the frequency increases as σ increases (*i.e.*, as the spring is made stronger), decreases as m increases (*i.e.*, as the mass is increased), and decreases as l_0 increases (*i.e.*, as the spring is made longer).　For example, if σ and m are fixed, then increasing l_0 by the factor 4 results in decreasing the frequency (and increasing the period) by the factor 2.

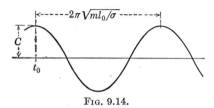

FIG. 9.14.

The above formulas have many applications; doubtless the reader has solved problems involving these formulas in courses in calculus, physics, or mechanics.　The formulas are useful; but because assumptions were made in arriving at the differential equation, they should not be applied with too much confidence to a particular problem until one has reason to believe that they are applicable.　In connection with this point, a student should think about the following two problems even though he may be unable to answer them satisfactorily:

Problem 9.16

One can easily imagine that, if a mass $m = 1{,}000$ grams (2.2046 pounds) were suspended by a suitable coil spring made of good spring steel with spring constant $\sigma = 400{,}000\pi^2$ and with length $l_0 = 100$ centimeters (39.37 inches), if the mass were displaced 2 centimeters from the equilibrium position and released with velocity 0 at time $t = 0$, and if the whole system were sealed in a high-vacuum glass container then the displacement $x(t)$ would appear for a long time to be given by

$$x = 2 \cos \sqrt{\frac{\sigma}{ml_0}}\, t = 2 \cos 2\pi t$$

and the oscillations would appear to have frequency 1.　Should you use the formula

(9.161) $$x = 2 \cos \sqrt{\frac{\sigma}{ml_0}}\, t$$

for the displacement and the formula $\sqrt{\sigma/ml_0}/2\pi$ for the frequency if all details were as above except that (*a*) m is some number between 500 and 2,000; (*b*) $m = 10^{20}$; (*c*) $m = 10^{-3}$?　Show that if the formula (9.161) is used for the case where $m = 10^{-23}$ (which is of the order of the mass of an atom) one arrives at the appalling conclusion that the mass completes 10^{13} oscillations and travels $8 \cdot 10^{13}$ centimeters in each second.　(The latter distance is about 16 times the distance from the earth to the sun and about 2,666 times the distance light travels in 1 second; thus the conclusion contradicts the popular belief that objects do not travel with speeds exceeding that of light.)

Problem 9.17

Could you construct a system composed of a spring with a suspended bobbing mass in such a way that, without application of external force, the displacement x of the mass from the equilibrium position would satisfy the equation $x = 10 \sin \pi t$

    a. Exactly for 5 minutes?
    b. Exactly for 150 years?
    c. Approximately for 5 minutes?
    d. Approximately for 150 years?

Problem 9.18

It is shown in mechanics (by use of the integral calculus) that the force on a particle inside a homogeneous spherical mass is directed toward the center of the sphere and has magnitude proportional to the first power of the distance from the center of the sphere. Assume the earth to be a stationary homogeneous sphere of radius 4,000 miles, that a hole is drilled through the center of the earth, and that a particle may move in the hole without friction. If a particle were dropped with initial velocity 0 into the hole how long would it take it to return to its starting point? *Ans.:* When units are feet and seconds so that $g = 32.2$, the answer is $1,600\pi \sqrt{33/g}$ seconds, or about 1 hour 25 minutes. Other problems arise when one assumes resistances of various sorts.

9.2. Free Damped Motion.—In this case $f(t) = 0$, $\delta > 0$, and the equation of motion (9.08) becomes

$$(9.21) \qquad x'' + \frac{\delta}{m} x' + \frac{\sigma}{ml_0} x = 0.$$

The roots of the characteristic equation are

$$(9.211) \qquad -\frac{\delta}{2m} - \sqrt{\frac{\delta^2}{4m^2} - \frac{\sigma}{ml_0}}, \qquad -\frac{\delta}{2m} + \sqrt{\frac{\delta^2}{4m^2} - \frac{\sigma}{ml_0}}.$$

We consider separately the cases in which the quantity under the radical is negative, positive, and 0. These are the cases in which, respectively, $\delta < \sqrt{4\sigma m/l_0}$, $\delta > \sqrt{4\sigma m/l_0}$, and $\delta = \sqrt{4\sigma m/l_0}$. The last case in which $\delta = \sqrt{4\sigma m/l_0}$ gives what is called *critical damping*.

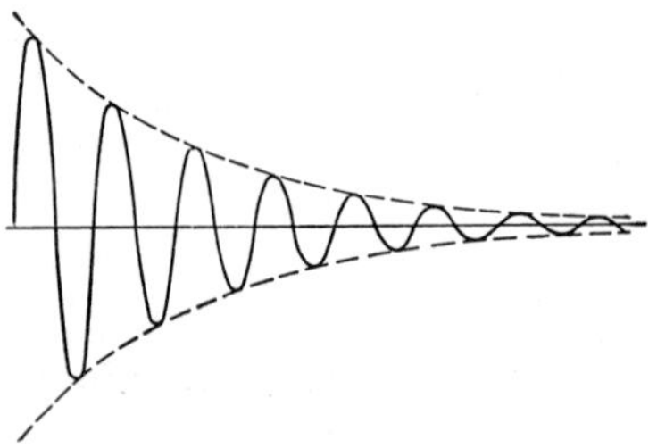

When $\delta < \sqrt{4\sigma m/l_0}$, the damping being less than critical damping, the general solution of (9.21) can be represented in the form

FIG. 9.221.

$$(9.22) \qquad x = Ce^{-(\delta/2m)t} \cos \sqrt{\frac{\sigma}{ml_0} - \frac{\delta^2}{4m^2}} (t - t_0)$$

where C and t_0 are constants and $C \geqq 0$. If $C = 0$, the mass simply stays at rest in the equilibrium position. If $C > 0$, the graph of (9.22) is as shown in Fig. 9.221. As time passes, the mass oscillates about the equilibrium position with smaller and smaller oscillations and approaches the equilibrium position.

Problem 9.23

Show that, if (9.22) holds, $x(0) = x_0 > 0$, and $x'(0) = 0$, then

$$t_0 = \frac{1}{\sqrt{\sigma/ml_0 - \delta^2/4m^2}} \left[2\nu\pi + \tan^{-1} \frac{\delta/2m}{\sqrt{\sigma/ml_0 - \delta^2/4m^2}} \right]$$

where ν is an integer, and

$$C = \frac{x_0}{\sqrt{1 - \delta^2 l_0/4\sigma m}}.$$

Problem 9.24

Show that, if (9.22) holds, then the mass passes through the equilibrium positions when $t = \tilde{t}_1, \tilde{t}_2, \tilde{t}_3, \cdots$ where, for each $n = 0, 1, 2, 3, \cdots$,

(9.241) $$\tilde{t}_n = t_0 + \frac{n\pi - \pi/2}{\sqrt{\sigma/ml_0 - \delta^2/4m^2}}.$$

Show that the velocity is positive (that is, that the mass is going down) at times $\tilde{t}_0, \tilde{t}_2, \tilde{t}_4, \cdots$ and is negative at times $\tilde{t}_1, \tilde{t}_2, \tilde{t}_3, \cdots$.

Problem 9.25

Assuming that (9.22) holds, show that x assumes relative maximum values at times $\hat{t}_0, \hat{t}_2, \hat{t}_4, \cdots$ and relative minimum values at times $\hat{t}_1, \hat{t}_3, \hat{t}_5, \cdots$ where

$$\hat{t}_n = t_0 + \frac{1}{\sqrt{\sigma/ml_0 - \delta^2/4m^2}} \left[n\pi - \tan^{-1} \frac{\delta/2m}{\sqrt{\sigma/ml_0 - \delta^2/4m^2}} \right].$$

Show that, if $\hat{x}_n = x(\hat{t}_n)$, then for each n

$$\log |\hat{x}_{n+1}| - \log |\hat{x}_n| = \log \frac{|\hat{x}_{n+1}|}{|\hat{x}_n|} = - \frac{\pi\delta/2m}{\sqrt{\sigma/ml_0 - \delta^2/4m^2}}.$$

This is independent of n and is called the *logarithmic decrement* of the motion.

When

(9.26) $$\delta > \sqrt{\frac{4\sigma m}{l_0}},$$

the damping being greater than critical damping, the general solution of (9.21) can be represented in the form

(9.261) $$x = c_1 e^{-(\alpha+\beta)t} + c_2 e^{-(\alpha-\beta)t}$$

where

(9.262) $$\alpha = \frac{\delta}{2m} > 0, \qquad \beta = \sqrt{\frac{\delta^2}{4m^2} - \frac{\sigma}{ml_0}} > 0.$$

Problem 9.27

Assuming (9.26), prove each of the following assertions involving (9.261) and (9.262): (1) $\alpha + \beta > 0$ and $\alpha - \beta > 0$.   (2) $x(t) \to 0$ as $t \to \infty$.   (3) If $c_1 \geqq 0$ and $c_2 \geqq 0$ while c_1 and c_2 are not both 0, then $x(t) > 0$ for each t; if $c_1 \leqq 0$ and $c_2 \leqq 0$ while c_1 and c_2 are not both 0, then $x(t) < 0$ for each t.   (4) If $c_1 c_2 > 0$, then $x(t)$ is never 0.   (5) If $c_1 c_2 < 0$, then $x(t) = 0$ if and only if

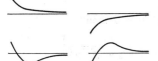

$$t = \frac{1}{2\beta} \log \left[-\frac{c_1}{c_2} \right].$$

Fig. 9.271.

(6) If $c_1 c_2 > 0$, then $x'(t)$ is never 0.   (7) If $c_1 c_2 < 0$, then $x'(t)$ is 0 if and only if

$$t = \frac{1}{2\beta} \log \left[-\frac{c_1(\alpha + \beta)}{c_2(\alpha - \beta)} \right].$$

(8) Show that the graph of (9.261) must have one of the four forms shown in Fig. 9.271 unless $x(t) = 0$ for all t.

When

(9.28) $$\delta = \sqrt{\frac{4m\sigma}{l_0}},$$

the damping being critical damping, the general solution of (9.21) is

(9.281) $$x = (c_1 + c_2 t)e^{-(\delta/2m)t}.$$

Problem 9.29

Show that under critical damping the graph of $x(t)$ must have one of the two forms show in Fig. 9.291 unless $x(t) = 0$ for all t.

It appears from the three cases of damped free motion that, when the damping is less than critical damping, the mass oscillates about the equilibrium position while approaching the equilibrium position; in the other two cases, the mass passes through the equilibrium position at most once and ultimately approaches the equilibrium position without oscillations. In each of the three cases, the displacement $x(t)$ is a *transient*.

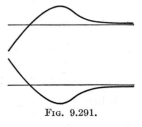

Fig. 9.291.

Problem 9.292

The damping constant δ can be changed in various ways, for example by changing the medium in which the mass oscillates. It being assumed that all constants except δ are fixed, there arises the problem of finding the value of δ such that, when the mass is given a displacement x_0 and released with velocity 0 at time $t = 0$, the mass will in some sense or other approach zero as quickly as possible. One could, for example, say that the approach to zero is "quickest" when the integral

$$\int_0^\infty |x(t)|^2 dt$$

is a minimum. Show that neither very great nor very small values of δ are desirable. Instruments for recording earthquakes are so constructed that the needle "returns as quickly as possible to its equilibrium position" after a quake so that it is ready to register another. Can you explain why the damping constant is given a critical value?

9.3. Forced Motion.—We now consider the equation (9.08) in which the impressed force $f(t)$ is a pure harmonic $E_0 \cos \omega t$ where E_0 and ω are positive constants. The differential equation is then

(9.31) $$x'' + \frac{\delta}{m} x' + \frac{\sigma}{ml_0} x = E_1 \cos \omega t$$

where $E_1 = E_0/m$. To simplify formulas, let

(9.311) $$b = \frac{\delta}{m}, \qquad c = \frac{\sigma}{ml_0}.$$

The real part of a solution of

(9.312) $$x'' + bx' + cx = E_1 e^{i\omega t}$$

is then a real particular solution of (9.31). The function $A e^{i\omega t}$ will be a solution of (9.312) provided that A satisfies the condition

(9.313) $$A[(c - \omega^2) + ib\omega] = E_1;$$

such a value of A can be found unless the impedance

(9.314) $$c - \omega^2 + ib\omega$$

of the equation (9.312) is 0. The impedance is 0 only if $b = 0$ so that there is no damping, and $\omega = \sqrt{c} = \sqrt{\sigma/ml_0}$ so that the frequency of the impressed force $E_0 \cos \omega t$ is the same as the frequency of the free undamped oscillations. The case in which the impedance is 0 is taken up in the next section; meanwhile, we denote the impedance by Z and assume that it is not zero. Thus

(9.315) $$Z = c - \omega^2 + ib\omega \neq 0.$$

The absolute value Z_0 and the phase angle $\omega\phi$ of the impedance are given by the formulas

(9.316) $$Z_0 = \sqrt{(c - \omega^2)^2 + b^2\omega^2}$$

and

(9.317) $$\cos \omega\phi = \frac{c - \omega^2}{Z_0}; \qquad \sin \omega\phi = \frac{b\omega}{Z_0}.$$

Using the theory of Section 8.5 (or formulas of this section and the formula $Z = Z_0 e^{i\omega\phi}$), we see that

(9.318)
$$\frac{E_1}{Z_0} e^{i\omega(t-\phi)}$$

is a solution of (9.312). Taking real parts gives

(9.32)
$$\frac{E_1}{Z_0} \cos \omega(t - \phi)$$

as a solution of (9.31). Each solution of (9.31) has, when $Z_0 \neq 0$, the form

(9.33)
$$x(t) = x_1(t) + \frac{E_1}{Z_0} \cos \omega(t - \phi)$$

where $x_1(t)$ is a solution of the homogeneous equation considered in Section 9.2. We give a brief discussion of this important formula.

When $\delta > 0$, $x_1(t) \to 0$ as t increases and accordingly the term $x_1(t)$ is a *transient*. As time passes, the displacement $x(t)$ tends toward the *steady state* in which

(9.34)
$$x(t) = \frac{E_1}{Z_0} \cos \omega(t - \phi).$$

This represents a simple harmonic motion with frequency the same as that of the impressed force; this frequency is entirely independent of the *natural frequency* $\sqrt{\sigma/ml_0}/2\pi$ of free undamped oscillation of the mass. When $\delta > 0$, the steady-state oscillations are always out of phase with the impressed force since, by (9.317), $\phi \neq 0$.

Problem 9.35

Show that, if $\delta > 0$ and the frequency of the impressed force is the same as the natural frequency of free undamped oscillation, then $\omega\phi = \pi/2$. What is the physical meaning of this result?

The amplitude E_1/Z_0 of the steady-state oscillations is both interesting and important. Using (9.311) and (9.316) we see that this amplitude is

(9.36)
$$\frac{E_1}{Z_0} = \frac{E_0}{m \sqrt{(\sigma/ml_0 - \omega^2)^2 + \delta^2\omega^2/m^2}}.$$

If the frequency of the impressed force is equal to the natural frequency of free undamped oscillations (that is, if $\omega = \sqrt{\sigma/ml_0}$), then the impressed force is said to be in *resonance;* in this case the amplitude (9.36) can be written in the interesting form

(9.361)
$$\frac{1}{2\pi} \frac{1}{\delta} E_0 \left\{ 2\pi \sqrt{\frac{ml_0}{\sigma}} \right\}$$

which shows that the resonant amplitude is inversely proportional to the damping constant δ, is proportional to the maximum value E_0 of the impressed force $E_0 \cos \omega t$, and is proportional to the period of free oscillation. This implies that a mass which oscillates slowly (and hence with a long period) and has a small damping factor must oscillate with small resonant amplitudes provided that the resonant force is sufficiently small; and that larger but nevertheless small resonant forces may produce prodigious resonant amplitudes which result in a broken spring or some other catastrophe. Automobile shock absorbers and the familiar devices on swinging doors are examples of mechanical contrivances designed to give very great damping constants and hence to tame these oscillations.

We consider now the case in which there is no damping but $\omega \neq \sqrt{\sigma/ml_0}$. In this case, $b = \delta = 0$; and (9.317) and (9.316) show that $\phi = 0$ and $Z_0 = |c - \omega^2|$. The general solution (9.33) of (9.31) now takes the form

$$(9.37) \qquad x = C \cos \sqrt{\frac{\sigma}{ml_0}} (t - t_0) + \frac{E_0}{m|\sigma/ml_0 - \omega^2|} \cos \omega t.$$

Here the displacement $x(t)$ is the sum of two cosine terms with different frequencies. The displacement assumes quite different forms for different relative values of the constants; some of these forms are described by the picturesque names given to them. For example, if the amplitude and period of the first term are large in comparison with the amplitude and period of the second term, then the first term is described as a *carrier wave* which *carries* the wave represented by the second term. Another phenomenon is discussed in the next section.

9.38. Beats.—If C and the second coefficient in (9.37) are of the same order of magnitude and ω is nearly equal to $\sqrt{\sigma/ml_0}$, then the amplitudes of the oscillations of $x(t)$ vary in such a way as to produce *beats*. This may be seen from the following: If

$$(9.381) \qquad x(t) = A \cos a(t - t_0) + B \cos b(t - t_1)$$

where A, B, a, b, t_0, and t_1 are real constants, then

$$(9.382) \qquad x(t) = \Re[Ae^{ia(t-t_0)} + Be^{ib(t-t_1)}]$$

$$= \Re[A + Be^{i(b-a)t+ic}]e^{ia(t-t_0)} = \Re We^{i\psi}e^{ia(t-t_0)} = \Re We^{i[a(t-t_0)+\psi]}$$

$$= \sqrt{\{A + B \cos [(b-a)t + c]\}^2 + \{B \sin [(b-a)t + c]\}^2}$$
$$\cos [a(t - t_0) + \psi]$$

$$= \sqrt{A^2 + 2AB \cos [(b-a)t + c] + B^2} \cos [a(t - t_0) + \psi]$$

where $\Re z$ means the real part of z; $c = at_0 - bt_1$; W is the above square root; and ψ is a phase angle, depending on t, such that

(9.383) $W \cos \psi = A + B \cos [(b - a)t + c]$
(9.384) $W \sin \psi = B \sin [(b - a)t + c]$.

When a and b are nearly equal but $a \neq b$, the coefficient

(9.385) $\sqrt{A^2 + 2AB \cos [(b - a)t + c] + B^2}$

changes slowly between the values $| A - B |$ and $| A + B |$, and the variable phase angle ψ changes slowly as t increases; thus (9.382) indicates that the graph of $x(t)$ is roughly that of a pure cosine curve

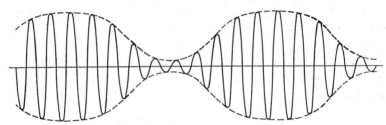

Fig. 9.386.

deformed by multiplying the ordinates by the variable factor (9.385). The graph of such a function $x(t)$ for which $A = 5.5$ and $B = 4.5$ is shown in Fig. 9.386.

9.4. Undamped Resonance.—In the preceding sections, we did not solve the equation

(9.41) $$x'' + \frac{\delta}{m} x' + \frac{\sigma}{ml_0} x = E_1 \cos \omega t$$

for the case in which the impedance is 0, that is,*

(9.42) $$Z \equiv \left(\frac{\sigma}{ml_0} - \omega^2\right) + i \frac{\delta\omega}{m} = 0.$$

If (9.42) holds and $\omega > 0$, it must be true that

(9.43) $$\delta = 0, \qquad \omega = \sqrt{\frac{\sigma}{ml_0}}.$$

---

* We have seen that, if $Z_0 \neq 0$, then

(9.421) $$\frac{E_1}{Z_0} \cos \omega(t - \phi)$$

is a particular solution of (9.41). To put $Z_0 = 0$ in (9.421), to say that $E_1/Z_0 = \infty$, and to assert that

$$\infty \cos \omega(t - \phi)$$

is a particular solution of (9.41) is one of those inglorious performances which cannot be tolerated in rational society.

This means that there is no damping and that the impressed force is resonant.   The differential equation (9.41) then becomes

$$(9.44) \qquad\qquad x'' + \frac{\sigma}{ml_0} x = E_1 \cos \sqrt{\frac{\sigma}{ml_0}} \, t.$$

To simplify writing, let $a = \sqrt{\frac{\sigma}{ml_0}}$.   The real part of a solution of

$$(9.441) \qquad\qquad x'' + a^2 x = E_1 e^{iat}$$

is then a particular solution of (9.44).   By Section 8.3, the function Ate^{iat} must be a solution of (9.441) provided that A is properly chosen. The required value of A is found to be $E_1/2ia$.   Thus

$$\Re \frac{E_1}{2ia} te^{iat} = \frac{E_1}{2a} t \sin at$$

is a particular solution of (9.44).   The general solution of (9.44) is therefore

$$(9.45) \qquad x = C \cos \sqrt{\frac{\sigma}{ml_0}} (t - t_0) + \frac{E_1}{2 \sqrt{\sigma/ml_0}} t \sin \sqrt{\frac{\sigma}{ml_0}} t$$

where C and t_0 are constants.

The first term in (9.45) represents a pure simple harmonic motion. The second term may be regarded as a sine wave distorted by the

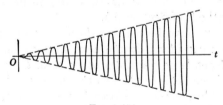

Fig. 9.451.

factor t which makes the oscillations greater and greater as t increases. A graph of the function $x(t)$, for the case in which $C = 0$, is shown in Fig. 9.451.

Only an impractical worshiper of equations would say that (9.45) implies that the oscillations become infinite as t becomes infinite.   A more practical individual must see that (9.45) implies that, as t increases, the oscillations increase until something happens to the mechanical system which we are studying.

9.5. Other Impressed Forces.—We have considered the equation

$$(9.51) \qquad\qquad mx'' + \delta x' + \frac{\sigma}{l_0} x = F$$

for the case in which $F = E_0 \cos \omega t$, a particular solution of (9.51) then being the real part of a solution of the equation obtained by setting $F = E_0 e^{i\omega t}$ in (9.51). The case in which $F = E_0 \cos \omega(t - t_0)$ can be handled by use of the identity

$$(9.511) \qquad E_0 e^{i\omega(t-t_0)} = E_0 e^{-i\omega t_0} e^{i\omega t} = E_1 e^{i\omega t}$$

where $E_1 = E_0 e^{-i\omega t_0}$. The case in which

$$(9.52) \qquad F = \sum_{k=1}^{n} a_k e^{i\omega_k(t-t_k)}$$

or

$$(9.521) \qquad F = \sum_{k=1}^{n} [A_k \cos \omega_k t + B_k \sin \omega_k t]$$

can now be handled. When (9.52) holds, a particular solution of (9.51) is the sum of particular solutions of the n equations obtained by setting $F = a_k e^{i\omega_k(t-t_k)}$ in (9.51). The procedure when F is a periodic function $f(t)$ was set forth in the section (Section 8.6) on Fourier series. Those who happen to know the theory of *almost periodic functions* should see other possibilities for use of (9.52).

The methods just described are those which feature the harmonics of the impressed force F and of the solution $x(t)$. In any case in which $F = f(t)$, $f(t)$ being bounded and having at most a finite set of discontinuities in each finite interval, (9.51) is linear and may be solved by the methods of Section 6.5.

The methods we have been using do not (except in some special cases such as that considered in the next section) enable us to solve (9.51) when F depends on variables other than t. Suppose that an impressed force $E_0 \cos \omega t$ is applied to the mass which is composed of iron and that in addition there is a force $H/(d - x)^2$ due to the presence of a magnet placed a distance d below the equilibrium position. The differential equation is then

$$(9.53) \qquad mx'' + \delta x' + \frac{\sigma}{l_0} x = E_0 \cos \omega t + \frac{H}{(d - x)^2}.$$

This equation is nonlinear; a student who has not yet attained a proper reverence for nonlinear equations may receive a good lesson by trying to solve (9.53) by methods heretofore used. One who wants to be able to handle equation (9.53) and other difficult equations should be familiar with the Picard method of successive approximations presented in Chapters 15 and 16.

9.54. Negative Damping.—It sometimes happens that the impressed force F considered in the last section has, at least for certain time intervals, the form $F = Bx'$ where B is a positive constant. In this case the equation (9.51) becomes

$$(9.55) \qquad mx'' + \delta x' + \frac{\sigma}{l_0} x = Bx'.$$

If $B > \delta$ and we set $d = B - \delta$, then $d > 0$ and (9.55) becomes

$$(9.551) \qquad mx'' - dx' + \frac{\sigma}{l_0} x = 0.$$

In such cases the impressed force Bx' is commonly said to be *self-induced* (or *self-excited*) because it is by virtue of the motion of the mass itself that the impressed force operates. Equation (9.551) is just like the equation (9.21) for free damped motion except that the coefficient of x' is now negative. A situation represented by (9.551) is commonly described as one in which *negative damping*** occurs. The roots of the characteristic equation of (9.551) are easily found, and the general solution of (9.551) can be conveniently represented in the form

$$(9.56) \qquad x = C e^{(d/2m)t} \cos \sqrt{\frac{\sigma}{ml_0} - \frac{d^2}{4m^2}} \, (t - t_0)$$

provided that the quantity under the radical is positive, that is, provided that d is sufficiently small. When $C \neq 0$, the motion defined by (9.56) consists of oscillations of increasing amplitudes; this portends destruction of the physical apparatus if the negative-damping force (or aggravating force) is permitted to operate for a sufficiently long time. For the cases in which the quantity under the radical in (9.56) is 0 and negative, appropriate forms of the general solution of (9.56) show that either $x(t) = 0$ or $|x(t)|$ increases without oscillations as t increases.

9.57. Degrees of Freedom.—A mechanical system is said to have *one degree of freedom* if the geometrical configuration at time t can be specified by one coordinate. This coordinate may represent a linear displacement of a point from its equilibrium position as in the problems previously considered in this chapter; hence the mechanical systems considered above have one degree of freedom. The coordinate may represent the angular displacement θ of a rotating line from its equilibrium position as in the pendulum problems considered in Chapter 11.

A mechanical system is said to have n *degrees of freedom* if the geometric configuration at time t can be specified by n coordinates. The *three-body problem* is the problem of determining, as functions of

---

* The term *aggravating force* has been proposed as an alternative for the term *negative-damping force*.

t, the three space coordinates of each of three mass points which, starting at specified positions with specified velocities, move through space subject only to their mutual attractive forces; thus the three-body problem deals with a system having nine degrees of freedom. It is a very difficult problem.

In the next section we derive and discuss briefly the differential equations governing a particular mechanical system which has two degrees of freedom since the geometrical configuration at time t can be specified by giving the displacements of two points from their equilibrium positions.

9.6. Two Degrees of Freedom.—Let three springs S_x, S_y, and S_z having spring constants σ_x, σ_y, and σ_z and natural lengths l_x, l_y, and l_z be used as in Fig. 9.61 to connect two masses m_1 and m_2 to each other and to two rigid supports a distance d apart. The term *spring* is to have, as in Section 9.01, a liberal interpretation; our discussion applies as well to rubber bands as to coiled springs. A trick which increases the number of applications of the system shown in Fig. 9.61 consists in

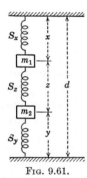

FIG. 9.61.

agreeing that if $\sigma_x = 0$ (or $\sigma_y = 0$ or $\sigma_z = 0$) then the spring S_x (or S_y or S_z) is absent from the figure. For example, $\sigma_y = 0$ implies that two masses are hanging tandem from the ceiling without a spring to the floor. If $\sigma_x = 0$, then S_y and S_z are to be regarded as compression springs; for example, S_y may be an automobile tire, m_2 may be the mass of a wheel and axle, S_z may be an automobile spring, and m_1 may be a part of the mass of the automobile. In every case we assume that $\sigma_z \neq 0$ and that either $\sigma_x \neq 0$ or $\sigma_y \neq 0$ or both, so that the masses are connected to each other and to either the ceiling or the floor or both. The problem in which we interest ourselves is that of determining the positions of the masses m_1 and m_2 as functions of the time t.

Let the forces be regarded as positive when they pull downward. Let x_0, y_0, and z_0 denote the values of x, y, and z (Fig. 9.61) when the masses are at rest in the equilibrium position. The equation which represents the fact that the algebraic sum of the forces acting on the mass m_1 vanishes is

(9.621)
$$-\sigma_x \frac{x_0 - l_x}{l_x} + m_1 g + \sigma_z \frac{y_0 - l_z}{l_z} = 0;$$

and the corresponding equation for the mass m_2 is

(9.622)
$$-\sigma_z \frac{y_0 - l_z}{l_z} + m_2 g + \sigma_y \frac{z_0 - l_y}{l_y} = 0;$$

these equations, together with the equation

(9.623) $$x_0 + y_0 + z_0 = d,$$

determine x_0, y_0, and z_0 in terms of the constants with which we started.

When the masses m_1 and m_2 are held at rest as in Fig. 9.61, but not necessarily in the equilibrium position, the sum of the spring and gravitational forces acting on the mass m_1 is the first of the expressions

(9.63)
$$\begin{cases} -\sigma_x \dfrac{x - l_x}{l_x} + m_1 g + \sigma_z \dfrac{z - l_z}{l_z}, \\ -\sigma_z \dfrac{z - l_z}{l_z} + m_2 g + \sigma_y \dfrac{y - l_y}{l_y}; \end{cases}$$

and the corresponding sum for the mass m_2 is the second. Using (9.621) and (9.622), we can write (9.63) in the form

(9.64) $$-k_1(x - x_0) + k_3(z - z_0), \qquad -k_3(z - z_0) + k_2(y - y_0)$$

where

(9.641) $$k_1 = \frac{\sigma_x}{l_x}, \qquad k_2 = \frac{\sigma_y}{l_y}, \qquad k_3 = \frac{\sigma_z}{l_z}.$$

It is convenient to determine the positions of m_1 and m_2 by finding their displacements x_1 and x_2 from their equilibrium positions. We see that $x_1 = x - x_0$ and $x_2 = (x + z) - (x_0 + z_0) = x_1 + (z - z_0)$ so that $z - z_0 = x_2 - x_1$. Also, $y - y_0 = -x_2$. Using these formulas with (9.641) and (9.642), we see that, when the masses m_1 and m_2 are held at rest with displacements x_1 and x_2, the sums of the spring forces and gravitational forces on m_1 and m_2 are, respectively,

(9.65) $$-(k_1 + k_3)x_1 + k_3 x_2, \qquad -(k_2 + k_3)x_2 + k_3 x_1;$$

we assume that these are also the forces when the masses are moving. Let $-\delta_1 x_1'$ and $-\delta_2 x_2'$ represent damping forces on m_1 and m_2, respectively, δ_1 and δ_2 being nonnegative constants; and let $f_1(t)$ and $f_2(t)$ denote impressed forces applied to m_1 and m_2, respectively. The external forces applied to the masses m_1 and m_2 are then, respectively,

(9.66)
$$\begin{cases} -(k_1 + k_3)x_1 + k_3 x_2 - \delta_1 x_1' + f_1(t), \\ -(k_2 + k_3)x_2 + k_3 x_1 - \delta_2 x_2' + f_2(t). \end{cases}$$

Using Newton's law $F = ma$ as an excuse for equating these expressions to $m_1 x_1''$ and $m_2 x_2''$, respectively, we obtain the two equations

(9.67)
$$\begin{cases} m_1 x_1'' + \delta_1 x_1' + (k_1 + k_3)x_1 - k_3 x_2 = f_1(t) \\ m_2 x_2'' + \delta_2 x_2' + (k_2 + k_3)x_2 - k_3 x_1 = f_2(t) \end{cases}$$

which govern the displacements x_1 and x_2 of the masses m_1 and m_2 from their equilibrium positions. Each equation is linear, of the second order, and has constant coefficients.

9.7. Solution of the System (9.67).—It is easy to start to solve the system (9.67) if $f_1(t)$ and $f_2(t)$ each have two derivatives. Inserting the operator $D = d/dt$ in (9.67), we can use the method of Section 8.8 to obtain the equation

$$(9.71) \quad \{m_1 m_2 D^4 + [m_2 \delta_1 + m_1 \delta_2]D^3$$
$$+ [m_2(k_1 + k_2) + m_1(k_2 + k_3) + \delta_1 \delta_2]D^2$$
$$+ [\delta_2(k_1 + k_2) + \delta_1(k_2 + k_3)]D + [(k_1 + k_3)(k_2 + k_3) - k_3^2]\}x_1$$
$$= m_2 f_1''(t) + \delta_2 f_1'(t) + (k_2 + k_3)f_1(t) + k_3 f_2(t)$$

which $x_1(t)$ must satisfy.

If there is no damping, so that $\delta_1 = \delta_2 = 0$, the equation (9.71) becomes

$$(9.72) \quad \left[D^4 + \left(\frac{k_1 + k_3}{m_1} + \frac{k_2 + k_3}{m_2} \right) D^2 + \frac{(k_1 + k_3)(k_2 + k_3) - k_3^2}{m_1 m_2} \right] x_1$$
$$= \frac{m_2 f_1''(t) + (k_2 + k_3)f_1(t) + k_3 f_2(t)}{m_1 m_2}.$$

The characteristic equation of the homogeneous equation is

$$(9.721) \quad m^4 + \left(\frac{k_1 + k_3}{m_1} + \frac{k_2 + k_3}{m_2} \right) m^2 + \frac{(k_1 + k_3)(k_2 + k_3) - k_3^2}{m_1 m_2} = 0.$$

This equation can be solved for m^2 by means of the quadratic formula; its roots are the four different numbers

$$i\beta_1, \ -i\beta_1, \ i\beta_2, \ -i\beta_2$$

where β_1 and β_2 are the positive numbers for which

$$(9.722) \quad \beta_1^2 = \frac{1}{2}\left(\frac{k_1 + k_3}{m_1} + \frac{k_2 + k_3}{m_2} \right)$$
$$+ \frac{1}{2}\sqrt{\left(\frac{k_1 + k_3}{m_1} - \frac{k_2 + k_3}{m_2} \right)^2 + \frac{4k_3^2}{m_1 m_2}}$$

and

$$(9.723) \quad \beta_2^2 = \frac{1}{2}\left(\frac{k_1 + k_3}{m_1} + \frac{k_2 + k_3}{m_2} \right)$$
$$- \frac{1}{2}\sqrt{\left(\frac{k_1 + k_3}{m_1} - \frac{k_2 + k_3}{m_2} \right)^2 + \frac{4k_3^2}{m_1 m_2}}.$$

It is easy to see that $0 < \beta_2 < \beta_1$. Hence each solution of the homogeneous equation corresponding to (9.72) must have the form

$$(9.724) \quad c_1 e^{i\beta_1 t} + c_2 e^{-i\beta_1 t} + c_3 e^{i\beta_2 t} + c_4 e^{-i\beta_2 t}.$$

Each solution of the system of homogeneous equations

$$(9.73) \qquad \begin{cases} m_1 x_1'' + (k_1 + k_3)x_1 - k_3 x_2 = 0 \\ m_2 x_2'' + (k_2 + k_3)x_2 - k_3 x_1 = 0 \end{cases}$$

must have the form

$$(9.74) \qquad \begin{cases} x_1 = c_1 e^{i\beta_1 t} + c_2 e^{-i\beta_1 t} + c_3 e^{i\beta_2 t} + c_4 e^{-i\beta_2 t} \\ x_2 = \dfrac{c_1}{k_3}(k_1 + k_3 - m_1\beta_1^2)e^{i\beta_1 t} + \dfrac{c_2}{k_3}(k_1 + k_3 - m_1\beta_1^2)e^{-i\beta_1 t} \\ \qquad + \dfrac{c_3}{k_3}(k_1 + k_3 - m_1\beta_2^2)e^{i\beta_2 t} + \dfrac{c_4}{k_3}(k_1 + k_3 - m_1\beta_2^2)e^{-i\beta_2 t}; \end{cases}$$

the fact regarding x_1 has been established, and x_2 is determined in terms of x_1 by the first of equations (9.73). Direct substitution shows that (9.74) is a solution of (9.73) for each set of constants c_1, c_2, c_3, c_4. Thus the equations (9.73) are solved; but further work is required to see what the solutions mean. The four constants c_1, c_2, c_3, and c_4 can be determined so that the four numbers $x_1(0)$, $x_1'(0)$, $x_2(0)$, and $x_2'(0)$ assume prescribed values. (Tell what this means physically, and prove the assertion.) Let N and P be the numbers defined by

$$(9.741) \qquad N = \frac{k_1 + k_3 - m_1\beta_1^2}{k_3}, \qquad P = \frac{k_1 + k_3 - m_1\beta_2^2}{k_3}.$$

These numbers are of interest since they appear in the second of equations (9.74). Using (9.722) and (9.723), we find that

$$(9.742) \qquad N = \frac{m_1}{2k_3}\left\{\left(\frac{k_1 + k_3}{m_1} - \frac{k_2 + k_3}{m_2}\right) \right.$$
$$\left. - \sqrt{\left(\frac{k_1 + k_3}{m_1} - \frac{k_2 + k_3}{m_2}\right)^2 + \frac{4k_3^2}{m_1 m_2}}\right\}$$

and

$$(9.743) \qquad P = \frac{m_1}{2k_3}\left\{\left(\frac{k_1 + k_3}{m_1} - \frac{k_2 + k_3}{m_2}\right) \right.$$
$$\left. + \sqrt{\left(\frac{k_1 + k_3}{m_1} - \frac{k_2 + k_3}{m_2}\right)^2 + \frac{4k_3^2}{m_1 m_2}}\right\}.$$

It is important to see that N is negative and P is positive. Using the abbreviations N and P and trigonometric rather than complex exponential functions, we can write the solutions (9.74) of (9.73) in the form

$$(9.75) \qquad \begin{cases} x_1 = A \sin \beta_1(t - t_1) + B \sin \beta_2(t - t_2) \\ x_2 = NA \sin \beta_1(t - t_1) + PB \sin \beta_2(t - t_2) \end{cases}$$

where A, B, t_1, and t_2 are constants which determine the different possible motions of the undamped unforced system. If $A > 0$ and $B = 0$, the motion is called a *natural motion* or a *fundamental motion* of the masses. Each mass executes a sinusoidal motion about its equilibrium position with *natural period* or *fundamental period* $2\pi/\beta_1$ and *natural frequency* or *fundamental frequency* $\beta_1/2\pi$. The motions are π radians (180 degrees) out of phase; the masses are in their equilibrium positions at the same times, but the fact that N is negative means that one mass is falling while the other is rising. Thus the motion of the masses is somewhat like the motion of a person's hands when he is applauding. The amplitude of the motion of the second mass is $|N|$ times the amplitude of the motion of the first mass; the equation for N shows when the amplitudes are equal. The case in which $A = 0$ and $B > 0$ represents another *fundamental motion* of the masses. Each mass executes a sinusoidal motion with *natural period* $2\pi/\beta_2$ and *natural frequency* $\beta_2/2\pi$. Since $P > 0$, the motions are in phase; the masses pass through their equilibrium positions at the same times, and each is rising when the other is rising.

The two natural frequencies $\beta_1/2\pi$ and $\beta_2/2\pi$ of the system are never equal; the frequency is always greater when the motions are out of phase than when they are in phase. According to the equations (9.75), each possible motion of the free undamped system is represented by a linear combination (or superposition) of two fundamental motions. The case in which A and B are both different from 0 can be studied by the method used in Section 9.38. One interesting result is that, if the frequencies β_1 and β_2 are nearly equal, A and B are nearly equal, and $-NA$ and PB are nearly equal, the two masses take turns standing essentially still; while one is essentially still, the other does essentially all the oscillating. Another result of both mathematical and physical interest is that neither $x_1(t)$ nor $x_2(t)$ can be periodic when A, $B \neq 0$ unless the quotient β_1/β_2 is a rational number, that is, the quotient of two integers; one who wants enlightenment on this subject can find it in a book on "Almost Periodic Functions."

When damping (positive or negative) is present, the finding of the roots of the characteristic equation of the homogeneous equation corresponding to (9.71) is not so simple; but sometimes engineers must find them whether the problem is simple or not. After having found these roots, the solutions of the homogeneous equation can be written down according to the rules given in Section 8.1.

Finding a particular solution of (9.72) or of the more general equation (9.71), can be accomplished by methods of Chapters 6 and 8; it is especially easy when f_1 and f_2 are pure harmonics with frequencies which are not natural frequencies of the system.

9.76. Steady-state Solutions of (9.67).—We consider now the system (9.67) for the case in which damping is present and the functions $f_1(t)$ and $f_2(t)$ are pure harmonics,

$$(9.761) \qquad f_1(t) = E_1 e^{i\omega_1 t}; \qquad f_2(t) = E_2 e^{i\omega_2 t}.$$

The system (9.67) now becomes

$$(9.77) \qquad \begin{cases} m_1 x_1'' + \delta_1 x_1' + (k_1 + k_3)x_1 - k_3 x_2 = E_1 e^{i\omega_1 t} \\ m_2 x_2'' + \delta_2 x_2' + (k_2 + k_3)x_2 - k_3 x_1 = E_2 e^{i\omega_2 t} \end{cases}$$

where $\delta_1 > 0$ and $\delta_2 > 0$. The right-hand members in this system may be harmonics of more general forces in which one is interested. It may be worth while to point out that the right members would not be more general if phase angles φ_1 and φ_2 were inserted since

$$A e^{i(\omega t - \varphi)} = A e^{-i\varphi} e^{i\omega t} = E e^{i\omega t}$$

where $E = A e^{-i\varphi}$.

The solutions of the homogeneous system corresponding to (9.77) are all transients (why?), and we do not concern ourselves with them. Our interest lies in the steady-state solutions.

Before going to work to find the steady-state solutions of the system (9.77) by the method of Section 8.8, it is advisable to introduce some notation. A little notation can save much writing. Let operators L_1 and L_2 be defined by

$$(9.771) \quad L_1 = m_1 D^2 + \delta_1 D + k_1 + k_3, \quad L_2 = m_2 D^2 + \delta_2 D + k_2 + k_3$$

where $D = d/dt$. Then the equations (9.77) can be written in the form

$$(9.772) \qquad \qquad L_1 x_1 - k_3 x_2 = E_1 e^{i\omega_1 t}$$
$$(9.773) \qquad \qquad L_2 x_2 - k_3 x_1 = E_2 e^{i\omega_2 t}.$$

Assuming that $x_1(t)$ and $x_2(t)$ are steady-state solutions of (9.772) and (9.773), we can multiply (9.772) by L_2 and (9.773) by k_3 and add to obtain

$$(9.774) \qquad L_2 L_1 x_1 - k_3^2 x_1 = L_2(i\omega_1)E_1 e^{i\omega_1 t} + k_3 E_2 e^{i\omega_2 t}.$$

Letting the operator L be defined by

$$(9.775) \qquad \qquad L = L_2 L_1 - k_3^2$$

we see that the steady-state solution of

$$(9.776) \qquad \qquad L x_1 = L_2(i\omega_1)E_1 e^{i\omega_1 t}$$

is (see Section 8.5 on Impedance)

$$(9.777) \qquad \qquad x_1 = \frac{L_2(i\omega_1)E_1}{L(i\omega_1)} e^{i\omega_1 t}$$

and that the steady-state solution of

$$(9.778) \qquad Lx_1 = k_3 E_2 e^{i\omega_2 t}$$

is

$$(9.779) \qquad x_1 = \frac{k_3 E_2}{L(i\omega_2)} e^{i\omega_2 t}.$$

Hence the steady-state solution of (9.774) is the sum of (9.777) and (9.779), that is,

$$(9.78) \qquad x_1(t) = \frac{L_2(i\omega_1) E_1}{L(i\omega_1)} e^{i\omega_1 t} + \frac{k_3 E_2}{L(i\omega_2)} e^{i\omega_2 t}.$$

Putting this function $x_1(t)$ in (9.772) gives

$$(9.781) \qquad x_2(t) = \frac{k_3 E_1}{L(i\omega_1)} e^{i\omega_1 t} + \frac{L_1(i\omega_2) E_2}{L(i\omega_2)} e^{i\omega_2 t}.$$

Direct substitution shows that these functions satisfy (9.773) as well as (9.772). Any other solution of the system (9.77) can differ by at most a transient from the steady-state solution given in (9.78) and (9.781).

The four coefficients in (9.78) and (9.781) may be evaluated by means of the formulas

$$(9.782) \qquad L_1(i\omega) = (k_1 + k_3 - m_1\omega^2) + i\,\delta_1\omega$$
$$(9.783) \qquad L_2(i\omega) = (k_2 + k_2 - m_2\omega^2) + i\,\delta_2\omega$$
$$(9.784) \qquad L(i\omega) = L_1(i\omega)L_2(i\omega) - k_3^2.$$

There is much to be said about the solutions and their applications. A student should be able to ask as well as answer many questions about them. One interesting question is the following. Suppose the m's, δ's, k's and E_1 are fixed positive constants and that $E_2 = 0$; for what frequency of $E_1 e^{i\omega t}$ would the oscillations of $x_2(t)$ be most violent?

9.8. Rods and Columns.—In this section we give problems involving elasticity in straight rods and columns.

Problem 9.81

A long steel rod is lying on the ground. Its length is a feet, it weighs w pounds per linear foot, and k is a constant (in fact, the product of Young's modulus and the area of a cross section of the rod) such that within elastic limits the force required to stretch or compress the rod to length b is $k(b - a)/a$. Let $u(x)$ be the function such that, when the rod hangs motionless from one end, the point which was x feet from that end will be $u(x)$ feet from the end. Draw figures and present an argument to show that

$$w(a - x) \sim k\,\frac{u(x + \Delta x) - u(x) - \Delta x}{\Delta x}$$

where [$\sim$] means is approximately equal to.   Make the necessary steps to obtain

(9.811) $$u(x) = x + \frac{w}{2k}[a^2 - (a - x)^2].$$

Can you see any connection between the fact that $u(a) = a + wa^2/2k$ and the fact that, when the rod is lying on the ground, a force equal to the weight of the rod stretches it to length $a + wa^2/k$?

Problem 9.82

Show that if the rod of the preceding problem is made to stand, as a vertical column, on one end then a point which was x feet from that end will be

(9.821) $$v(x) = x - \frac{w}{2k}[a^2 - (a - x)^2]$$

feet from the base.

Problem 9.83

Using the result of the previous problem, show that a steel rod whose length is the height of the Empire State Building would be compressed 1.7 inches when it is stood on one end.   Assume that the steel weighs .3 pounds per cubic inch, that Young's modulus for the steel is $32 \cdot 10^6$ when units are pounds and inches, and that the height of the building is 15,000 inches (1,250 feet).

Problem 9.9

A particle slides without friction in a long slender tube which rotates in a vertical plane about its center with constant angular velocity $\omega > 0$.   Let $u(t)$ denote the displacement of the particle from the center at time t, and suppose the time origin to be so chosen that at time $t = 0$ the tube is horizontal.   Show that

$$\frac{d^2u}{dt^2} - \omega^2 u = -g \sin \omega t$$

and that, if the initial velocity and displacement of the particle are $u(0) = A$ and $u'(0) = B$, then

$$u = \frac{1}{2}\left[A + \frac{B}{\omega} - \frac{g}{2\omega^2}\right]e^{\omega t} + \frac{1}{2}\left[A - \frac{B}{\omega} + \frac{g}{2\omega^2}\right]e^{-\omega t} + \frac{g}{2\omega^2}\sin \omega t.$$

Show that $u(t)$ is bounded if and only if $2A\omega^2 + 2B\omega = g$ and that $u(t)$ is periodic if and only if $A = 0$ and $2B\omega = g$.

CHAPTER 10

ELECTRIC CIRCUITS

10.0. Introduction.—In this chapter we show how differential equations are used in electric-circuit analysis. Sections 10.1 and 10.2 introduce physical laws and concepts and give the rules for setting up the differential equations governing flow of current in electric circuits and networks. The remainder of the chapter is concerned with setting up equations, solving the equations, and interpreting the solutions.

Throughout the chapter, $E(t)$ represents an impressed electromotive force. For reasons set forth in Section 3.9, it is not good strategy to require that $E(t)$ be everywhere continuous.

10.1. A Simple Circuit.—We begin by considering the simple *circuit* of Fig. 10.11 containing an *inductor* (coil) represented by the letter L, a *resistor* (resistance) represented by the letter R, and a *capacitor* (condenser) represented by the letter C. The letter E represents an applied electromotive force which in many applications has the form $E_0 \sin \omega t$.

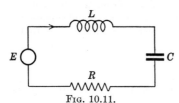

FIG. 10.11.

Let Q denote the *charge* on the capacitor, and let I denote the current in the circuit. Both Q and I are functions of the time t. We assume that no current flows through the capacitor and that units of time, charge, and current are so adjusted that at all times

$$(10.12) \qquad \frac{dQ}{dt} = I.$$

If units are not properly adjusted, then the time rate of change of the charge Q would be merely proportional to the current I; we leave all questions involving units to physicists and engineers. It may serve the purpose of the nonscientific (and amuse the scientific) to think of Q as being a number of pints and I as being a number of pints per second. The electricity "circulates" as an incompressible fluid; at each time the current I is the same at all points of the circuit. It is as though the two horizontal lines at C were storage tanks and E were a pump circulating fluid from one tank to the other.

We are now ready to use some physical concepts and laws to set up the differential equation for the circuit in Fig. 10.11. The applied electromotive force E represents an applied *potential difference*, or *voltage drop*. This voltage drop must, by a physical law, be equal to the sum of the voltage drops due to the inductor, resistor, and capacitor. The last three voltage drops are computed, under conditions which it is the business of physicists and engineers to know about, by use of the following three laws:

(i) There is a positive constant L, called the *inductance* of the inductor, such that the voltage drop due to the inductor is equal to

$$(10.131) \qquad\qquad L\frac{dI}{dt}.$$

(ii) There is a positive constant R, called the *resistance* of the resistor, such that the voltage drop due to the resistor is equal to

$$(10.132) \qquad\qquad RI.$$

(iii) There is a positive constant C, called the *capacitance* of the capacitor, such that the voltage drop due to the capacitor is Q/C. For reasons more cogent than a desire to eliminate fractions, the number $1/C$ is given a name and symbol; it is called the *elastance* of the capacitor, and we denote it by Γ to remind us of C. Thus the voltage drop due to a capacitor is

$$(10.133) \qquad\qquad \Gamma Q \quad\text{or}\quad \frac{Q}{C}.$$

Thus we obtain

$$(10.14) \qquad\qquad L\frac{dI}{dt} + RI + \Gamma Q = E$$

as a differential equation governing the circuit of Fig. 10.11. This equation contains, in addition to the constants L, R, and Γ and the electromotive force E which are assumed to be known, two functions $I = I(t)$ and $Q = Q(t)$ which are related by the formula (10.12).

One way of using (10.12) and (10.14) to obtain an equation involving only one unknown function is to obtain

$$(10.141) \qquad\qquad Q = Q(t_0) + \int_{t_0}^{t} I(s)\,ds$$

from (10.12) (see Section 2.5) and to substitute in (10.14) to obtain

$$(10.142) \qquad L\frac{dI}{dt} + RI + \Gamma\left(Q(t_0) + \int_{t_0}^{t} I(s)\,ds\right) = E(t).$$

This is, according to Chapter 1, a differential equation; but it contains the unknown function under an integral sign and is also an *integral equation*. In fact, (10.142) is called an *integrodifferential equation*. If $E(t)$ is differentiable and (10.142) holds, we can differentiate (10.142) to obtain the pure differential equation

$$(10.15) \qquad L\frac{d^2I}{dt^2} + R\frac{dI}{dt} + \Gamma I = E'(t).$$

Another (and simpler) way to use (10.12) and (10.14) to obtain an equation involving only one unknown function is to use (10.12) to obtain

$$I = \frac{dQ}{dt}, \qquad \frac{dI}{dt} = \frac{d^2Q}{dt^2}$$

and substitute in (10.14) to obtain

$$(10.16) \qquad L\frac{d^2Q}{dt^2} + R\frac{dQ}{dt} + \Gamma Q = E(t).$$

If each term in (10.16) has a t derivative, then we can differentiate (10.16) and use (10.12) to obtain (10.15).

One who has read Chapter 9 (this is not assumed) should note the similarity between (10.16) and the equation

$$m\frac{d^2x}{dt^2} + \delta\frac{dx}{dt} + \frac{\sigma}{l_0}x = f(t)$$

which governs the displacement x of an oscillating mass. *Charge Q corresponds to displacement x; inductance L to mass m; resistance R to damping δ; elastance Γ to modified spring constant σ/l_0; and impressed electromotive force $E(t)$ to impressed force $f(t)$. The current $I(t) \equiv Q'(t)$ corresponds to velocity $x'(t)$.*

Solution of equations (10.15) and (10.16) involves an easy application of Chapters 6 and 8; we return to these equations later in this chapter. One who has mastered Chapter 9 should have many ideas about the solutions. This illustrates the important point that knowledge of mechanical systems can be transferred to knowledge of electrical systems. Of course, transfer can (and often does) proceed in the opposite direction.

10.2. Networks.—A *network* is an electric circuit consisting of one or more branches. The network in Fig. 10.21 is sufficiently complicated to illustrate the terminology and to provide many problems. The points marked V_1, V_2, $\cdots$, V_5 are *vertices*, or *junction points*, or *terminals* of the network. The lines joining the vertices are *branches* of the network. The resistors, inductors, capacitors, and impressed electromotive forces are the *elements* of the network. A branch may contain any combination of none, some, or all of the elements.*

With the currents I_1, I_2, $\cdots$, I_8 in the eight branches of the network in Fig. 10.21 are associated arrowheads. When a branch contains an impressed (or applied) electromotive force E, we shall always point the arrow on the branch in the direction in which E tends (when positive) to produce a flow of current. Arrows on other branches are assigned in purely arbitrary directions; the point is that one puts on the arrows and does not change them throughout discussion of a network. If the direction of the arrowhead on the branch from V_1 to V_5

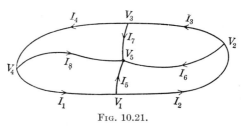

FIG. 10.21.

were reversed, the current I_5 would have its sign reversed (perhaps I_5 would be changed from cos ωt to $-$ cos ωt); thus one could change the direction of the arrow by prefixing a negative sign to I_5, but there is no point in doing this. It is often convenient to regard current I flowing from a vertex V as being the same thing as a current $-I$ flowing into the vertex V.

The branches $V_1 V_2$, $V_2 V_5$, and $V_5 V_1$ form a *closed circuit* of the network; likewise, the branches $V_1 V_2$, $V_2 V_3$, $V_3 V_5$, and $V_5 V_1$ form a *closed circuit*. The branches $V_1 V_2$ and $V_2 V_3$ form an *open circuit* of the network. A closed circuit begins and ends at each of its vertices; an open circuit does not. We are now in a position to state the two following *Kirchhoff laws* which govern the electromotive forces and currents in a network in which arrows have been inserted.

* To be accurate, one should recognize the fact that each branch necessarily has positive inductance L, positive resistance R, and positive elastance Γ and that the voltage drop due to them is

$$(10.22) \qquad L\frac{dI}{dt} + RI + \Gamma\left(A + \int_{t_0}^{t} I(s)ds\right)$$

when current I is flowing in the branch, A being a constant. If there is no capacitor in the branch, Γ *may* be so near 0 that the term involving Γ can be neglected without damaging results. If the branch has no turns or coils, L *may* be so near 0 that the term $L\,dI/dt$ can be similarly neglected. Sometimes the term RI is so small in comparison with the other terms that it is neglected. If each of the three terms is negligible and if the branch contains no impressed electromotive force, the branch may be eliminated from engineers' drawings of the network; the vertices at the ends of the branch are placed in coincidence, and the branch disappears. By reversing the process, a branch without elements may be created (see Problem 10.27). The idea of a branch containing inductance but no resistance or elastance is another one of those convenient fictions which simplify problems.

Law 10.221.—*The sum of the currents flowing into each vertex is equal to the sum of the currents flowing from the vertex.*

Law 10.222.—*The sum of the impressed electromotive forces in each closed circuit of the network is equal to the sum of the voltage drops due to the resistors, inductors, and capacitors in the closed circuit.*

In the following applications of the first law, one must pay attention to the arrows which assign directions to the currents.

Problem 10.231

By applying Kirchhoff's first law (Law 10.221) to the network of Fig. 10.21, show that $I_5 = I_1 - I_2, I_6 = I_2 - I_3, I_7 = I_4 - I_3,$ and

$$I_8 = -I_5 - I_6 - I_7 = I_4 - I_1.$$

Notice that the four currents $I_1, I_2, I_3,$ and I_4 determine the other four. Pick out four closed circuits which, collectively, contain each branch at least once.

Problem 10.232

Determine the vertices and branches in the network of Fig. 10.66, and express the currents in each branch in terms of $I_1, I_2,$ and I_3. Pick out three closed circuits which, collectively, contain each branch at least once.

Problem 10.233

Draw the network obtained by removing V_5 from the network of Fig. 10.21, the branches V_1V_5 and V_3V_5 being joined below the plane of the paper, and the branches V_2V_5 and V_4V_5 being joined above the plane of the paper. Show how the currents $I_1, I_2,$ and I_3 determine the currents in the other three branches of your network. Pick out three closed circuits which, collectively, contain each branch at least once.

In applying the second law of Kirchhoff to a closed circuit, we must choose one of the two directions along the circuit and, when writing the equations mentioned in the law, prefix a negative sign to each term arising from a current whose arrow is not in the chosen direction and to each electromotive force which (when positive) does not tend to produce current in the chosen direction. The voltage drops due to resistors, inductors, and capacitors are computed by use of (10.131), (10.132), and (10.133). If $Q_k(t_0)$ is the charge on capacitor C_k at time t_0, then the charge at time t is given by

$$Q_k(t) = Q_k(t_0) + \int_{t_0}^{t} I(s)ds$$

where $I(t)$ is the current at time t in the branch containing the capacitor C_k. The following examples illustrate the points:

Let E_1 and E_2 be two electromotive forces which, when positive, tend to produce currents in the directions assigned to I_1 and I_2 in Fig. 10.24. The current in the central branch of the network is, since the arrow is directed downward, $I_1 - I_2$.

Consider first the closed circuit, on the left in Fig. 10.24, which contains E_1 and the elements with constants L_1, R_1, $\Gamma_1 \equiv 1/C_1$, and $\Gamma_3 \equiv 1/C_3$. Application of Law 10.222 gives

$$(10.251) \quad L_1 \frac{dI_1}{dt} + R_1 I_1 + \Gamma_1 \left\{ Q_1(t_0) + \int_{t_0}^{t} I_1(s)ds \right\}$$
$$+ \Gamma_3 \left\{ Q_3(t_0) + \int_{t_0}^{t} [I_1(s) - I_2(s)]ds \right\} = E_1.$$

Applying Law 10.222 to the closed circuit on the right in Fig. 10.24 gives

$$(10.252) \quad L_2 \frac{dI_2}{dt} + R_2 I_2 + \Gamma_2 \left\{ Q_2(t_0) + \int_{t_0}^{t} I_2(s)ds \right\}$$
$$- \Gamma_3 \left\{ Q_3(t_0) + \int_{t_0}^{t} [I_1(s) - I_2(s)]ds \right\} = E_2.$$

Our interest lies at present in setting up differential equations; we postpone the problem of solving the equations. However, we may notice that, if we set

$$q_k(t) = \int_{t_0}^{t} I_k(s)ds \qquad k = 1, 2,$$

then (10.251) and (10.252) take the form

$$L_1 q_1'' + R_1 q_1' + (\Gamma_1 + \Gamma_3)q_1 - \Gamma_3 q_2 = E_1 - \Gamma_1 Q_1(t_0) - \Gamma_3 Q_3(t_0)$$
$$L_2 q_2'' + R_2 q_2' + (\Gamma_2 + \Gamma_3)q_2 - \Gamma_3 q_1 = E_2 - \Gamma_2 Q_2(t_0) + \Gamma_3 Q_3(t_0).$$

These equations are, except for differences in the names of the constants and functions, identical with the equations (9.67) which were discussed and solved in special cases in Sections 9.7 and 9.76. Thus the network in Fig. 10.24 is the *electrical equivalent* of the mechanical system illustrated in Fig. 9.61. One who has mastered Sections 9.7 and 9.76 should have many ideas about solutions of the

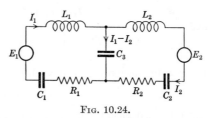

FIG. 10.24.

equations. This demonstrates again the important point that knowledge of mechanical systems can be transferred to knowledge of electrical systems.

Problem 10.261

Apply Law 10.222 to the "outside" circuit in Fig. 10.24 to obtain a new equation. Show that the new equation can also be obtained by adding (10.251) and (10.252). Can you explain this phenomenon without writing down the equations?

Problem 10.262

Find the equations which govern the network obtained from Fig. 10.24 by removing element X and soldering a wire across the gap, if X is the elemented associated with (1) E_2; (2) L_2; (3) R_2; (4) C_2; (5) C_3. Comment upon the last case. *Ans.:* Equations (10.251) and (10.252) with (1) $E_2 = 0$; (2) $L_2 = 0$; (3) $R_2 = 0$; (4) $\Gamma_2 = 0$; (5) $\Gamma_3 = 0$. In the last case, the equations show that I_1 is independent of E_2 and I_2 is independent of E_1.

Problem 10.263

What equations govern the network obtained from Fig. 10.24 by removing completely the central branch containing the condenser with capacitance C_3 and elastance Γ_3? *Ans.:* $I_2 = I_1$ and equation (10.41) with $I = I_1$, $L = L_1 + L_2$, $R = R_1 + R_2$, $Q = Q_1 + Q_2$, and $E = E_1 + E_2$.

Problem 10.264

What equations govern the network obtained from Fig. 10.24 by removing the inductors represented by L_1 and L_2, soldering wires across the gaps, and connecting the inductors, respectively, between C and R_1 and between R_2 and C_2? *Ans.:* Equations (10.251) and (10.252).

Problem 10.265

What equations govern the network obtained from Fig. 10.24 by changing the direction of the electromotive force E_2 [perhaps by keeping $E_2(t)$ the same but interchanging the connections] and reversing the direction of the I_2 arrowhead? *Ans.:* The equations obtained from (10.251) and (10.252) by replacing all negative signs by positive signs.

Problem 10.27

By applying Kirchhoff's laws to the networks in Figs. 10.271 and 10.272, show that in each case the currents I_1, I_2, I_3, and I_4 satisfy the equations

$$I_1 = I_2 + I_3 + I_4, \qquad RI_2 = E,$$

and

$$L\frac{dI_3}{dt} = E, \qquad \Gamma\left[A + \int_{t_0}^t I_4(s)ds\right] = E.$$

Let $E = 120 \sin 120\pi t$, as in 120-volt 60-cycle "house" voltage; and let

$$I_2 = I_3 = I_4 = 0$$

and $\Gamma Q = 360$ when $t = 0$. Show that in this case

$$I_2 = \frac{120}{R} \sin 120\pi t, \qquad I_3 = \frac{1}{\pi L}(1 - \cos 120\pi t)$$

$$I_4 = \frac{120^2\pi}{\Gamma} \cos 120\pi t, \qquad Q_4 = \frac{120}{\Gamma}(3 + \sin 120\pi t).$$

Remark 10.28

Many problems involve pure harmonic electromotive forces of the form

$$E(t) = E_0 \sin(\omega t + \alpha)$$

where $E_0 \geqq 0$, $\omega \geqq 0$, and α is real. The coefficient E_0 is an amplitude or maximum voltage, and α is a phase angle. If $\omega > 0$, then $E(t)$ is periodic with period $2\pi/\omega$ and frequency $\omega/2\pi$; if $\omega = 0$, then $E(t)$ is a constant. There are reasons why such electromotive forces are important. In the first place, when $\omega > 0$, this

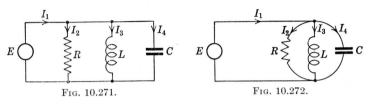

FIG. 10.271.   FIG. 10.272.

is precisely the form of electromotive force produced by an ordinary alternating-current generator. In the second place, solutions of problems involving electromotive forces $f(t)$ which are periodic but not pure harmonic can (Theorem 8.63) be approximated as closely as one desires by adding solutions of equations obtained by replacing $f(t)$ by harmonics of $f(t)$.* For the case of a single isolated circuit containing a single pure-harmonic electromotive force, the phase angle α is not important; one who prefers $\sin \omega t$ may take $\alpha = 0$, and one who prefers $\cos \omega t$ may take $\alpha = \pi/2$. But for the case of *polyphase* problems, the phase angles must be kept.

Since L means inductance in circuit theory, it is inconvenient to use L to denote linear operators. Engineers use Z, doubtless because the impedance $Z(i\omega)$ is usually not real and Z makes one think of complex numbers. Some physicists and engineers use j for i and ϵ for e; others use i and e even when such symbols as i_1, i_2, e_1, and e_2 denote currents and electromotive forces.

10.3. The Harmonic Oscillator.—The circuit of Fig. 10.31, containing an inductor and capacitor but no resistor, is known as the *harmonic oscillator.* Using Kirchhoff's second law, we obtain the equation (where, as usual, $\Gamma = 1/C$)

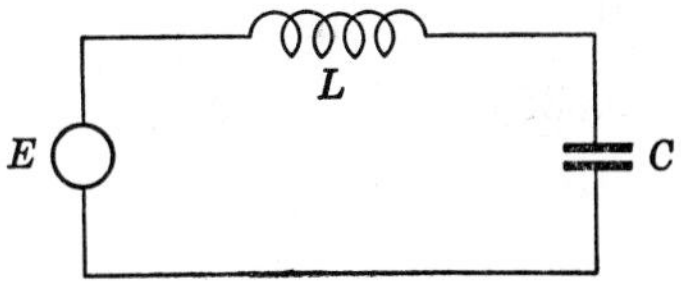

$$(10.32) \qquad L\frac{dI}{dt} + \Gamma Q = E(t).$$

FIG. 10.31.

One approaches this differential equation from the correct point of view when he assumes that he knows nothing whatever about currents and charges in the harmonic oscillator and forces the differential equation to furnish all information. For our first problem, let us suppose that the impressed voltage $E(t)$ is identically 0 when $t > t_0$. Since $I'(t) = Q''(t)$, the equation (10.32) becomes in this case

$$(10.33) \qquad Q''(t) + \frac{\Gamma}{L} Q(t) = 0,$$

when $t > t_0$. From this equation, it follows, as we have seen many

* Even periodicity of $f(t)$ is not required when one is interested in obtaining a solution valid only for a given finite time interval. The use of harmonics covers "almost periodic" as well as periodic functions $f(t)$.

times, that $Q(t)$ must be given by the formula

(10.331) $Q(t) = c_1 \cos a(t - t_0) + c_2 \sin a(t - t_0)$

where c_1 and c_2 are constants and $a = \sqrt{\Gamma/L}$. Setting $t = t_0$ shows that c_1 must be $Q(t_0)$, the charge at time t_0. Differentiating (10.331) and setting $t = t_0$ in the result give $I(t_0) = ac_2$. Thus (10.33) implies that

(10.332) $Q(t) = Q(t_0) \cos a(t - t_0) + \dfrac{I(t_0)}{a} \sin a(t - t_0)$

and hence also, as differentiation shows,

(10.333) $I(t) = -aQ(t_0) \sin a(t - t_0) + I(t_0) \cos a(t - t_0).$

Thus the differential equation (10.33) shows, in a very simple way, that the charge on the capacitor and the current in the harmonic oscillator will vary as time passes unless the charge $Q(t)$ at time t_0 and the current $I(t)$ at time t_0 are both 0. This fact alone is of interest since we are pretending that we know nothing about the harmonic oscillator and are trying to learn something. The terms in the right members of the formulas for $Q(t)$ and $I(t)$ may be combined in the usual way. Letting Z_0 be defined by

(10.334) $Z_0 = \sqrt{[aQ(t_0)]^2 + [I(t_0)]^2}$

and, assuming $Z_0 \neq 0$, letting ϕ be the angle such that $-\pi < \phi \leqq \pi$ and

(10.335) $\cos \phi = \dfrac{I(t_0)}{Z_0}, \qquad \sin \phi = \dfrac{aQ(t_0)}{Z_0},$

we obtain

(10.336) $Q(t) = \dfrac{Z_0}{a} \sin [a(t - t_0) + \phi]$

(10.337) $I(t) = Z_0 \cos [a(t - t_0) + \phi].$

Thus both the charge on the capacitor and the current in the harmonic oscillator are simple harmonic functions of t. The amplitudes Z_0/a and Z_0 depend both upon the circuit constants L and Γ and upon the charge and current at time t_0. The frequency ν_0 of the oscillations is given by the formula

(10.338) $\nu_0 = \dfrac{a}{2\pi} = \dfrac{1}{2\pi} \sqrt{\dfrac{\Gamma}{L}} = \dfrac{1}{2\pi} \sqrt{\dfrac{1}{LC}}.$

This frequency, which is called the *natural frequency* of the harmonic oscillator, depends only on the circuit constants L and Γ, being independent of the charge and current. It is apparent from this formula that high-frequency oscillations occur when the elastance is large (that is, when the capacitor and capacitance are small) and the inductance is small (that is, when there are relatively few turns in the coil).

We consider now the equation (10.32) for the case in which $E(t)$ is not necessarily 0, the problem being that of finding the solution of (10.32) for which $Q(t_0)$ and $I(t_0)$ have prescribed values. The problem can be solved by methods of Chapter 6. However, we go rabbit hunting with a cannon by using the method of inverse operators described in Chapter 8. The object is of course to illustrate methods used when problems are more difficult. Let (10.32) be written in the form

$$(10.34) \qquad L\frac{dI}{dt} + \Gamma\left[Q(t_0) + \int_{t_0}^{t} I(s)ds\right] = E(t).$$

Let D and D^{-1} be operators with independent variable t so that

$$DI = \frac{dI}{dt}, \qquad D^{-1}I = \int_{t_0}^{t} I(s)ds.$$

Then (10.34) becomes

$$(10.341) \qquad (LD + \Gamma D^{-1})I = E - \Gamma Q(t_0).$$

Since

$$D^{-1}DI = \int_{t_0}^{t} I'(s)ds = I(t) - I(t_0),$$

application of the operator D^{-1} to the members of (10.341) gives

$$(10.342) \qquad (L + \Gamma D^{-2})I = D^{-1}[E - \Gamma Q(t_0)] + LI(t_0).$$

The next step is to solve this equation for I exactly as one would if D were a number. Multiplying by D^2 eliminates reciprocals, and then dividing by $LD^2 + \Gamma$ gives

$$(10.343) \qquad I = \frac{D}{LD^2 + \Gamma}[E - \Gamma Q(t_0)] + \frac{LD^2}{LD^2 + \Gamma}I(t_0).$$

Setting $a = \sqrt{\Gamma/L}$, we find that

$$\frac{D}{LD^2 + \Gamma} = \frac{1}{L}\frac{D}{D^2 + a^2} = \frac{1}{2L}\left(\frac{1}{D + ia} + \frac{1}{D + ia}\right)$$

and

$$\frac{LD^2}{LD^2 + \Gamma} = \frac{D^2}{D^2 + a^2} = 1 + \frac{a}{2i}\left(\frac{1}{D + ia} - \frac{1}{D - ia}\right);$$

this gives the partial-fraction expansions of the quotients in the right-hand member of (10.343), and accordingly

$$(10.344) \quad I = \frac{1}{2L} \left(\frac{1}{D + ia} + \frac{1}{D - ia} \right) [E - \Gamma Q(t_0)]$$
$$+ \left[1 - \frac{a}{2i} \left(\frac{1}{D + ai} - \frac{1}{D + ai} \right) \right] I(t_0).$$

The symbol D is now to be interpreted as an operator. There is nothing ambiguous about the right-hand member since (Section 8.9) $(D - m)^{-1}f$ is always to be evaluated by use of the formula

$$\frac{1}{D - m} f = e^{mt} \int_{t_0}^{t} e^{-ms} f(s) ds = \int_{t_0}^{t} e^{m(t-s)} f(s) ds$$

when m is a constant. Using this formula and the Euler formulas, we can put (10.344) in the form

$$(10.345) \quad I(t) = \frac{1}{L} \int_{t_0}^{t} E(s) \cos a(t - s) ds$$
$$- aQ(t_0) \sin a(t - t_0) + I(t_0) \cos a(t - t_0).$$

This expresses the current $I(t)$ at time $t > t_0$ as the sum of three terms: one due to action of the impressed force over the time interval $t_0 \leqq s \leqq t$; one due to the charge $Q(t)$ at time t_0; and one due to the current $I(t)$ at time t_0. If $E(s) = 0$ when $t_0 \leqq s \leqq t$, the formula is of course in agreement with (10.333).

Problem 10.35

Show that the solution $I(t)$ of the equation

$$(10.351) \qquad\qquad L \frac{dI}{dt} + \Gamma Q = E_0 \sin (\omega t + \alpha),$$

for which

$$(10.352) \qquad\qquad Q(t_0) = I(t_0) = 0,$$

can, when $L > 0$, $\Gamma > 0$, $E_0 \geqq 0$, $\omega \geqq 0$, and $a = \sqrt{\Gamma/L} \neq \omega$, be written in the form

$$(10.353) \quad I(t) = \frac{E_0 \omega}{\Gamma - \omega^2 L} \cos (\omega t + \alpha) + \frac{a E_0}{\Gamma - \omega^2 L} \sin (\omega t_0 + \alpha) \sin a(t - t_0)$$
$$- \frac{E_0 \omega}{\Gamma - \omega^2 L} \cos (\omega t_0 + \alpha) \cos a(t - t_0).$$

Assuming all constants except ω to be fixed, discuss the amplitudes and phases in the case when $\omega = 0$; in the *low-frequency* case when ω is near 0; in the *high-frequency* case when ω is very great; and in the two cases of *near resonance* when ω is a little less and a little greater than $\sqrt{\Gamma/L}$.

Problem 10.36

Show that in case of resonance (the frequency of the impressed electromotive force being the same as the natural frequency of the harmonic oscillator, that is, $\omega = a = \sqrt{\Gamma/L}$), the function $I(t)$ satisfying (10.351) and (10.352) is given by the formula

$$(10.361) \quad I(t) = \frac{E_0}{2L} (t - t_0) \sin (at + \alpha) - \frac{E_0}{2aL} \cos (at + \alpha)$$

$$+ \frac{E_0}{2aL} \cos (at_0 + \alpha) \cos a(t - t_0).$$

Remark: The last two terms represent periodic currents; the first represents a sinusoidal current, in phase with the impressed electromotive force, whose oscillations are distorted by the factor $t - t_0$ which increases steadily as t increases. Of course, this increase in violence of the oscillations can continue only until "something happens." On the one hand the resistance can no longer be neglected when the current is very great, and resistance may keep the oscillations within safe bounds. On the other hand the electrical equipment may blow up.

Problem 10.37

Suppose an electromotive force $E(t)$ is applied to the harmonic oscillator (by a battery and suitable switching apparatus) in such a way that $E(t)$ is alternately V and $-V$ over alternate time intervals of length h. Let V and h be positive constants, and let the time origin be so chosen that $E(t) = -V$ when $-h < t < 0$ and $E(t) = V$ when $0 < t < h$. Using the method of Section 8.6 and an interval of length $2h$, show that the Fourier coefficients E_0, E_{-1}, E_1, $\cdots$ of $E(t)$ have the following values: $E_n = 0$ when n is even and $E_n = iV/n\pi$ when n is odd. Show by use of Theorem 8.63 that the odd harmonics of a solution of the equation

$$(10.371) \qquad L \frac{d^2Q}{dt^2} + \Gamma Q = E(t)$$

are solutions of the equations

$$(10.372) \qquad L \frac{d^2Q}{dt^2} + \Gamma Q = - \frac{iV}{n\pi} e^{in(\pi/h)t}$$

in which $n = \pm 1, \pm 3, \pm 5, \cdots$. Using Theorem 8.63, show that

$$Q(t) = \sum_{n=0}^{\infty} \frac{2h^2V \sin [(2n + 1)\pi/h]t}{(2n + 1)\pi[h^2\Gamma - (2n + 1)^2\pi^2L]}$$

is a particular solution of (10.392) provided that none of the denominators vanishes. The series can be differential termwise to give

$$I(t) = \sum_{n=0}^{\infty} \frac{2hV}{h^2\Gamma - (2n + 1)^2\pi^2L} \cos \frac{(2n + 1)\pi}{h} t.$$

Show that, when h and all the physical constants are fixed, the harmonics of the current in the oscillator for which the amplitude is greatest are those for which n has odd integer values nearest to $\frac{1}{2} + h \nu_0/\sqrt{2\pi}$, ν_0 being the natural frequency of the oscillator.

10.4. The Damped Harmonic Oscillator.—In this section we consider the harmonic oscillator for the case in which a resistor with resistance $R > 0$ has been added to the circuit. This is of course the circuit of Fig. 10.11 to which equations (10.142), (10.15), and (10.16) apply. For the case of the pure-harmonic impressed electromotive force

$$(10.41) \qquad E(t) = E_0 \sin (\omega t + \alpha)$$

in which E_0 and ω are positive constants, an application of Kirchhoff's second law gives the equation

$$(10.42) \qquad LDI + RI + \Gamma Q = E_0 \sin (\omega t + \alpha)$$

which governs the circuit. This equation may be written in the forms

$$(10.421) \qquad (LD^2 + RD + \Gamma)Q = E_0 \sin (\omega t + \alpha)$$

and (as differentiation shows)

$$(10.422) \qquad (LD^2 + RD + \Gamma)I = \omega E_0 \cos (\omega t + \alpha).$$

One may solve (10.421) for $Q(t)$ and differentiate to obtain $I(t)$, or one may solve (10.422) for $I(t)$, using complex exponentials in the process. However, when one uses (10.421) or (10.422), there is a little troublesome detail involved in writing the current $I(t)$ in such a way as to display in simple terms the phase relation between $I(t)$ and $E(t)$. Largely for this reason, it is best to work with (10.42) itself.

Since L, R, and D are positive, the solutions of the homogeneous equations are all transients (see Section 8.4). Our first step is to neglect transients and to find the steady-state solution. For this purpose, we may suppose that $Q(t_0) = 0$ and write (10.42) in the form

$$(10.43) \qquad (LD + R + \Gamma D^{-1})I = E_0 \sin (\omega t + \alpha).$$

The steady-state solution of (10.43) is obtained by taking the *imaginary* part of the steady-state solution $I(t)$ of the equation

$$(10.431) \qquad (LD + R + \Gamma D^{-1})I = E_0 e^{i(\omega t + \alpha)}.$$

Let Z denote the operator in (10.431) so that

$$Z = LD + R + \Gamma D^{-1}.$$

The impedance of the equation is then*

---

* We have now reached a point where we may use the term *impedance* as it is used in the theory of circuits. The term $i\omega L$ is the impedance (sometimes called complex impedance) of the inductor, R is the impedance of the resistor, and $\Gamma/i\omega$ is

(10.432) $$Z(i\omega) = i\omega L + R + \frac{\Gamma}{i\omega}.$$

The absolute value of the impedance is

(10.433) $$| Z(i\omega) | = \sqrt{R^2 + \left(\omega L - \frac{\Gamma}{\omega}\right)^2},$$

and the phase angle ϕ is determined by the formulas

(10.434) $$\cos \phi = \frac{R}{| Z(i\omega) |}, \quad \sin \phi = \frac{\omega L - \Gamma/\omega}{| Z(i\omega) |}.$$

The steady-state solution of (10.431) is

$$I = \frac{E_0}{| Z(i\omega) |} e^{i(\omega t + \alpha - \phi)},$$

and the steady-state solution of (10.43) is

(10.44) $$I = \frac{E_0}{\sqrt{R^2 + (\omega L - \Gamma/\omega)^2}} \sin (\omega t + \alpha - \phi).$$

One can easily deduce important fundamental ideas of circuit theory by study of (10.44). Suppose that E_0, and R are fixed positive constants; we investigate the manner in which the amplitude and phase of the current I depend on the other circuit parameters L, Γ, and ω. Since the amplitude is greatest when the denominator in (10.44) is least, it is obvious that the amplitude has its greatest value E_0/R when $\omega L - \Gamma/\omega = 0$, that is, when $\omega = \sqrt{\Gamma/L}$; in this case the frequency of the impressed force is the same as the natural frequency of the (imaginary) oscillator obtained by removing the resistance, and the oscillator is said to be in *resonance*. When the oscillator is in resonance, (10.434) shows that $\phi = 0$, that is, the electromotive force and current are in phase. If $\omega < \sqrt{\Gamma/L}$, then the current is less

---

the impedance of the capacitor. We see that

$$\frac{\Gamma}{i\omega} = -\frac{i\Gamma}{\omega} = -\frac{i}{\omega C}$$

where C is the capacitance of the capacitor (or condenser). The sum $Z(i\omega)$ of the three impedances is the *impedance of the circuit*. The real part of the impedance is the resistance R of the circuit. The imaginary part of the impedance (that is, the coefficient of i) $\omega L - \Gamma/\omega$ is called the *reactance* of the circuit. The absolute value of the impedance is the ratio of the amplitudes of the electromotive force and current, and the phase angle of the impedance gives the phase difference between the electromotive force and current. This shows why electrical engineers are interested in impedance.

than the resonant current, and (10.434) shows that $-\pi/2 < \phi < 0$ and hence that the current *lags* the force. If $\omega > \sqrt{\Gamma/L}$, then again the current is less than the resonant current but now (10.434) shows that $0 < \phi < \pi/2$ and hence that the current *leads* the force.

It often happens that a circuit contains known fixed resistance R and inductance L which cannot be changed without destroying the usefulness of the circuit, and that a force $E_0 \sin \omega t$ (in which E_0 and ω are known fixed positive constants) is applied. If this circuit contains no capacitor, then we may set $\Gamma = 0$ in (10.44) to see that the current I has amplitude $E_0/\sqrt{R^2 + \omega^2 L^2}$; this amplitude is less than the resonant amplitude E_0/R. Suppose we now put into the circuit a *variable capacitor* (condenser), that is, one whose capacitance C and elastance Γ can be varied by turning a knob. By looking at (10.44) we see that, as we start Γ at 0 and increase it, the amplitude of I starts at $E_0/\sqrt{R^2 + \omega^2 L^2}$ and increases steadily to the maximum resonant amplitude E_0/R as Γ increases to the value for which $\omega = \sqrt{\Gamma/L}$ and the oscillator is in resonance. When Γ is increased beyond the value giving resonance, the current steadily decreases and is near 0 when Γ is large. If R is very small in comparison to ωL, the resonant amplitude E_0/R obtained by insertion of a properly adjusted capacitor is much greater than the original amplitude $E_0/\sqrt{R^2 + \omega^2 L^2}$. In many practical circuits, the factor involved is enormous.

The process of adjusting a capacitor to produce resonance is known as a process *tuning the circuit.* * When resonance is attained, the circuit is said to be *balanced;* the point being that the capacitor "balances" the inductor, the circuit behaving as though neither were present. It is characteristic of balanced circuits that the currents are in phase with the electromotive forces producing them.

In many problems in electric circuits the steady-state solutions of the equations are the only solutions required, the transients being of no interest. In other problems, notably those involving telephone, telegraph, and cable circuits, the transient currents must be computed. Accordingly, it is worth while to look at a standard method of finding the current $I(t)$ determined, when $t \geq t_0$, by the equation

$$(10.45) \qquad LDI + RI + \Gamma Q = E(t)$$

and the two conditions

$$(10.451) \qquad Q(t_0) = q_0, \qquad I(t_0) = i_0.$$

---

* This is the process involved in turning the knob of a radio to "tune in" KDKA; one adjusts the capacitor to produce resonance at the broadcast frequency of the broadcasting station.

Since

$$D^{-1}I = \int_{t_0}^t Q(s)ds = Q(t) - Q(t_0) = Q(t) - q_0,$$

(10.45) may be written in the form

(10.452) $(LD + R + \Gamma D^{-1})I = E - \Gamma q_0.$

Moreover, since

$$D^{-1}DI = \int_{t_0}^t I'(s)ds = I(t) - I(t_0) = I(t) - i_0,$$

we can apply the operator D^{-1} to the members of (10.452) to obtain

(10.453) $(L + RD^{-1} + \Gamma D^{-2})I = D^{-1}(E - \Gamma q_0) + Li_0.$

This equation is analogous to (10.342), and the same procedure is applied. Treating D momentarily as a number, we multiply by D^2 and divide by the coefficient of I to obtain

(10.454) $I = \dfrac{D}{LD^2 + RD + \Gamma}(E - \Gamma q_0) + \dfrac{LD^2}{LD^2 + RD + \Gamma}\,i_0.$

This equation is analogous to (10.343). The next step is to obtain the partial-fraction expansions of the operators; and the solution is obtained by use of (10.345). The formula for the solution is not so simple as the formula for the steady-state current; but the essential point is that one can get the formula by straightforward methods when he must have it.

Problem 10.46

Let $E(t) = E_0 \sin \omega t$, and discuss completely the circuit obtained from that in Fig. 10.11 by eliminating (i) the capacitor; (ii) the inductor; (iii) both the capacitor and the inductor.

10.5. The Operational Method.—The standard *operational method* of computing the precise currents in a network may be illustrated by solving the problem for the network of Fig. 10.24. Let the charges on the three capacitors at time t_0 be, respectively, q_1, q_2, and q_3; and let the two currents at time t_0 be, respectively, i_1 and i_2. The electromotive forces $E_1(t)$ and $E_2(t)$ are supposed to be given functions which are bounded and have at most a finite set of discontinuities in some interval $t_0 \leq t \leq t_1$. The values of $E_1(t)$ and $E_2(t)$ when $t < t_0$ and when $t > t_1$ do not enter into the determination of $I_1(t)$ and $I_2(t)$ when $t_0 \leq t \leq t_1$; this is obvious from both physical and mathematical considerations. We use inverse operators (Chapter 8). The equations (10.251) and (10.252) governing the circuit take the form

$$[L_1 D + R_1 + (\Gamma_1 + \Gamma_3)D^{-1}]I_1 - \Gamma_3 I_2 = E_1 - \Gamma_1 q_1 - \Gamma_3 q_3.$$
$$[L_2 D + R_2 + (\Gamma_2 + \Gamma_3)D^{-1}]I_2 - \Gamma_3 I_1 = E_2 - \Gamma_2 q_2 + \Gamma_3 q_3.$$

Since, when $k = 1, 2$,

$$D^{-1}DI_k = \int_{t_0}^{t} I_k'(s)ds = I_k(t) - I_k(t_0) = I_k - i_k,$$

application of the operator D^{-1} to these equations gives

$$[L_1 + R_1D^{-1} + (\Gamma_1 + \Gamma_3)D^{-2}]I_1 - \Gamma_3D^{-1}I_2$$
$$= D^{-1}(E_1 - \Gamma_1q_1 - \Gamma_3q_3) + L_1i_1$$
$$[L_2 + R_2D^{-1} + (\Gamma_2 + \Gamma_3)D^{-2}]I_2 - \Gamma_3D^{-1}I_1$$
$$= D^{-1}(E_2 - \Gamma_2q_2 + \Gamma_3q_3) + L_2i_2.$$

The next step is to pretend that D is a number and to solve for I_1 and I_2; justification of the process must depend upon Chapter 8. Multiplying the equations by D^2 gives

$$Z_1I_1 - \Gamma_3DI_2 = D(E_1 - \Gamma_1q_1 - \Gamma_3q_3) + D^2L_1i_1$$
$$-\Gamma_3DI_1 + Z_2I_2 = D(E_2 - \Gamma_2q_2 + \Gamma_3q_3) + D^2L_2i_2$$

where Z_1 and Z_2 are operators defined by

$$Z_k = L_kD^2 + R_kD + (\Gamma_k + \Gamma_3) \qquad k = 1, 2.$$

Solving for I_1 gives

$$(10.51) \quad I_1(t) = \frac{Z_2D}{Z_1Z_2 - \Gamma_3^2D^2} E_1 + \frac{\Gamma_3D^2}{Z_1Z_2 - \Gamma_3^2D} E_2 + \cdots$$

where the dots indicate quotients of operators, operating on constants involving q_1, q_2, q_3, i_1, and i_2. The formula for I_2 is similar. When the quotients of operators in (10.51) are replaced by their partial-fraction expansions, we have the Heaviside expansion (Chapter 8) of $I_1(t)$. The process of obtaining this expansion requires determination of the roots of the characteristic equation $Z_1(m)Z_2(m) - \Gamma_3^2m^2 = 0$ which is of the fourth degree in m. These roots can be found in a satisfactory way only when the circuit constants have specific numerical values; this is unfortunate, since it makes it impossible to obtain formulas which show how the currents depend upon the circuit constants and hence makes it difficult to design circuits in which prescribed electromotive forces produce desired currents.

When the circuit constants have been assigned numerical values and the algebraic manipulations are completed, computation of $I_1(t)$ is especially simple when $E_1(t)$ and $E_2(t)$ are constants and is always manageable when $E_1(t)$ and $E_2(t)$ are represented (or approximated) by linear combinations of functions of the form $e^{i\omega t}$.

Problem 10.52

Would the labor of solving the problem of this section be essentially reduced if $E_2(t)$ were always 0, that is, if the element E_2 were removed from the network of Fig. 10.24 and the right side replaced by an unbroken line?

10.6. Steady-state Currents.—The problem of computing the steady-state currents in networks is very much simpler than the problem of computing the precise currents depending upon the state of the circuit at a given time as well as upon the electromotive force or forces at later times. When all solutions of the homogeneous equations are transients, one may simplify the statements and solutions of steady-state problems by assuming that all currents and charges are 0 at an initial time which may be taken to be $t = 0$. In this case the charge $Q(t)$ in a capacitor at time t is given by the formula

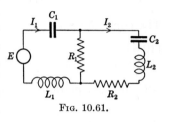

FIG. 10.61.

$$Q(t) = \int_0^t I(s)ds = D^{-1}I$$

where I is the current in the branch containing the capacitor.

Consider the circuit of Fig. 10.61; it represents a damped harmonic oscillator with an "$L_2 - R_2 - C_2$ wave trap" appended at the right side. Let $E(t)$ be a sinusoidal electromotive force given by

(10.62) $$E(t) = E_0 \sin (\omega t + \alpha).$$

Applying the Kirchhoff laws gives, for the equations governing the currents,

(10.631) $$(L_1 D + R_1 + \Gamma_1 D^{-1})I_1 - R_1 I_2 = E_0 \sin (\omega t + \alpha)$$
(10.632) $$-R_1 I_1 + (L_2 D + R_1 + R_2 + \Gamma_2 D^{-1})I_2 = 0.$$

The steady-state solutions of these equations are obtained by taking the imaginary parts of the steady-state solutions of the equations

(10.633) $$(L_1 D + R_1 + \Gamma_1 D^{-1})I_1 - R_1 I_2 = E_0 e^{i(\omega t + \alpha)}$$
(10.634) $$-R_1 I_1 + (L_2 D + R_1 + R_2 + \Gamma_2 D^{-1})I_2 = 0.$$

The next step is to replace D by $i\omega$ and simply solve the equations to get the steady-state currents.* Replacing D by $i\omega$ gives

(10.635) $$\left[R_1 + i\left(\omega L_1 - \frac{\Gamma_1}{\omega} \right) \right] I_1 - R_1 I_2 = E_0 e^{i(\omega t + \alpha)}$$

(10.636) $$-R_1 I_1 + \left[R_1 + R_2 + i\left(\omega L_2 - \frac{\Gamma_2}{\omega} \right) \right] I_2 = 0.$$

---

* That this procedure actually gives the steady-state currents is not hard to see. Since $D^{-1}DI_1 = I_1$ and $D^{-1}DI_2 = I_2$, one can apply D^{-1} to equations (10.633) and (10.634) and (as in Chapter 8) work with the equations as though D were a number until one is ready to replace D by $i\omega$. The same result is obtained by replacing D by $i\omega$ at the start.

A glance at these equations shows that the inductances and elastances enter only in combinations $\omega L_1 - \Gamma_1/\omega$ and $\omega L_2 - \Gamma_2/\omega$. These combinations are reactances, and we denote them by Y_1 and Y_2 so that

$$(10.637) \qquad Y_k = \omega L_k - \frac{\Gamma_k}{\omega} \qquad\qquad k = 1, 2.$$

The equations for I_1 and I_2 can now be written

$$(10.638) \qquad (R_1 + iY_1)I_1 - R_1I_2 = E_0 e^{i(\omega t + \alpha)}$$
$$(10.639) \qquad -R_1I_1 + (R_1 + R_2 + iY_2)I_2 = 0.$$

Solving the equations for I_1 and I_2 gives

$$(10.641) \qquad I_1 = \frac{(R_1 + R_2 + iY_2)E_0}{(R_1 + iY_1)(R_1 + R_2 + iY_2) - R_1^2}\, e^{i(\omega t + \alpha)}$$

and

$$(10.642) \qquad I_2 = \frac{R_1 E_0}{(R_1 + iY_1)(R_1 + R_2 + iY_2) - R_1^2}\, e^{i(\omega t + \alpha)};$$

and we may obtain also

$$(10.643) \qquad I_2 = \frac{R_1}{R_1 + R_2 + iY_2}\, I_1.$$

The quotient in the right-hand member of (10.641) is a complex number which may be written in the form $\rho_1 e^{i\phi_1}$ where $\rho_1 > 0$ and $-\pi < \phi_1 \leqq \pi$; hence,

$$I_1(t) = \rho_1 e^{i(\omega t + \alpha - \phi_1)}$$

and the steady-state current $I_1(t)$ in the circuit in Fig. 10.61 is

$$(10.644) \qquad I_1(t) = \rho_1 \sin (\omega t + \alpha - \phi_1).$$

The amplitude of $I_1(t)$ is ρ_1, and the phase difference between the current $I_1(t)$ and the electromotive force $\sin (\omega t + \alpha)$ is ϕ_1. In the same way, (10.642) determines $I_2(t)$; and (10.643) determines a simple relation between $I_2(t)$ and $I_1(t)$.

It is easy to formulate rules, very similar to the laws of Kirchhoff, for writing down at once the equations (10.638) and (10.639) without writing the differential equations. By use of these rules, solution of steady-state problems becomes a matter of pure algebra involving no differential equations or derivatives or integrals. The algebra is of the most elementary type, involving only solving systems of linear algebraic equations with constant coefficients and finding the absolute value and *angle* of a quotient of two complex numbers.* In partic-

---

* Some companies engaged in designing electric circuits have machines for performing the two operations.

ular, it is not necessary to find the roots of characteristic equations. It is of course to the credit rather than to the discredit of differential equations that they can be used to provide simple rules for computing steady-state sinusoidal currents in a network.

One of the fundamental results of the theory is the fact that *each steady-state current in a network, containing a single sinusoidal electromotive force, must have the same frequency as the electromotive force* provided that one does not make the assumption (which is always false) that some circuit in the network involves no resistance.

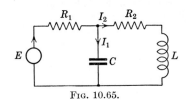

FIG. 10.65.

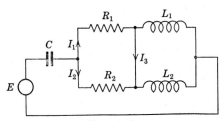

FIG. 10.66.

If a network contains impressed electromotive forces having different frequencies, the problem of finding the steady-state currents may (because the equations are linear) be simplified by obtaining the harmonics of the currents one at a time. The harmonic due to one of the electromotive forces is obtained from the system of equations in which all other electromotive forces are replaced by 0.

Problem 10.651

Find the steady-state currents $I_1(t)$ and $I_2(t)$ in the network of Fig. 10.65 when $E(t) = E_0 \sin \omega t$. *Ans. (partial):* $I_1(t)$ and $I_2(t)$ are the imaginary parts of

$$J_1(t) = \frac{R_2 + iL\omega}{R_1R_2 + \Gamma L + i[R_1L\omega - (R_1 + R_2)\Gamma/\omega]} E_0 e^{i\omega t}$$

$$J_2(t) = \frac{-i\Gamma/\omega}{R_1R_2 + \Gamma L + i[R_1L\omega - (R_1 + R_2)\Gamma/\omega]} E_0 e^{i\omega t}.$$

Show that an assumption that the terms involving R_1 and R_2 are negligible leads to the formulas

$$I_1(t) = \frac{\omega E_0}{\Gamma} \sin\left(\omega t + \frac{\pi}{2}\right), \qquad I_2(t) = \frac{E_0}{\omega L} \sin\left(\omega t - \frac{\pi}{2}\right).$$

Show that, if the elastance Γ is 0 (that is, if the capacitor is removed from the network, the branch being left intact), then

$$I_1(t) = \frac{E_0}{R_1} \sin \omega t, \qquad I_2(t) = 0.$$

What happens if $L = R_2 = 0$? Assuming that E_0, ω, R_1, R_2, and L are fixed positive constants, find the elastance Γ of the capacitor C which makes the amplitude of $I_2(t)$ a maximum. *Ans.* $\Gamma = (R_2^2 + L^2\omega^2)/L$.

Problem 10.661

Find the steady-state currents in the six branches of the network in Fig. 10.66 when $E = E_0 \sin \omega t$. Find the conditions, if any, under which the network is "balanced," that is, under which the currents are all in phase with the electromotive force. Formulate and answer a good question about $I_3(t)$. *Ans.* (partial): Kirchhoff's laws give the equations

$$R_1 I_1 - R_2 I_2 = 0$$
$$L_1 D(I_1 - I_3) - L_2 D(I_2 + I_3) = 0$$
$$L_1 D(I_1 - I_3) + R_1 I_1 + \Gamma D^{-1}(I_1 + I_2) = E_0 \sin \omega t$$

which govern the circuit when the initial charge on the capacitor is 0. The next step is to replace $\sin \omega t$ by $e^{i\omega t}$ and D by $i\omega$. The first two equations alone give

$$I_2 = \frac{R_1}{R_2} I_1, \qquad I_1 + I_2 = \frac{R_1 + R_2}{R_2} I_1, \qquad I_3 = \frac{L_1 R_2 - L_2 R_1}{R_2(L_1 + L_2)} I_1$$

$$I_1 - I_3 = \frac{L_2(R_1 + R_2)}{R_2(L_1 + L_2)} I_1, \qquad I_2 + I_3 = \frac{L_1(R_1 + R_2)}{R_2(L_1 + L_2)} I_1;$$

and these equations together with the third show that $I_1(t)$ is the imaginary part of

$$I_1 = \frac{R_2(L_1 + L_2)E_0}{R_1 R_2(L_1 + L_2) + i[\omega L_1 L_2(R_1 + R_2) - \omega^{-1}\Gamma(L_1 + L_2)(R_1 + R_2)]} e^{i\omega t}.$$

The currents all have the same phase, and they are in phase with the electromotive force if and only if $(L_1 + L_2)\Gamma = \omega^2 L_1 L_2$.

Problem 10.662

Show that if the network of Problem 10.661 is balanced (in the sense that all currents are in phase with the electromotive force), then the steady-state currents $I_1(t)$ and $I_2(t)$ [and hence also the current $I_1(t) + I_2(t)$ through the branch containing the electromotive force] are exactly what they would be if the capacitor and inductors were removed from the circuit.

Problem 10.67

Draw the network obtained from Fig. 10.66, by adding a resistance to the branch containing E and interchanging the elements L_1 and R_2. Find the steady-state currents when $E(t) = E_0 \sin \omega t$.

Problem 10.68

Find the steady-state currents in the network of Fig. 10.24 when

$$E_1(t) = A \sin \omega t, \qquad E_2(t) = B \sin \omega t.$$

CHAPTER 11

NEWTON'S EQUATION my″ = f(y) AND THE PENDULUM PROBLEM

11.1. The Equation my″ = f(y).—The differential equation

$$(11.11) \qquad m\frac{d^2y}{dx^2} = f(y),$$

in which m is a positive constant, arises in various ways. If, for example, x represents time measured in seconds and y represents a displacement of a particle of mass m from an origin on a line, and if the particle moves on the line subject to a force f which depends only on the position so that $f = f(y)$, then Newton's fundamental law

$$\text{Mass} \times \text{acceleration} = \text{force}$$

takes the form (11.11) since $y'(x)$ is the velocity $v(x)$ and $y''(x)$ is the acceleration. It is interesting to observe that each equation of the form (11.11) can be given this mechanical interpretation even though the equation may have arisen in connection with a totally different problem.

The equation (11.11) is of the second order and is nonlinear except in the important case in which $f(y) = ky + a$ where k and a are constants. Attempts to solve (11.11) by assuming a series representation of $y(x)$ are usually unsatisfactory because of difficulties with $f(y(x))$. The problem of solving (11.11) is reduced quickly to the problem of solving a first-order equation by the following special trick. Assuming that $f(y)$ is continuous and that $y(x)$ is a solution of (11.11) for which $y_0 = y(x_0)$ and $v_0 = y'(x_0)$ we can multiply (11.11) by $y'(x)$ to obtain

$$m\frac{dy}{dx}\frac{d^2y}{dx^2} = f(y)\frac{dy}{dx}$$

or

$$(11.12) \qquad \frac{m}{2}\frac{d}{dx}\left(\frac{dy}{dx}\right)^2 = \frac{d}{dx}P(y)$$

where $P(y)$ is a function whose derivative is $f(y)$, say

$$(11.13) \qquad P(y) = \int_{y_0}^{y} f(\alpha)d\alpha.$$

239

From (11.12) we obtain

(11.14) $$\frac{m}{2}\left(\frac{dy}{dx}\right)^2 = \frac{m}{2}v_0^2 + P(y).$$

This equation has a simple mechanical interpretation. The left-hand member is $\frac{1}{2}mv^2$, the kinetic energy of the particle at time x; $\frac{1}{2}mv_0^2$ is the kinetic energy at time x_0; and $P(y)$ is the work done by the force f as the particle moves from y_0 to y. The term $P(y)$ may otherwise be described as the difference of the potential energies of the particle at the points y and y_0; and if the potential energy at y_0 is defined to be 0, then $P(y)$ is the potential energy at y. Thus (11.14) is a form of the law of conservation of energy.

From (11.14) we obtain

(11.15) $$\frac{dy}{dx} = \pm\sqrt{v_0^2 + \frac{2P(y)}{m}}$$

The ambiguity in sign in (11.15) is painful; it is a sad fact that (11.14) simply does not determine the sign of dy/dx. Since dy/dx must be continuous, dy/dx must have the same sign over each interval of values of x for which $v_0^2 + 2P(y)/m > 0$; but in many problems dy/dx *must* change sign each time $v_0^2 + 2P(y)/m = 0$, and accordingly (11.15) holds with the positive sign over some intervals and with the negative sign over the remaining intervals. If x_0 is a point of an interval I over which $v_0^2 + 2P(y)/m$ is positive, we can separate the variables in (11.15) to obtain

$$dx = \pm \frac{1}{\sqrt{v_0^2 + 2P(y)/m}}\,dy$$

and hence

(11.16) $$x = x_0 \pm \int_{y_0}^{y} \frac{1}{\sqrt{v_0^2 + 2P(\beta)/m}}\,d\beta$$

when x lies in I. Though (11.16) may in a sense be regarded as a solution of (11.11), it is often true that difficulties begin only when one has reached (11.16). Determination of the sign in (11.16) must be made for each interval I over which the denominator of the integrand is positive. One who expects the integral in (11.16) to be an elementary function of y is usually doomed to disappointment. Moreover even when the integral in (11.16) has been evaluated by some method or other, one obtains x as a function of y and it is necessary to get the inverse function to obtain the function $y(x)$.

Problems

Use the method (but not the formulas) of this section to solve the following equations in which a is a positive constant:

(11.17) $\quad \dfrac{d^2y}{dx^2} = a^2y$ $\qquad\qquad\qquad$ *Ans.*: $y = c_1e^{at} + c_2e^{-at}$

(11.18) $\quad \dfrac{d^2y}{dx^2} = -a^2y$ $\qquad\qquad\quad$ *Ans.*: $y = c_1 \sin(at + c_2)$

(11.19) $\quad \dfrac{d^2y}{dx^2} = 0$ $\qquad\qquad\qquad\quad$ *Ans.*: $y = c_1t + c_2$

These equations have been previously solved by simpler methods.

Problem 11.191

A flexible chain 6 feet long is placed at rest with 5 feet stretched out on a slick horizontal table and the other foot hanging over the edge of the table. Show that, insofar as friction is negligible, the chain will slide off the table in such a way that the length of the part off the table t seconds later is

$$\frac{e^{at} + e^{-at}}{2},$$

where $a = \sqrt{g/6}$, until the chain flies off the table or the bottom of the chain hits the floor.

11.2. Motion of a Pendulum.—We now consider the motion of a pendulum which swings (or rotates), in a vertical plane. All forces except gravitational forces will be disregarded, and the pendulum will be considered inelastic. Thus it may be said that we are going to find what the motion of a pendulum would be if there were no friction and if the pendulum were inelastic. Since some friction and elasticity are always present when a physical pendulum swings, our results can at best give an approximate description of the motion of a physical pendulum. Our first step is to derive a differential equation which governs the motion of the pendulum.

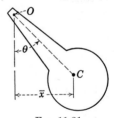

FIG. 11.21.

Let m and I denote the mass of the pendulum and its moment of inertia about the axis which passes through the point of suspension O (see Fig. 11.21) and is perpendicular to the plane of the paper. Let l (the effective length of the pendulum) denote the distance from O to the centroid (or center of gravity) C of the pendulum. Let θ, measured positive in a counterclockwise direction, be the angular displacement of the line OC from the vertical line drawn downward from 0. Under our assumptions, the point C must move on a circle with center at O, and the only force having a moment which produces angular acceleration is the gravitational force on the pendulum. This moment, being positive when it produces positive angular acceleration, is equal by definition of $\bar{x}$ (see Fig. 11.21) to $-mg\bar{x}$ and hence is equal to $-mgl \sin \theta$.

We are now in a position to use the formula

(Moment of inertia) $\times$ (angular acceleration) = moment,

which governs angular acceleration in the same way that the formula

Mass $\times$ acceleration = force

governs linear acceleration, to obtain

(11.22) $$I \frac{d^2\theta}{dt^2} = -mgl \sin \theta;$$

this is the differential equation we sought.*

11.3. Solution of the Pendulum Equation (11.22).—Our next step is to solve equation (11.22). We make a slight simplification of our work by supposing the time origin so chosen that $\theta = 0$ when $t = 0$ and that the angular velocity ω_0 at time $t = 0$ is positive. This means merely that at time $t = 0$ the pendulum is swinging toward the right with its centroid in the lowest possible position. The equation has the form (11.11), and we use the method of Section 11.1. Multiplying (11.22) by $2\theta'(t)$ we find that

$$\frac{d}{dt} \left(\frac{d\theta}{dt} \right)^2 = -\frac{2mgl}{I} \sin \theta \frac{d\theta}{dt}$$

so that

$$\left(\frac{d\theta}{dt} \right)^2 = c_1 + \frac{2mgl}{I} \cos \theta.$$

Setting $t = 0$ gives $\omega_0^2 = c_1 + 2mgl/I$ and hence

(11.301) $$\left(\frac{d\theta}{dt} \right)^2 = \omega_0^2 - \frac{2mgl}{I} (1 - \cos \theta).$$

It is convenient to use the trigonometric identity $1 - \cos \theta = 2 \sin^2 \frac{1}{2}\theta$ and to write (11.301) in the form

(11.31) $$\left(\frac{d\theta}{dt} \right)^2 = \omega_0^2 \left[1 - \frac{4mgl}{I\omega_0^2} \sin^2 \frac{1}{2} \theta \right].$$

---

* In case the pendulum consists of a small mass at the end of a light wire, it is a common trick to neglect the mass of the wire, to regard the mass as concentrated at a point C, and to use ml^2 as an approximation for I; the differential equation (11.22) then becomes

$$\frac{d^2\theta}{dt^2} = -\frac{g}{l} \sin \theta.$$

To simplify discussion and formulas, let k be the positive constant such that

$$(11.311) \qquad k^2 = \frac{4mgl}{I\omega_0^2}.$$

It will turn out that the character of the motion of the pendulum depends upon whether $k < 1$, $k = 1$, or $k > 1$. We discuss the three cases separately. Although there is some point in learning to solve problems without the assistance of physical intuition and good sense, it is very much worth while to think of the physical meanings of mathematical conditions. The condition $k < 1$ means (since $k > 0$) the same thing as the condition $k^2 < 1$ and hence also the condition

$$(2l)(mg) < \tfrac{1}{2}I\omega_0^2.$$

This says that the work required to raise the centroid from its lowest to its highest position is less than the kinetic energy of the pendulum when it is in its lowest position. Similar interpretations apply to $k = 1$ and to $k > 1$ and give a reasonably good physicist a basis for feeling that the results which we are going to obtain are sensible.

In case $k < 1$, (11.31) implies that

$$[\theta'(t)]^2 \geqq \omega_0^2(1 - k^2) > 0.$$

The hypothesis that $\theta(t)$ satisfies (11.22) implies that $\theta''(t)$ exists and hence that $\theta'(t)$ is continuous. Since $\theta'(t) = \omega_0 > 0$ when $t = 0$ and $\theta'(t)$ is never 0, it follows that $\theta'(t)$ is positive for all t. Hence,

$$(11.32) \qquad \theta'(t) = \omega_0 \sqrt{1 - k^2 \sin^2 \tfrac{1}{2}\theta} \geqq \omega_0 \sqrt{1 - k^2}.$$

This implies that the pendulum rotates repeatedly completely around the point of suspension O with variable angular velocity $\theta'(t)$ which attains its minimum value $\omega_0(1 - k^2)^{\frac{1}{2}}$ when θ is an odd multiple of π and its maximum value ω_0 when θ is an even multiple of π. Separating the variables in (11.32) and integrating give

$$(11.321) \qquad t = \frac{1}{\omega_0} \int_0^\theta \frac{1}{\sqrt{1 - k^2 \sin^2 \tfrac{1}{2}u}} \, du,$$

and changing the "dummy" variable of integration by setting $x = \tfrac{1}{2}u$ gives

$$(11.322) \qquad t = \frac{2}{\omega_0} \int_0^{\theta/2} \frac{1}{\sqrt{1 - k^2 \sin^2 x}} \, dx.$$

The time T_1 required for the angular displacement θ to increase from 0 to π is

$$(11.323) \qquad T_1 = \frac{2}{\omega_0} \int_0^{\pi/2} \frac{1}{\sqrt{1 - k^2 \sin^2 x}} \, dx.$$

Since $\sin (\pi - x) = \sin x$, it is easy to show that the integral which gives the time required for θ to increase from 0 to 2π is $2T_1$; thus $2T_1$ is the time required for a complete revolution of the pendulum.

The integrals appearing in (11.322) and (11.323) are known as *elliptic integrals of the first kind*, that in (11.322) being called *incomplete* and that in (11.323) being called *complete*. Many integral tables and other mathematical tables tabulate the complete elliptic integral

$$K = \int_0^{\pi/2} \frac{1}{\sqrt{1 - k^2 \sin^2 x}}\, dx$$

for certain values of k between 0 and 1. Tables of the incomplete elliptic integral

$$F(k, \phi) = \int_0^{\phi} \frac{1}{\sqrt{1 - k^2 \sin^2 x}}\, dx$$

can be used with (11.322) when k and ω_0 are known to find corresponding pairs of values of θ and t and hence to obtain a graph of the function $\theta(t)$. The numbers k and ϕ are called, respectively, the *modulus* and the *amplitude* of the integral.

In case $k = 1$, (11.31) becomes

(11.33) $$[\theta'(t)]^2 = \omega_0^2 \cos^2 \tfrac{1}{2}\theta.$$

In the interval I of values of t containing $t = 0$ over which $-\pi < \theta < \pi$, the function $\cos \tfrac{1}{2}\theta$ and the right-hand member of (11.33) are positive. Since $\theta'(0) = \omega_0 > 0$, $\theta'(t)$ must be positive and

(11.331) $$\theta'(t) = \omega_0 \cos \tfrac{1}{2}\theta$$

for each t in the interval I. When t is in the interval I, we can use (11.331) to obtain

$$t = \frac{1}{\omega_0} \int_0^{\theta} \sec \frac{1}{2} u\, du = \frac{2}{\omega_0} \log \tan \frac{\theta + \pi}{4}$$

and hence

$$\theta = -\pi + 4 \tan^{-1} e^{\omega_0 t/2}.$$

Thus in this case we obtain θ as an elementary function of t, and we see that $-\pi < \theta < \pi$ for all values of t. It is easy to verify that $\theta(0) = 0$ and that, as t increases, $\theta(t)$ increases and approaches π as $t \to \infty$. Thus the pendulum simply swings, with angular velocity approaching 0, toward the unstable equilibrium position in which the centroid is directly above the point of suspension. In this case, trigonometric and logarithmic tables permit graphing $\theta(t)$.

We come now to the most complicated and interesting case in which $k > 1$. The left member of the equation

(11.34) $$[\theta'(t)]^2 = \omega_0^2(1 - k^2 \sin^2 \tfrac{1}{2}\theta)$$

is either 0 or positive; hence

$$\sin^2 \frac{1}{2}\theta \leq \frac{1}{k^2}.$$

This implies, since $\theta(0)=0$ and $\theta(t)$ is continuous, that

$$-\alpha \leq \theta(t) \leq \alpha \qquad\qquad -\infty < t < \infty$$

where α is the angle between 0 and π such that

$$\sin \frac{1}{2}\alpha = \frac{1}{k}.$$

To determine the form of the function $\theta(t)$, let t_n be a time at which $\theta = 0$. We know that t_n may be taken to be 0, and one who does not suspect that θ may be zero at other times has not been thinking extensively about the problem we are solving. Let I_n be the interval of values of t containing t_n over which $|\theta(t)| < \alpha$ and accordingly

$$1 - k^2 \sin^2 \tfrac{1}{2}\theta > 0.$$

Then (11.34) gives, for t in I_n,

$$\theta'(t) = \sigma_n \omega_0 \sqrt{1 - k^2 \sin^2 \tfrac{1}{2}\theta}$$

where σ_n is $+1$ if $\theta'(t_n) > 0$ and is -1 if $\theta'(t_n) < 0$. Hence, when t is in I_n

(11.341) $$t = t_n + \frac{1}{\sigma_n \omega_0} \int_0^\theta \frac{1}{\sqrt{1 - k^2 \sin^2 \tfrac{1}{2}u}} \, du.$$

The integral in (11.341) looks the same as the integral in (11.321), but in (11.341) we have $k > 1$ whereas in (11.321) we had $k < 1$. It is, so far as use of tables is concerned, an important fact that a shrewd change of the dummy variable of integration throws the integral in (11.341) into an elliptic integral with modulus less than 1. When $-\alpha < u < \alpha$, there is a unique angle x such that $-\pi/2 < x < \pi/2$ and

$$k \sin \tfrac{1}{2}u = \sin x.$$

Using the formulas

$$\sqrt{1 - k^2 \sin^2 \tfrac{1}{2}u} = \sqrt{1 - \sin^2 x} = \cos x$$

and

$$du = \left\{ \frac{2}{k} \Big/ \sqrt{1 - \left(\frac{1}{k}\right)^2 \sin^2 x} \right\} \cos x \, dx$$

to change the variable of integration in (11.341), we obtain

$$(11.35) \quad t = t_n + \frac{2}{\sigma_n k \omega_0} \int_0^{\sin^{-1}(k\sin\frac{1}{2}\theta)} \frac{1}{\sqrt{1 - (1/k)^2 \sin^2 x}} \, dx.$$

In view of (11.311), (11.35) can be written in the alternative form

$$(11.36) \quad t = t_n + \sigma_n \sqrt{\frac{I}{mgl}} \int_0^{\sin^{-1}(k\sin\frac{1}{2}\theta)} \frac{1}{\sqrt{1 - (1/k)^2 \sin^2 x}} \, dx.$$

The coefficient of $\sin^2 x$, which is the modulus of the elliptic integral in (11.36), is less than 1 since $k > 1$. Hence, when I, m, g, l, and k are known, tables of trigonometric functions and incomplete elliptic integrals can be used to obtain corresponding values of θ and t when t lies in the interval I_n. Let T_1 be the constant defined by

$$(11.37) \qquad T_1 = \sqrt{\frac{I}{mgl}} \int_0^{\pi/2} \frac{1}{\sqrt{1 - (1/k)^2 \sin^2 x}} \, dx.$$

In case $\sigma_n = 1$, it can be seen from (11.36) that as t increases over the interval $t_n - T_1 < t < t_n + T_1$ the angular displacement $\theta(t)$ increases over the interval $-\alpha < \theta < \alpha$; and since $\theta(t)$ must be continuous, we conclude that $\theta(t_n - T_1) = -\alpha$ and $\theta(t_n + T_1) = \alpha$. This gives results illustrated schematically in Fig. 11.38; and similar consideration of the case in which $\sigma_n = -1$ gives Fig. 11.381.

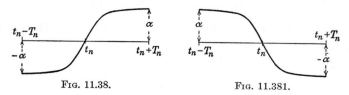

FIG. 11.38.   FIG. 11.381.

To describe the motion of the pendulum, let I_0 be the interval containing the time origin over which $-\alpha < \theta(t) < \alpha$. Then $\sigma_n = 1$, and we see that θ increases from $-\alpha$ to α as t increases from $-T_1$ to T_1. At time T_1, the angular velocity $\theta'(t)$ is 0 since

$$\theta'(T_1) = \sqrt{1 - k^2 \sin^2 \tfrac{1}{2}\alpha} = 0.$$

From the differential equation

$$\theta''(t) = -\frac{mgl}{I} \sin \theta$$

with which we started, we see that $\theta''(t)$ is negative and $\theta'(t)$ is decreasing when $0 < \theta \leq \alpha$; hence, $\theta'(t)$ is negative and $\sigma_n = -1$ over a time interval I_1 after $t = T_1$. In the interval I_1 the graph of $\theta(t)$ must have the form exhibited in Fig. 11.381, and $\theta(t)$ decreases from α to $-\alpha$ as t increases from T_1 to $3T_1$. In the time interval I_2 after $t = 3T_1$ over which $-\alpha < \theta(t) < \alpha$, $\theta'(t)$ must be positive and $\theta(t)$ increases from $-\alpha$ to α as t increases from $3T_1$ to $5T_1$. Thus the pendulum swings alternately to the right and left, stopping between with angular displacements α and $-\alpha$. Of course, one gets different graphs of $\theta(t)$ for different values of the constants; but the graphs all have the character of the curve obtained by sliding Figs. 11.38 and 11.381 together and making a periodic extension of the result.

11.4. Periods of the Motion of the Pendulum.—The considerations which led to the graphs in Figs. 11.38 and 11.381 and the manner in which they fit together show that the graph of $\theta(t)$ over the interval $4T_1 \leq t \leq 8T_1$ is an exact copy of the graph of $\theta(t)$ over the interval $0 \leq t \leq 4T_1$. The graph is similarly copied over other intervals of length $4T_1$; this means that $\theta(t + 4T_1) = \theta(t)$ and that $\theta(t)$ has *period* $4T_1$. Denoting this period by $T = 4T_1$, we can use (11.37) to obtain the formula

$$(11.41) \qquad T = 4 \sqrt{\frac{I}{mgl}} \int_0^{\pi/2} \frac{1}{\sqrt{1 - \sin^2 \frac{1}{2}\alpha \sin^2 x}} \, dx$$

for the period of the pendulum. If α, the maximum displacement of the pendulum, is near 0, then $\sin^2 \frac{1}{2}\alpha$ is near 0 and the integrand in (11.41) is near 1 over the range $0 \leq x \leq \pi/2$; hence the value of the integral is near $\pi/2$ when α is near 0.* This implies that, when α is near 0, the formula

$$(11.42) \qquad T = 2\pi \sqrt{\frac{I}{mgl}}$$

is approximately true.

In case the pendulum consists of a small mass which may (insofar as satisfactory approximations are concerned) be regarded as concentrated at a point C at the end of a weightless string of length l, the moment of inertia I becomes ml^2 and the approximate formula for the period becomes

$$(11.43) \qquad T = 2\pi \sqrt{\frac{l}{g}}.$$

The approximations for periods given in (11.42) and (11.43) are often used; most students of differential equations have seen them before.

---

* A skeptic may either look at a table of elliptic integrals to see that this is true or try to prove that it must be true.

Problem 11.44

A pendulum is swinging in such a way that the centroid C rises exactly to the level of the point of support O at the end of each swing. By use of the approximate formula (11.42), computation gives $T = 1$ second. What value of T would be obtained from (11.41)? Give your answer in the form of an integral and, if possible, as a decimal expansion of a number.

Problem 11.45

Show that if an inelastic pendulum swings or rotates with damping (see Section 9.01) proportional to the angular speed, then the equation of motion is

$$I \frac{d^2\theta}{dt^2} + \delta \frac{d\theta}{dt} + mgl \sin \theta = 0$$

where δ is a damping constant and other constants have the same meanings as above.

11.5. Plane Motion of a Simple Elastic Pendulum.—A differential-equations text which proposes only such problems as it can solve by elementary methods may be very comforting to a student and teacher. However, it commits an unpardonable sin when it fails to point out that many simple problems lead to complicated differential equations which, insofar as the thought of obtaining exact solutions is concerned, horrify pure and applied mathematicians who are far more experienced than a student taking a first course in differential equations. The best one can do is obtain approximations to solutions and perhaps know that the exact solution is the limit of a sequence of the approximations to solutions.

We now consider the motion of a mass m which moves in a vertical plane at the end of an elastic string or spring (which may be a rubber band or a steel wire) OC which is tied at a fixed point of suspension O. Several simplifying assumptions will be made. The mass of the string will be neglected, the mass m will be considered as concentrated at a point C, and all frictional forces will be disregarded. Moreover, it is assumed that the mass moves in such a way that the string is always taut and the force on the string is always within the elastic limits of the string. Let l be the length of the string when no weights or other forces tend to stretch it, and let E be the *spring constant* of the string, that is, the constant such that the force $F(r)$ required to stretch the string to length r is

$$F(r) = \frac{E(r - l)}{l}.$$

Let θ and r denote the angle (as in Fig. 11.21) and the length of the string at time t; thus θ and r are polar coordinates of the mass m.

In order to have a definite problem to solve, we assume the position and velocity of the mass to be known at some time t_0, say

(11.51) $\theta(t_0) = \theta_0,$ $\theta'(t_0) = \omega_0,$ $r(t_0) = r_1,$ $r'(t_0) = r_1'$

where θ_0, ω_0, r_1, and r_1' are known constants. The position of the mass at time t is to be determined by finding the polar coordinates $r(t)$ and $\theta(t)$ of the mass at time t. Thus the system under discussion has two degrees of freedom (Section 9.59).

It is helpful to draw a figure and to indicate the following three forces: (i) the gravitational force mg; (ii) the force $E(r - l)/l$ in the wire which tends to accelerate the mass toward O; and (iii) the centrifugal force $mr[\theta'(t)]^2$ which tends to accelerate the mass outward from O. Of these three forces, only the first tends to produce angular acceleration whereas each of the three tends to produce radial acceleration. Using principles of elementary physics, we arrive at the equations

$$(11.52) \qquad \frac{d^2\theta}{dt^2} = -\frac{g}{r}\sin\theta$$

$$(11.53) \qquad \frac{d^2r}{dt^2} = g\cos\theta - \frac{E}{ml}(r-l) + r\left(\frac{d\theta}{dt}\right)^2.$$

Each of these equations involves the two functions $r(t)$ and $\theta(t)$ which are sought.

A realization of the fact that this system of differential equations has many solutions corresponding to different initial conditions (11.51) can be attained by playing with a weight attached to a couple of feet of elastic constructed from rubber bands; but of course it is hard to tell how long the gyrations continue before the effect of damping (due to frictional forces) becomes significant.

11.6. Approximations.—When a differential equation or a system of differential equations is complicated, it is a standard trick to resort to approximations. One method of procedure is set forth in Chapters 15 and 16.

Another method of procedure is to obtain new and simpler equations by replacing some of the terms of the equations by new and simpler terms to which they are almost equal. In some simple cases it is possible to prove precise statements about the manner in which solutions of the simpler equations represent approximations to solutions of the original equations; usually however, this cannot be done.

The plain truth is that many differential equations, of which applied mathematicians require solutions, simply cannot be solved in any satisfactory way. In such cases an attempt is made to use good sense in making approximations to obtain simpler equations of which at least approximations to solutions can be obtained. There is usually no mathematical theory which tells the applied mathematician whether the results which he obtains are sufficiently accurate for his purposes: it is to the credit of a good applied mathematician that his training and good sense often lead him to make approximations which give useful results. Many times there is genuine doubt whether results obtained are trustworthy; and of course there are times when results thought to be trustworthy lead to catastrophe. In particular, many of the differential equations involved in problems of airplane design are so difficult that dubious approximations must be made, and we may conclude these remarks by mentioning the fact that test pilots wear parachutes.

Problem 11.61

The following attempt to simplify the system of equations (11.52) and (11.53) involves at least one very faulty step; find one or more steps of this kind. Consider the case in which the number E/ml is very large, that is, the case in which the string is strong and the mass m does not stretch it very much. Let the equation (11.53) be written in the form

$$r - l = \frac{g\cos\theta + r(d\theta/dt)^2 - (d^2r/dt^2)}{\dfrac{E}{ml}}.$$

Since $g\cos\theta$, r, the angular velocity $\theta'(t)$, and the radial acceleration are never very large, the numerator is never very large. But the denominator is very large, and so the quotient on the right is near 0. Thus r is near l, and we can set $r = l$ in the right-hand members of (11.52) and (11.53) to obtain

(11.62) $$\frac{d^2\theta}{dt^2} = -\frac{g}{l}\sin\theta, \qquad \frac{d^2r}{dt^2} = g\cos\theta + l\left(\frac{d\theta}{dt}\right)^2.$$

If the angular displacement is always small and accordingly the angular velocity is always small, θ and $\theta'(t)$ are nearly 0, $\sin\theta$ is nearly θ, $\cos\theta$ is nearly 1, and we can substitute in (11.62) to obtain

(11.63) $$\frac{d^2\theta}{dt^2} = -\frac{g}{l}\theta, \qquad \frac{d^2r}{dt^2} = g.$$

Can you eliminate the really bad mistake and do something with your more satisfactory results?

Problem 11.64

If you happen to be a good physicist, set up differential equations governing motion in three dimensions of an inelastic (or elastic) pendulum.

Problem 11.65

An ordinary wooden pencil with a sharp point at one end and a rubber eraser at the other end is placed in a nearly vertical position on a slippery table and allowed to fall. If the point is on the table, the first motion of the point is in the direction opposite to that of the fall. If the eraser is on the table, the first motion of the eraser is in the direction of the fall. Can you explain this by means of differential equations or otherwise?

CHAPTER 12

EIGENVALUES, FOURIER SERIES,
AND PARTIAL DIFFERENTIAL EQUATIONS

12.0. Introduction.—This chapter is designed to give an introduction to and to set forth relations among several important concepts such as *exact linear equation, integrating factor, adjoint equation, Lagrange's formula, Green's formula, self-adjoint operator, eigenvalue* (characteristic value) *and eigenfunction* (characteristic function), *Sturm-Liouville equation and system, orthonormal set, completeness,* and *Fourier series in general as well as in trigonometric and complex exponential functions.* In Section 12.9, we show how these concepts are used in the Fourier method of solving boundary-value problems involving partial differential equations.

These concepts appear in many phases of science, and it is not unlikely that the reader has been mystified by one or more of them in courses in Mathematics, Physics, Chemistry, or Engineering. It is impossible to give in this book or in any other single book a thorough treatment of these concepts which adequately covers their theory and applications.* However, it is possible to set forth fundamental definitions of, properties of, and relations among these concepts in a few pages. We proceed.

12.1. Exact Linear Equations.—The linear equation

$$(12.11) \qquad \frac{d^2y}{dx^2} + x\frac{dy}{dx} + y = \sin x$$

may be written in the form

$$(12.12) \qquad \frac{d}{dx}\left\{\frac{dy}{dx} + xy\right\} = \sin x.$$

---

* In fact, it is impossible to give a reasonably short list of references to works which, collectively, are adequate. One who wishes to make a serious study of these concepts and their applications may find plenty of references by consulting the subject index at the end of a volume of *Mathematical Reviews.* This periodical, giving abstracts of current mathematical literature, is published by the American Mathematical Society, New York, N. Y. An excellent way to accumulate references is to look up books and papers to which references are made by *Mathematical Reviews;* to look up books and papers to which references are made in the books and papers already found; and to continue the process until one has an abundance of references. The results will amaze a person who is unfamiliar with the scope of scientific literature.

These equations hold if and only if

(12.121) $$\frac{dy}{dx} + xy = c_1 - \cos x;$$

thus the problem of solving (12.11) is reduced to the simpler problem of solving the first-order linear differential equation (12.121). By use of the operator D, (12.11) and (12.12) can be written, respectively,

(12.13) $(D^2 + xD + 1)y = \sin x, \qquad D(D + x)y = \sin x.$

We see that the differential equation (12.13) and the operator $D^2 + xD + 1$ are *exact* in accordance with the following definition:

DEFINITION 12.14.—*A differential equation*

(12.141) $(a_0 D^n + a_1 D^{n-1} + \cdots + a_{n-1}D + a_n)y = f$

and the operator

(12.142) $L_a = a_0 D^n + a_1 D^{n-1} + \cdots + a_{n-1}D + a_n$

are said to be exact if there exists an operator

(12.143) $L_b = b_0 D^{n-1} + b_1 D^{n-2} + \cdots + b_{n-2}D + b_{n-1}$

of order one less than the order of L_a such that $L_a = DL_b$.

Thus, to say that an operator is exact means merely that it can be factored (see Section 6.4) in a simple special way. The following theorem furnishes an easy method of determining whether a given second-order operator is exact:

THEOREM 12.15.—*If a_0, a_1, and a_2 are functions of x for which $a_0''(x)$ and $a_1'(x)$ exist, then the equation*

(12.151) $$a_0 y'' + a_1 y' + a_2 y = f$$

and the operator

(12.152) $$L_a = a_0 D^2 + a_1 D + a_2$$

are exact if and only if

(12.153) $$a_0'' - a_1' + a_2 = 0.$$

Suppose first that (12.151) and (12.152) are exact. Then functions $b_0(x)$ and $b_1(x)$ exist such that
$$a_0 D^2 + a_1 D + a_2 = D(b_0 D + b_1),$$
that is, such that

(12.154) $$a_0 \frac{d^2 y}{dx^2} + a_1 \frac{dy}{dx} + a_2 y = \frac{d}{dx}\left(b_0 \frac{dy}{dx} + b_1 y\right)$$

for each function $y(x)$ having two derivatives.   Considering in turn the functions $y = 1$ and $y = x$, we see that the derivatives b_1' and b_0' must exist.   Hence the right member of (12.154) can be written in the form

$$b_0 \frac{d^2y}{dx^2} + (b_0' + b_1) \frac{dy}{dx} + b_1'y.$$

Hence, we can set in turn $y = 1$, $y = x$, and $y = x^2$ to obtain

$$a_2 = b_1', \qquad a_1 = b_0' + b_1, \qquad a_0 = b_0.$$

Therefore,

$$a_1' = b_0'' + b_1' = a_0'' + a_2,$$

and consequently (12.153) holds.

Suppose now that (12.153) holds; we are required to show that (12.151) and (12.152) are exact.   Using (12.153) we obtain, when $y(x)$ has two derivatives,

$$a_0 \frac{d^2y}{dx^2} + a_1 \frac{dy}{dx} + a_2y = a_0 \frac{d^2y}{dx^2} + a_1 \frac{dy}{dx} + (a_1' - a_0'')y$$

$$= \left(a_0 \frac{d^2y}{dx^2} - a_0''y \right) + \left(a_1 \frac{dy}{dx} + a_1'y \right) = \frac{d}{dx} \left[\left(a_0 \frac{dy}{dx} - a_0'y \right) + a_1y \right]$$

$$= \frac{d}{dx} \left[a_0 \frac{dy}{dx} + (a_1 - a_0')y \right]$$

so that

$$a_0D^2 + a_1D + a_2 = D[a_0D + (a_1 - a_0')]$$

and therefore (12.151) and (12.152) are exact.   This proves Theorem 12.15.

Problem 12.16

Show that, if a_0, a_1, and a_2 are constants, then

$$a_0D^2 + a_1D + a_2$$

is exact if and only if $a_2 = 0$.

Problem 12.17

State and prove a theorem analogous to Theorem 12.15 which applies to linear operators of order 4.

12.2. Integrating Factors and Adjoint Equations.—In this section, we use $\bar{w}$ to denote the conjugate $u - iv$ of a complex number $w = u + iv$ in which u and v are real.   Insofar as real solutions of differential equations with real coefficients are concerned, the bars have no significance since $\bar{w} = w$ when w is real.

A function $\mu(x)$ is called an *integrating factor* of an equation $Ly = f$ and of the operator L if the equation $\mu Ly = \mu f$ and the operator μL are exact.   We confine our attention to differential equations and operators of the second order.

THEOREM 12.21.—*If a_0, a_1, and a_2 are continuous functions of x for which a_0'' and a_1' exist, then $\mu(x)$ is an integrating factor of the equation*

$$(12.211) \qquad a_0y'' + a_1y' + a_2y = f$$

if and only if

(12.212) $a_0\mu'' + (2a_0' - a_1)\mu' + (a_0'' - a_1' + a_2)\mu = 0.$

By Theorem 12.15 the equation

$$(a_0\mu)y'' + (a_1\mu)y' + (a_2\mu)y = \mu f$$

is exact if and only if

(12.213) $(a_0\mu)'' - (a_1\mu)' + (a_2\mu) = 0;$

and (12.212) is merely an expanded form of (12.213). This proves Theorem 12.21.

The equation (12.212) can be written in the form

(12.214) $\bar{a}_0\bar{\mu}'' + (2\bar{a}_0' - \bar{a}_1)\bar{\mu}' + (\bar{a}_0'' - \bar{a}_1' + \bar{a}_2)\bar{\mu} = 0.$

Hence, Theorem 12.21 can be stated in the following form:

THEOREM 12.22.—*Under the hypothesis of Theorem 12.21, a function* μ *is an integrating factor of the equation*

(12.221) $a_0y'' + a_1y' + a_2y = f$

if and only if $\bar{\mu}$ *is a solution of the equation*

(12.222) $\bar{a}_0y'' + (2\bar{a}_0' - \bar{a}_1)y' + (\bar{a}_0'' - \bar{a}_1' + \bar{a}_2)y = 0.$

The equation (12.222) is called the *adjoint* (or *adjoint equation*) of (12.221). The adjoint of an operator is often indicated by an asterisk superscript which is commonly called a *star*. Thus, if L denotes the operator

(12.23) $L = a_0D^2 + a_1D + a_2,$

then the *adjoint* (or *adjoint operator*) is†

(12.24) $L^* = \bar{a}_0D^2 + (2\bar{a}_0' - \bar{a}_1)D + (\bar{a}_0'' - \bar{a}_1' + \bar{a}_2).$

Problem 12.241

Prove that the adjoint of the adjoint of the operator L in (12.23) is L itself; that is, $L^{**} = L$. Find whether the formula

$$(L_1 + L_2)^* = L_1^* + L_2^*$$

is correct when L_1 and L_2 are second-order operators.

The most obvious connection between the operators L and L^* lies in the fact that the integrating factors of $Ly = f$ are the conjugates of the solutions of $L^*y = 0$. An important connection between L and

---

† In case the a's are real, the bars may naturally be omitted; but, when the a's are not real, omission of the bars leads to confusion.

L^* is set forth in the following theorem which is one of various theorems known as *Lagrange's theorem.*†

THEOREM 12.25.—If

$$L = a_0 D^2 + a_1 D + a_2$$

where a_0, a_1, and a_2 are functions of x for which a_0'' and a_1' exist and if $y_m(x)$ and $y_n(x)$ are two functions each having two derivatives, then‡

$$(12.26) \quad y_m \overline{L^* y_n} - \bar{y}_n L y_m = \frac{d}{dx} [a_0 (y_m \bar{y}_n' - y_m' \bar{y}_n) - (a_1 - a_0') y_m \bar{y}_n].$$

The simplest way to prove this theorem is to expand both sides of (12.26) [using (12.23) and (12.24) in the left-hand member] and to show that the terms all cancel. A formula obtained by integrating *Lagrange's formula* (12.26) is one of various formulas known as *Green's formula*.

12.27. Self-adjoint Operators.—An operator L is called *self-adjoint* if $L^* = L$. If a_0, a_1, and a_2 are real, the conditions for $L^* = L$ are

$$a_0 = a_0, \qquad a_1 = 2a_0' - a_1, \qquad a_2 = a_0'' - a_1' + a_2$$

and these three conditions are satisfied if and only if $a_1 = a_0'$. Therefore, each self-adjoint linear operator of the second order with real coefficients has the form

$$(12.28) \qquad L = a_0(x) D^2 + a_0'(x) D + a_2(x).$$

This can of course be written in the form $L = D(a_0 D) + a_2$. For this operator, $L^* = L$ and $\overline{Ly} = L\bar{y}$ so that Lagrange's formula (12.26) becomes

$$(12.29) \qquad y_m L \bar{y}_n - \bar{y}_n L y_m = \frac{d}{dx} [a_0 (y_m \bar{y}_n' - y_m' \bar{y}_n)].$$

The fact that (12.29) is simpler than (12.26) shows why self-adjoint operators are more tractable than others.

Problem 12.291

Show that, if $a_0(x)$, $a_1(x)$, and $a_2(x)$ are real continuous functions of x for which $a_0''(x)$ and $a_1'(x)$ exist, then a factor $\nu(x)$ makes the operator

$$a_0(x)\nu(x) D^2 + a_1(x)\nu(x) D + a_2(x)\nu(x)$$

† Joseph Louis Lagrange (1736–1813) was a great French mathematician who is best known for his work in analytical mechanics.

‡ It is somewhat absurd to call two functions by the names $y_m(x)$ and $y_n(x)$; names such as $y_1(x)$ and $y_2(x)$ would seem more appropriate. However, this notation results in formulas written exactly the way we want to use them later.

self-adjoint if and only if $\nu(x)$ is a solution of the first-order equation

$$a_0(x)\nu' + [a_0'(x) - a_1(x)]\nu = 0.$$

Problem 12.292

Derive (12.29) directly from (12.28) without use of (12.26).

12.3. Eigenvalue Problems.—Differential equations of the form $Ly = -\lambda y$, in which L is a linear operator and λ is a parameter, arise in many problems. It is often true that special solutions, called *eigenfunctions* or *characteristic functions*, are required which are not identically 0 and which satisfy one or more supplementary conditions pertinent to the problem being solved. In important cases, eigenfunctions exist only for special values of the parameter λ; these values of λ are called *eigenvalues* or *characteristic values*. If λ_n is an eigenvalue and y_n is a solution of $Ly = -\lambda_n y$ which is not identically 0 and which satisfies the supplementary conditions, then y_n is called an *eigenfunction belonging to* λ_n. It is customary to think of the differential equation and the supplementary conditions together as constituting a *system;* the eigenvalues and eigenfunctions are then *eigenvalues and eigenfunctions of the system.*

It is impossible to indicate in a paragraph the role which eigenvalues play in science, but we can see clearly the meaning of the equation $Ly = -\lambda y$. Though certain functions may be drastically changed when the operator L is applied to them, the eigenfunctions enjoy a very special status; *an eigenfunction y_n belonging to λ_n is merely multiplied by $-\lambda_n$.* Moreover, if $y_1, y_2, \cdots, y_n$ are eigenfunctions belonging to $\lambda_1, \lambda_2, \cdots, \lambda_n$, respectively, and

$$g = c_1 y_1 + c_2 y_2 + \cdots + c_n y_n,$$

then linearity of L implies that

$$Lg = -c_1 \lambda_1 y_1 - c_2 \lambda_2 y_2 - \cdots - c_n \lambda_n y_n;$$

thus an expression for Lg is quickly obtained when g is a given linear combination of eigenfunctions. It is a more significant observation that it is easy to write out a solution of the equation

$$(12.31) \qquad Ly = c_1 y_1 + c_2 y_2 + \cdots + c_n y_n$$

when $\lambda_k \neq 0$ for each k; a solution is

$$(12.32) \qquad y = -\frac{c_1}{\lambda_1} y_1 - \frac{c_2}{\lambda_2} y_2 - \cdots - \frac{c_n}{\lambda_n} y_n.$$

In case the supplementary conditions are linear (that is, such that they are satisfied by each linear combination of functions which satisfy them), then not only is (12.32) a solution of (12.31); (12.32) *is a solution of* (12.31) *which satisfies the supplementary conditions.*

These considerations indicate that it should be useful to know what functions g can be expressed as linear combinations of eigenfunctions, either exactly or approximately in some sense satisfying to an applied mathematician who is always ready to use good approximations. The following sections consider an important class of eigenvalue problems.

12.33. Sturm-Liouville Equations.—We consider here the case in which L is a second-order operator,

$$L = a_0(x)D^2 + a_1(x)D + a_2(x),$$

and x lies in an open interval $a < x < b$ over which $a_0(x)$, $a_1(x)$, and $a_2(x)$ are real and continuous and $a_0(x)$ is positive. For example, with the Bessel operator $L = x^2 D^2 + xD + (x^2 - \alpha^2)$ we can take $a = 0$, $b = 1$; likewise for the self-adjoint operator $\mathfrak{L} = xD^2 + D + (x - \alpha^2/x)$ we can take $a = 0$, $b = 1$. In case $a_0(x) = 1 - x^2$ while $a_1(x)$ and $a_2(x)$ are continuous, we can take $a = -1$, $b = 1$.

The equation $Ly = -\lambda y$ is then

$$(12.34) \qquad a_0(x)\frac{d^2y}{dx^2} + a_1(x)\frac{dy}{dx} + a_2(x)y = -\lambda y.$$

Having seen (Section 12.27) that self-adjoint operators are more tractable than others, we introduce the factor

$$p(x) = \frac{A}{a_0(x)} \exp \int_{x_0}^{x} \frac{a_1(t)}{a_0(t)} \, dt$$

in which x_0 is a point of the interval $a < x < b$ and A is a conveniently chosen positive constant, and set

$$q(x) = a_0(x)p(x), \qquad r(x) = a_2(x)p(x)$$

to obtain the *Sturm-Liouville equation*

$$(12.35) \qquad \frac{d}{dx}[q(x)y'] + r(x)y = -\lambda p(x)y,$$

in which the operator

$$(12.36) \qquad \mathfrak{L} \equiv D(qD) + r \equiv qD^2 + q'D + r$$

is self-adjoint.* The coefficients $p(x)$ and $q(x)$ are positive over

---

* The equation (12.35), which may of course be written in the form

$$q(x)\frac{d^2y}{dx^2} + q'(x)\frac{dy}{dx} + [\lambda p(x) + r(x)]y = 0,$$

is known as a Sturm-Liouville equation of second order. Theorem 6.04 guarantees existence of solutions over $a < x < b$ for each λ.

$a < x < b$. In case L is self-adjoint, we may take $p(x) = 1$ so that the operators L and $\mathcal{L}$ are identical.

Now let λ_m and λ_n be two numbers and let $y_m(x)$ and $y_n(x)$ be two functions such that, when $a < x < b$,

$$Ly_m = -\lambda_m y_m, \qquad Ly_n = -\lambda_n y_n$$

or (what amounts to the same thing)

$$\mathcal{L}y_m = -\lambda_m p y_m, \qquad \mathcal{L}y_n = -\lambda_n p y_n.$$

Since $\mathcal{L}$ is self-adjoint, we can substitute in the Lagrange formula (12.29) to obtain, when $a < x < b$,

$$(12.37) \qquad (\lambda_m - \bar{\lambda}_n) p y_m \bar{y}_n = \frac{d}{dx}[q(y_m \bar{y}_n' - y_m' \bar{y}_n)].$$

The two members of (12.37) are certainly (why?) continuous over the open interval $a < x < b$; but they may either be or fail to be continuous over the closed interval $a \leqq x \leqq b$. We can (why?) integrate (12.37) over $x_1 \leqq x \leqq x_2$ when $a < x_1 < x_2 < b$ and then let $x_1 \to a$ and $x_2 \to b$ to obtain (see Section 2.4 on Cauchy integrals)

$$(12.38) \quad (\lambda_m - \bar{\lambda}_n) \int_a^b p(x) y_m(x) \bar{y}_n(x) dx = \lim_{x \to b} [q(x)$$
$$\{y_m(x)\bar{y}_n'(x) - y_m'(x)\bar{y}_n(x)\}] - \lim_{x \to a}[q(x)\{y_m(x)\bar{y}_n'(x) - y_m'(x)\bar{y}_n(x)\}]$$

whenever the limits on the right exist. In case the functions

$$p(x), \qquad q(x), \qquad y_m(x), \qquad y_m'(x), \qquad y_n(x), \qquad y_n'(x)$$

are continuous over $a \leqq x \leqq b$, (12.38) can be written in the form

$$(12.39) \quad (\lambda_m - \bar{\lambda}_n) \int_a^b p(x) y_m(x) \bar{y}_n(x) dx$$
$$= q(b)[y_m(b)\bar{y}_n'(b) - y_m'(b)\bar{y}_n(b)] - q(a)[y_m(a)\bar{y}_n'(a) - y_m'(a)\bar{y}_n(a)],$$

the integral on the left now being a Riemann integral with a continuous integrand.

Conditions under which the second member of (12.38) is 0 are of great interest; one obvious fact is that vanishing of the second member implies that the integral in (12.38) must be 0 unless $\lambda_m = \bar{\lambda}_n$.

12.4. Sturm-Liouville Systems.—A *Sturm-Liouville system* is a system composed of (i) a Sturm-Liouville equation

$$(12.41) \qquad \frac{d}{dx}[q(x)y'(x)] + r(x)y(x) = -\lambda p(x)y(x)$$

and (ii) a set of supplementary conditions on $p(x)$, $q(x)$, $r(x)$, and $y(x)$ which, among other things, implies that each pair of functions $y_m(x)$

and $y_n(x)$ satisfying the conditions imposed upon $y(x)$ is a pair for which the right-hand member of (12.38) is 0.

One important system is composed of (12.41) and the conditions that $p(x)$ be positive and $r(x)$ be continuous over $a < x < b$; that $p(x)$, $q(x)$, $y(x)$, and $y'(x)$ be continuous over $a \leqq x \leqq b$; that $q(x)$ be positive over $a \leqq x \leqq b$; and that

$$(12.42) \qquad A_1 y(a) + A_2 y'(a) = 0, \qquad B_1 y(b) + B_2 y'(b) = 0$$

where A_1 and A_2 are real constants not both 0 and likewise B_1 and B_2 are real constants not both 0. The special case in which (12.42) takes the form

$$(12.43) \qquad\qquad y(a) = y(b) = 0$$

and that in which (12.42) takes the form

$$(12.44) \qquad\qquad y'(a) = y'(b) = 0$$

frequently occur.

Another type of system is just like the preceding except that the function $q(x)$ satisfies the additional condition $q(a) = q(b)$ and (12.42) is replaced by the so-called *periodic boundary condition*

$$(12.45) \qquad\qquad y(a) = y(b), \qquad y'(a) = y'(b).$$

For each of these systems, an *eigenvalue of the system* is a value of λ for which a function $y_\lambda(x)$ not identically 0 over $a < x < b$ exists which satisfies (12.41) and the specified supplementary conditions; the function $y_\lambda(x)$ is an *eigenfunction belonging to* λ.

Formulation of satisfactory supplementary conditions when $q(a) = 0$ or $q(b) = 0$ or both is a more delicate matter. The footnote below* contains a discussion of this point more easily understood after a preliminary reading of this chapter.

---

* When the coefficient $q(x)$ in (12.41) is such that $q(a) = 0$ or $q(b) = 0$ or both, it sometimes happens that some or all [except the function $y(x) \equiv 0$] of the functions $y(x)$ which satisfy the differential equation over the interval $a < x < b$ fail to be such that $y(x)$ and $y'(x)$ have limits as $x \to a$ and as $x \to b$. In such cases the formula (12.39) and such conditions as (12.42) cannot be used; to obtain supplementary conditions which yield a satisfactory Sturm-Liouville system, it is necessary to formulate conditions on $y(x)$ in such a way that the right-hand member of (12.38) may be used. We do not go into details in this matter; the essential point is that the conditions are so formulated that each eigenfunction satisfies (12.41) over the interval $a < x < b$; that, if $y_m(x)$ and $y_n(x)$ are two eigenfunctions, then the right-hand member of (12.38) is 0; that, if $y_n(x)$ is an eigenfunction belonging to λ, then $\bar{y}_n(x)$ is an eigenfunction belonging to λ; and that, if $y_n(x)$ is an eigenfunction, then $p(x) | y_n(x) |^2$ has a Cauchy integral (Section 2.4) over $a \leqq x \leqq b$, the value of the integral being positive.

It is easy to see that the eigenvalues must be real. If $\lambda_m = \alpha + i\beta$ is an eigenvalue with eigenfunction $y_m(x) = u(x) + iv(x)$, then $\lambda_n = \alpha - i\beta$ must be an eigenvalue with eigenfunction

$$y_n(x) = u(x) - iv(x).$$

The equation (12.38) is in this case

$$2\beta \int_a^b p(x)[u^2(x) + v^2(x)]dx = 0.$$

Since the integral is not 0, β must be 0 and the eigenvalue λ_m must be real.

It thus appears that if $y_m(x)$ and $y_n(x)$ are eigenfunctions belonging to λ_m and λ_n, respectively, then

(12.46) $$(\lambda_m - \lambda_n) \int_a^b p(x)y_m(x)\bar{y}_n(x)dx = 0.$$

If $\lambda_m \neq \lambda_n$, this implies that the integral must be 0. In this case, we can write (12.46) in the form

(12.47) $$\int_a^b \{\sqrt{p(x)}\, y_m(x)\}\{\sqrt{p(x)}\, \bar{y}_n(x)\}dx = 0.$$

Thus we are led to the developments of the next sections.

12.5. Orthonormal Sets.—Two functions $\phi(x)$ and $\psi(x)$ are said to be *orthogonal* over an interval $a \leq x \leq b$ if

(12.51) $$\int_a^b \phi(x)\bar{\psi}(x)dx = 0.$$

One function $\phi(x)$ is said to be *normal* (or *normalized*) if

(12.52) $$\int_a^b |\phi(x)|^2\, dx = 1.$$

A set of functions

$$\phi_1(x), \qquad \phi_2(x), \qquad \phi_3(x), \qquad \cdots$$

is said to form a *normal and orthogonal set of functions*, or, briefly, an *orthonormal set*, over an interval $a \leq x \leq b$ if

(12.53) $$\int_a^b \phi_m(x)\bar{\phi}_n(x)dx = 0 \qquad\qquad m \neq n$$
$$= 1 \qquad\qquad m = n$$

A set $\psi_1(x)$, $\psi_2(x)$, $\cdots$ is said to form an *orthogonal set* over $a \leq x \leq b$ if

$$\int_a^b \psi_m(x)\bar{\psi}_n(x)dx = 0 \qquad\qquad m \neq n.$$

It is clear that each orthonormal set is an orthogonal set and that an orthogonal set may fail to be orthonormal.

Each Riemann integrable function $\psi(x)$ for which $\int_a^b |\psi(x)|^2\,dx \neq 0$ can be normalized by multiplication by an appropriate constant Q. Thus, if we set

$$\phi(x) = Q\psi(x),$$

then

$$\int_a^b |\phi(x)|^2\,dx = |Q|^2 \int_a^b |\psi(x)|^2\,dx;$$

and $\phi(x)$ will be normal if we set

$$Q = \left[\int_a^b |\psi(x)|^2\,dx \right]^{-\frac{1}{2}}.$$

Suppose now $\lambda_1, \lambda_2, \lambda_3, \cdots$ is an infinite set of different eigenvalues of a Sturm-Liouville system and that $y_1(x), y_2(x), \cdots$ is an infinite set of eigenfunctions such that $y_n(x)$ belongs to λ_n for each $n = 1, 2, 3, \cdots$. Let

$$(12.54) \qquad\qquad \phi_n(x) = Q_n \sqrt{p(x)}\, y_n(x)$$

where Q_n is the constant,

$$(12.541) \qquad\qquad Q_n = \left[\int_a^b p(x)|y_n(x)|^2\,dx \right]^{-\frac{1}{2}}.$$

Then obviously

$$(12.55) \qquad\qquad \int_a^b |\phi_n(x)|^2\,dx = 1 \qquad\qquad n = 1, 2, 3, \cdots$$

so that the set

$$(12.56) \qquad\qquad \phi_1(x), \qquad \phi_2(x), \qquad \phi_3(x), \qquad \cdots$$

is normal. If $m \neq n$, we can use (12.54) and (12.46) to obtain

$$\int_a^b \phi_m(x)\bar{\phi}_n(x)\,dx = Q_m Q_n \int_a^b p(x)y_m(x)\bar{y}_n(x)\,dx = 0;$$

hence the set (12.56) must be orthogonal. The set of functions

$$\psi_n(x) = \sqrt{p(x)}\, y_n(x)$$

is orthogonal but is not normal unless by accident or design the functions $y_n(x)$ were so chosen that the integral in (12.541) is 1.

Thus we have shown that *if $y_1(x), y_2(x), \cdots$ is a set of eigenfunctions, of a Sturm-Liouville system, belonging to distinct eigenvalues $\lambda_1, \lambda_2, \cdots$, then the functions*

$$(12.57) \qquad\qquad \phi_n(x) = Q_n \sqrt{p(x)}\, y_n(x) \qquad\qquad n = 1, 2, \cdots$$

constitute an orthonormal set.

In cases in which $p(x) = 1$ for all x, the functions $Q_n y_n(x)$ themselves constitute an orthonormal set; in case $p(x)$ is not always 1, the functions $y_n(x)$ are said to be *orthogonal with weight function* $p(x)$.

Problem 12.581

Verify each of the following assertions: The operator

$$L = D^2$$

is a self-adjoint linear operator of the second order with real coefficients. The equation $D^2 y = -\lambda y$ together with the boundary conditions $y(0) = y(\pi) = 0$ constitutes a Sturm-Liouville system. The eigenvalues (and the only eigenvalues) are $\lambda_1 = 1^2$, $\lambda_2 = 2^2$, $\lambda_3 = 3^2$, $\cdots$; the eigenfunctions (and the only eigenfunctions) are $y_1 = c_1 \sin x$, $y_2 = c_2 \sin 2x$, $y_3 = c_3 \sin 3x$, $\cdots$ where $c_1 \neq 0$, $c_2 \neq 0$, $c_3 \neq 0$, $\cdots$. In this example, $p(x) = 1$ for all x, and the functions $y_n(x)$ are orthogonal. Since

$$\int_0^\pi \sin^2 nx \, dx = \frac{1}{2} \int_0^\pi (1 - \cos 2nx) dx = \frac{\pi}{2} \qquad n = 1, 2, 3, \cdots,$$

the functions

$$\phi_n(x) = \sqrt{\frac{2}{\pi}} \sin nx \qquad n = 1, 2, 3, \cdots$$

constitute an orthonormal system over $0 \leq x \leq \pi$.

Problem 12.582

Establish the formula

$$\int_0^\pi \left(\sqrt{\frac{2}{\pi}} \sin mx \right) \left(\sqrt{\frac{2}{\pi}} \sin nx \right) dx = 0 \qquad m \neq n$$

by a method simpler than that used in the previous problem.

Problem 12.583

Show that if, in Problem 12.581, the boundary conditions $y(0) = y(\pi) = 0$ are replaced by the so-called *periodic boundary conditions*

$$y(0) = y(2\pi), \qquad y'(0) = y'(2\pi)$$

then the eigenvalues become 0, 1^2, 2^2, 3^2, $\cdots$ and the corresponding eigenfunctions become

$$\alpha_n e^{inx} + \beta_n e^{-inx} \qquad n = 0, 1, 2, \cdots$$

or

$$A_n \cos nx + B_n \sin nx \qquad n = 0, 1, 2, \cdots.$$

Except in the case $n = 0$, there are two linearly independent eigenfunctions belonging to each eigenvalue. Show that nevertheless if we set

$$\phi_n(x) = \frac{1}{\sqrt{2\pi}} e^{inx} \qquad n = 0, \pm 1, \pm 2, \cdots$$

then

(12.5831) $$\int_0^{2\pi} \phi_m(x) \overline{\phi_n(x)} dx = 0 \qquad m \neq n$$

$$= 1 \qquad m = n.$$

Show also that if we set

$$\phi_0(x) = \frac{1}{\sqrt{2\pi}}$$

$$\phi_{2n}(x) = \frac{\cos nx}{\sqrt{\pi}} \qquad n = 1, 2, 3, \cdots$$

$$\phi_{2n-1}(x) = \frac{\sin nx}{\sqrt{\pi}} \qquad n = 1, 2, 3, \cdots$$

then (12.5831) holds.

12.6. Existence of Eigenvalues and Completeness of Orthonormal Sets.

—For the Sturm-Liouville systems in Problems 12.581 and 12.582, it was easy to show existence of an infinite set of nonnegative real eigenvalues and, in fact, to find them. These eigenvalues led to orthonormal sets having an important property, completeness, which we shall discuss presently.

We give now without proof an indication of results which are of great interest in pure and applied mathematics; accurate statements of the results are too involved to be given here.

Under quite general conditions, all eigenvalues of a Sturm-Liouville system are real and nonnegative. There is an infinite set of eigenvalues; and these eigenvalues can be named $\lambda_1, \lambda_2, \lambda_3, \cdots$ in such a way that

$$(12.61) \qquad 0 \leq \lambda_1 < \lambda_2 < \lambda_3 < \lambda_4 < \cdots$$

and $\lambda_n \to \infty$ as $n \to \infty$. The eigenfunctions belonging to an eigenvalue λ_n are in some cases simply nonzero constant multiples of a single eigenfunction, say $y_n(x)$; in other cases they are linear combinations, with coefficients not both 0, of two linearly independent eigenfunctions, say $y_n(x)$ and $Y_n(x)$. In the latter case it is always possible to choose the linearly independent eigenfunctions $y_n(x)$ and $Y_n(x)$ in such a way that each eigenfunction belonging to λ_n is a linear combination of $y_n(x)$ and $Y_n(x)$ and moreover the two functions $y_n(x)$ and $Y_n(x)$ are *orthogonal with weight function* $p(x)$ in the sense that

$$\int_a^b [\sqrt{p(x)}\, y_n(x)][\sqrt{p(x)}\, \bar{Y}_n(x)]dx = 0.$$

For each n, let Q_n be a constant such that the function

$$(12.62) \qquad Q_n \sqrt{p(x)}\, y_n(x)$$

is normal; and, for values of n for which $Y_n(x)$ is present, let R_n be a constant such that the function

$$(12.63) \qquad R_n \sqrt{p(x)}\, Y_n(x)$$

is normal. Let the functions in (12.62) and (12.63) be denoted in some order by*

(12.64) $\phi_1(x), \ \phi_2(x), \ \phi_3(x), \ \cdots$.

These functions always form an orthonormal set over the interval $a \leqq x \leqq b$.

The most useful theorems involving Sturm-Liouville systems are those which show that, under conditions which we cannot set forth here, the orthonormal set (12.64) is *complete*. It is possible to define *complete orthonormal set* in several equivalent ways which appear to be quite different. In the next section we give some remarks designed to sophisticate rather than educate; in Section 12.7 we go to work.

12.65. Use of Lebesgue Integrals.—The simplest discussions of orthonormal sets are those in which the integrals used are Lebesgue integrals. We neither assume knowledge of nor use Lebesgue integrals, but this is no reason why a student should not be interested in the subject. If a function $f(x)$ is Riemann integrable over an interval $a \leqq x \leqq b$, then it is Lebesgue integrable over the same interval and the integrals are equal. However, there are functions not Riemann integrable which are Lebesgue integrable. The definition of the Lebesgue integral is more complicated than that of the Riemann integral because it requires a working knowledge of *Lebesgue measure;* but those who understand both integrals find the Lebesgue integral much the easier to work with because it has many useful properties which the Riemann integral lacks.

An orthonormal set of functions

$$\phi_1(x), \ \phi_2(x), \ \phi_3(x), \ \cdots ,$$

which may be continuous but in any case must be *measurable,* is said to be *complete* if there exists no function $\phi_0(x)$ such that the set of functions

$$\phi_0(x), \ \phi_1(x), \ \phi_2(x), \ \cdots$$

is an orthonormal set. This simple definition, based on Lebesgue integration, says that an orthonormal set is complete if no new function can be added. Of course, it implies that the set obtained by removing one or more functions from a complete set is not complete. It can be shown that this definition of completeness is equivalent to the definition given in the next section; that is, if a set is complete in one sense, then it is also complete in the other sense.

It is possible to define an orthonormal set $\phi_1(x), \ \phi_2(x), \ \cdots$ of continuous functions to be *complete with respect to continuous functions* if there is no *continuous* function $\phi_0(x)$ such that the set $\phi_0(x), \ \phi_1(x), \ \cdots$ is an orthonormal set; but this property of orthonormal sets is by no means so strong as the property of completeness and serves no useful purpose in our theory.

One who knows the appropriate mathematics finds it very easy to prove that a definition of completeness equivalent to that given in the next section is obtained by replacing the condition that $f(x)$ be Riemann integrable by (i) the condition that $f(x)$ be continuous, or (ii) the condition that $f(x)$ have two continuous derivatives,

---

* In some cases it is convenient to denote the functions by $\phi_0, \ \phi_{-1}, \ \phi_1, \ \phi_{-2}, \ \phi_2,$ $\cdots$, but after all it makes no difference how the functions are named; the important thing is that none be lost.

or (iii) the condition that $f(x)$ and $|f(x)|^2$ have Cauchy integrals, or (iv) the condition that $f(x)$ be measurable and $|f(x)|^2$ be Lebesgue integrable. The term *closed* is sometimes used in place of the term *complete*.

12.7. Completeness of Orthonormal Sets.

—An orthonormal set

$$(12.71) \qquad \phi_1(x), \ \phi_2(x), \ \phi_3(x), \ \cdots$$

is said to be *complete* if, corresponding to each function $f(x)$ which is Riemann integrable* over $a \leq x \leq b$ and each $\epsilon > 0$, there exist an index n and constants $c_1, c_2, \cdots, c_n$ such that

$$(12.72) \qquad \int_a^b \left| f(x) - \sum_{k=1}^n c_k \phi_k(x) \right|^2 dx < \epsilon.$$

The meaning of this definition may perhaps be made apparent by the following statement: If the orthonormal set is complete, then when $f(x)$ and ϵ are given it is possible to find a linear combination of the ϕ's which is so close to $f(x)$ so much of the time that the integral in (12.72) is less than ϵ.

When $f(x)$ is fixed, the value of the integral in (12.72) depends only on $c_1, c_2, \cdots, c_n$. As we shall see, an attempt to discuss the integral is facilitated by defining constants $a_1, a_2, a_3, \cdots$ by the formulas

$$(12.73) \qquad a_k = \int_a^b f(x) \bar{\phi}_k(x) dx \qquad k = 1, 2, \cdots;$$

these constants are called the *Fourier coefficients* of the function $f(x)$. Using the simple formula $|z|^2 = z\bar{z}$ to expand the integrand in (12.72), and using (12.73) and the orthonormality of the ϕ's, we obtain

$$(12.74) \quad \int_a^b \left| f(x) - \sum_{k=1}^n c_k \phi_k(x) \right|^2 dx$$

$$= \int_a^b \left[f(x) - \sum_{k=1}^n c_k \phi_k(x) \right]\left[\bar{f}(x) - \sum_{l=1}^n \bar{c}_l \bar{\phi}_l(x) \right] dx$$

$$= \int_a^b |f(x)|^2 dx - \sum_{l=1}^n \bar{c}_l \int_a^b f(x) \bar{\phi}_l(x) dx$$

$$- \sum_{k=1}^n c_k \int_a^b \bar{f}(x) \phi_k(x) dx + \sum_{k=1}^n \sum_{l=1}^n c_k \bar{c}_l \int_a^b \phi_k(x) \bar{\phi}_l(x) dx$$

$$= \int_a^b |f(x)|^2 dx + \sum_{k=1}^n \left[-\bar{c}_k a_k - c_k \bar{a}_k + c_k \bar{c}_k \right].$$

$$= \int_a^b |f(x)|^2 dx - \sum_{k=1}^n |a_k|^2 + \sum_{k=1}^n |c_k - a_k|^2.$$

* It should be recognized that each Riemann integrable function $f(x)$ is bounded and such that $|f(x)|^2$ is integrable, and that each bounded function $f(x)$ having at most a finite set of discontinuities is such that $f(x)$ and $|f(x)|^2$ are both integrable.

Since $| c_k - a_k |$ is never negative and is 0 only when $c_k = a_k$, this shows that the integral is a minimum when $c_k = a_k$ for each k; in other words, $c_1\phi_1(x) + \cdots + c_n(x)$ is the best approximation to $f(x)$ in the sense of *least squares* and in the sense of *approximation in mean* when the c's are the Fourier coefficients of $f(x)$. This type of approximation is held in highest esteem by all experts in the theory of approximation. If

$$\int_a^b | f(x) - \sum_{k=1}^n c_k\phi_k(x) |^2 \, dx$$

is "small" then the function

$$\sum_{k=1}^n c_k\phi_k(x)$$

is regarded as a "good" approximation to $f(x)$.

Setting $c_k = a_k$ in (12.74) gives the important formula

$$(12.75) \qquad \int_a^b | f(x) - \sum_{k=1}^n a_k\phi_k(x) |^2 \, dx = \int_a^b | f(x) |^2 \, dx - \sum_{k=1}^n | a_k |^2$$

$$n = 1, 2, 3, \cdots$$

which holds whether the orthonormal set is complete or not. Since the left side of (12.75) is never negative, we obtain

$$(12.751) \qquad \sum_{k=1}^n | a_k |^2 \leqq \int_a^b | f(x) |^2 \, dx \qquad n = 1, 2, 3, \cdots.$$

Thus the partial sums of the series

$$| a_1 |^2 + | a_2 |^2 + | a_3 |^2 + \cdots$$

are bounded, and since the terms are nonnegative the series must converge. Using (12.751) we obtain the inequality

$$(12.76) \qquad \sum_{k=1}^\infty | a_k |^2 \leqq \int_a^b | f(x) |^2 \, dx$$

which is known as *Bessel's inequality;* it holds whether the orthonormal set is complete or not.

When the orthonormal set is complete, the estimate in (12.76) can be strengthened by removal of the inequality sign. To be precise, we state and prove the following theorem:

THEOREM 12.77.—*If $\phi_1(x)$, $\phi_2(x)$, $\cdots$ is a complete orthonormal set over $a \leqq x \leqq b$, if $f(x)$ is Riemann integrable over $a \leqq x \leqq b$, and if the constants*

$$a_n = \int_a^b f(x)\bar{\phi}_n(x)dx \qquad n \doteq 1, 2, 3, \cdots$$

are the Fourier coefficients of $f(x)$, *then the Parseval equality*

$$(12.78) \qquad \sum_{n=1}^{\infty} |\, a_n \,|^2 = \int_a^b |\, f(x) \,|^2 \, dx$$

holds.

To prove this theorem, let the hypotheses be satisfied. Let $\epsilon > 0$. Then an integer n and constants $c_1, c_2, \cdots, c_n$ exist such that (12.72) holds. Using the equality (12.74) we obtain

$$\left\{ \int_a^b |\, f(x) \,|^2 \, dx - \sum_{k=1}^{n} |\, a_k \,|^2 \right\} + \left\{ \sum_{k=1}^{n} |\, c_k - a_k \,|^2 \right\} < \epsilon.$$

The second quantity in braces is nonnegative. Therefore

$$\int_a^b |\, f(x) \,|^2 \, dx - \sum_{k=1}^{n} |\, a_k \,|^2 < \epsilon$$

and hence

$$\sum_{k=1}^{n} |\, a_k \,|^2 > \int_a^b |\, f(x) \,|^2 \, dx - \epsilon$$

so that

$$(12.781) \qquad \sum_{k=1}^{\infty} |\, a_k \,|^2 > \int_a^b |\, f(x) \,|^2 \, dx - \epsilon.$$

Since (12.781) holds for each $\epsilon > 0$, it follows that

$$\sum_{k=1}^{\infty} |\, a_k \,|^2 \geq \int_a^b |\, f(x) \,|^2 \, dx;$$

and this, together with Bessel's inequality (12.76), establishes the desired Parseval equality (12.78).

We give without proof the following facts: *The orthonormal set*

$$(12.791) \qquad \sqrt{\frac{2}{b}} \sin \frac{n\pi x}{b} \qquad\qquad n = 1, 2, 3, \cdots$$

is complete over the interval $0 \leq x \leq b$. *The orthonormal set*

$$(12.792) \qquad \sqrt{\frac{1}{b}}, \quad \sqrt{\frac{2}{b}} \cos \frac{n\pi x}{b} \qquad\qquad n = 1, 2, 3, \cdots$$

is complete over the interval $0 \leq x \leq b$. *The orthonormal set*

$$(12.793) \qquad \sqrt{\frac{1}{2b}} e^{in(\pi/b)x} \qquad\qquad n = 0, \pm 1, \pm 2, \cdots$$

is complete over the interval $-b \leqq x \leqq b$.   *The orthonormal set*

$$(12.794) \qquad \sqrt{\frac{1}{2b}}, \qquad \sqrt{\frac{1}{b}} \cos \frac{n\pi x}{b}, \qquad \sqrt{\frac{1}{b}} \sin \frac{n\pi x}{b} \qquad n = 1, 2, 3, \cdots$$

is complete over the interval $-b \leqq x \leqq b$.   *The orthonormal set of normalized Legendre polynomials* $\tilde{P}_n(x)$ *defined by*

$$(12.795) \qquad \tilde{P}_n(x) = \sqrt{\frac{2n+1}{2}} \, P_n(x) \qquad n = 0, 1, 2, \cdots$$

(see Section 7.9) is complete over the interval $-1 \leqq x \leqq 1$.

Problem 12.796

Prove that if

$$(12.797) \qquad f(x) = a_1\phi_1(x) + a_2\phi_2(x) + a_3\phi_3(x) + \cdots \qquad a \leqq x \leqq b$$

where $\phi_1, \phi_2, \cdots$ constitute an orthonormal set over $a \leqq x \leqq b$, and if (12.797) can be multiplied by $\bar{\phi}_k(x)$ and integrated termwise over $a \leqq x \leqq b$ for each $k = 1, 2, \cdots$, then the constants $a_1, a_2, \cdots$ must be the Fourier coefficients of $f(x)$.

12.8. Fourier Series.—Let $\phi_1(x)$, $\phi_2(x)$, $\cdots$ be an orthonormal set over $a \leqq x \leqq b$, let $f(x)$ be Riemann integrable over $a \leqq x \leqq b$, and, as in Section 12.7, let

$$(12.81) \qquad a_k = \int_a^b f(x)\bar{\phi}_k(x)dx \qquad k = 1, 2, 3, \cdots$$

be the Fourier coefficients of $f(x)$.   Then the infinite series

$$(12.82) \qquad a_1\phi_1(x) + a_2\phi_2(x) + a_3\phi_3(x) + \cdots$$

is called the *Fourier series* (or *Fourier expansion* or *Fourier development* or *orthogonal series*, etc.) of $f(x)$.   It is customary and convenient to write

$$(12.83) \qquad f(x) \sim a_1\phi_1(x) + a_2\phi_2(x) + a_3\phi_3(x) + \cdots$$

where the $[\sim]$ means merely that the series on the right is the Fourier series of $f(x)$.

The sequence

$$(12.84) \qquad \sum_{k=1}^{n} a_k\phi_k(x) \qquad n = 1, 2, 3, \cdots$$

which appeared in (12.75) is, of course, the sequence of partial sums of the Fourier series.   We recall from Section 12.7 the formula

$$(12.85) \qquad \int_a^b \Big| f(x) - \sum_{k=1}^{n} a_k\phi_k(x) \Big|^2 dx = \int_a^b |f(x)|^2 dx - \sum_{k=1}^{n} |a_k|^2,$$

which holds whether the set $\phi_n(x)$ is complete or not, and the Parseval equality

$$(12.86) \qquad \int_a^b |f(x)|^2 \, dx = \sum_{k=1}^\infty |a_k|^2,$$

which holds when the set $\phi_n(x)$ is complete.

The three formulas (12.81), (12.85), and (12.86) alone constitute a very useful theory of expansion of functions into Fourier series. Starting with a given function $f(x)$, one uses (12.81) to compute Fourier coefficients $a_1, \cdots, a_n$; the aim is to get enough a's to make the right-hand member of (12.85) small enough to suit one's purpose. If the orthonormal set is complete and one knows that it is complete, then by use of (12.86) one can tell in advance that the aim can be realized. If one does not know whether or not the set is complete, one can try to realize the aim; if one succeeds, then the goal is attained whether the orthonormal set be complete or incomplete. The coefficients $a_1, a_2, \cdots, a_n$ having been computed to make the right-hand member of (12.85) "small," the formula (12.85) shows that the partial sum (12.84) is a "good" approximation to $f(x)$, and one uses the formula

$$f(x) = \sum_{k=1}^n c_k \phi_k(x)$$

which is usually incorrect but sufficiently accurate for many practical purposes.

The theory of Fourier series has a long and honorable history. Since the time of Fourier (1768–1830), hundreds of thousands of pages have been written on the subject. The first developments of the subject involved the trigonometric orthonormal set; in our discussion we may think of $\phi_1, \phi_2, \phi_3, \cdots$ as being the trigonometric, complex exponential, or any other *complete* orthonormal set. When Fourier announced that "an arbitrary function $f(x)$ can be expanded into a series $c_1\phi_1 + c_2\phi_2 + \cdots$," the mathematicians of his day were, as the story goes, "filled with incredulity and amazement." The idea of Fourier has been developed into a standard method of solving diverse problems. Soon after the time of Fourier, the question of convergence of Fourier series was investigated (see Section 8.6). Of course, any Riemann integrable function $f(x)$ can be expanded into a Fourier series, but it was found that some further conditions must be placed upon $f(x)$ before one can be sure that the expansion converges to $f(x)$. For a long time, pure mathematicians insisted that Fourier series (and other series as well) could not be used unless the series were known to be convergent. During this time, there was continual controversy between pure mathematicians and applied mathematicians who got satisfactory answers without paying attention to questions of convergence. Fortunately, this war is now over. Everyone knows that, if a function $f(x)$ satisfies one or another of certain conditions, then the Fourier series of $f(x)$ will converge to $f(x)$. On the other hand, everyone knows that in many problems there is no reason for paying attention to the question of convergence of

Fourier series; it makes no difference whether the Fourier series converges or diverges.

Problem 12.87

When the complex exponential set (12.793) is used, it is customary to write the Fourier series of $f(x)$ in the form

$$(12.871) \qquad f(x) \sim \frac{a_0}{\sqrt{2b}} + \sum_{n=1}^{\infty} \left[a_n \frac{e^{in(\pi/b)x}}{\sqrt{2b}} + a_{-n} \frac{e^{-in(\pi/b)x}}{\sqrt{2b}} \right]$$

where a_n is, for each $n = 0, \pm 1, \pm 2, \cdots$, the Fourier coefficient

$$a_n = \sqrt{\frac{1}{2b}} \int_{-b}^{b} f(x) e^{-in(\pi/b)x} \, dx.$$

Considering the case in which $b = \pi$ and

$$(12.872) \qquad\qquad\qquad f(x) = x \qquad\qquad\qquad -\pi < x < \pi$$

show that $a_0 = 0$ and

$$(12.873) \qquad\qquad\qquad a_n = \frac{(-1)^n \sqrt{2\pi}\, i}{n} \qquad\qquad n = \pm 1, \pm 2, \cdots.$$

Show that the Parseval equality

$$\int_{-\pi}^{\pi} | f(x) |^2 \, dx = \sum_{n=-\infty}^{\infty} | a_n |^2$$

becomes in this case

$$\frac{2\pi^3}{3} = 2 \sum_{n=1}^{\infty} \frac{2\pi}{n^2}$$

so that

$$(12.874) \qquad\qquad\qquad \frac{\pi^2}{6} = 1 + \frac{1}{2^2} + \frac{1}{3^2} + \frac{1}{4^2} + \cdots.$$

Show that (12.871) becomes in this case

$$x \sim \tfrac{2}{1} \sin x - \tfrac{2}{2} \sin 2x + \tfrac{2}{3} \sin 3x - \tfrac{2}{4} \sin 4x + \tfrac{2}{5} \sin 5x - \cdots.$$

Graphs which show how the partial sums of the series on the right approximate the function x may be found in some books on Fourier series.* The formula (12.874) is frequently encountered in advanced mathematics.

Problem 12.88

If $F(x)$ and $G(x)$ have at most a finite set of discontinuities in an interval $a \leqq x \leqq b$ and if the two integrals in the right member of the inequality

$$(12.881) \qquad \int_{a}^{b} | F(x)G(x) | \, dx \leqq \sqrt{\int_{a}^{b} | F(x) |^2 \, dx} \sqrt{\int_{a}^{b} | G(x) |^2 \, dx}$$

* See, for example, H. S. Carslaw, "Fourier Series and Integrals," The Macmillan Company, New York, 1930.

exist as Riemann or Cauchy integrals, then the integral on the left exists and the inequality holds. This inequality is the *Schwarz inequality*. It is also true that

$$(12.882) \qquad \left| \int_a^b F(x)\bar{G}(x)dx \right| \leqq \int_a^b |F(x)G(x)|\,dx.$$

Let f and g be functions satisfying the conditions imposed above on F and G. Using (12.881) and (12.882), show that if

$$f \sim a_1\phi_1 + a_2\phi_2 + \cdots$$

where ϕ_1, ϕ_2, $\cdots$ is a complete orthonormal set over $a \leqq x \leqq b$, then

$$\lim_{n \to \infty} \int_a^b \left[f(x) - \sum_{k=1}^n a_k\phi_k(x) \right] \bar{g}(x)dx = 0$$

and hence

$$\int_a^b f(x)\bar{g}(x)dx = a_1 \int_a^b \bar{g}(x)\phi_1(x)dx + a_2 \int_a^b \bar{g}(x)\phi_2(x)dx + \cdots.$$

Show that if also

$$g \sim b_1\phi_1 + b_2\phi_2 + \cdots$$

then

$$\int_a^b f(x)\bar{g}(x)dx = a_1\bar{b}_1 + a_2\bar{b}_2 + \cdots.$$

To what does the last equality reduce when $g = f$? *Ans.:* The Parseval equality.

12.9. Partial Differential Equations.—Many problems in mathematical physics are solved by finding a function of two or more variables which satisfies a partial differential equation and supplementary conditions called *boundary conditions* (or *initial conditions*). Frequently, one of the independent variables represents a time coordinate, and the others represent space coordinates.

We give a brief discussion of the *Fourier method* of finding such functions. The equation

$$(12.91) \qquad A\,\frac{\partial^2 u}{\partial x^2} + B\,\frac{\partial u}{\partial x} + C\,\frac{\partial^2 u}{\partial y^2} + D\,\frac{\partial u}{\partial y} + Eu = 0,$$

in which A and B are functions of x and C, D, and E are functions of y, is sufficiently complicated for significant illustration of the method. In case $A = C = 1$ and $B = D = E = 0$, this becomes the *Laplace equation;* in case $A = 1$, $C = -a^2$, and $B = D = E = 0$, it becomes the *wave equation;* and in case $A = a^2$, $D = -1$, $B = D = E = 0$, it becomes the *heat equation*. Other determinations of the functions A, B, C, D, E yield other important equations. Different boundary conditions correspond to different problems.

The procedure of the Fourier method is as follows: First determine functions $u_1(x, y)$, $u_2(x, y)$, $\cdots$ of the form

$$(12.92) \qquad u_n(x, y) = X_n(x)Y_n(y).$$

such that, for each n, $u_n(x, y)$ satisfies the differential equation (12.91) and *some* of the boundary conditions; then determine constants $A_1, A_2, \cdots$ such that the series

$$A_1 u_1(x, y) + A_2 u_2(x, y) + A_3 u_3(x, y) + \cdots$$

represents the required function $u(x, y)$ satisfying the differential equation (12.91) and *all* the boundary conditions. We simplify our discussion by referring to the functions in (12.92) as *harmonics* of $u(x, y)$; the term harmonic is ordinarily used only when the differential equation involved is the Laplace equation.

The first step can be described in simple language: we seek harmonics of the required solution. A function of the form

$$u_0(x, y) = X(x)Y(y),$$

where X is a function of x alone and Y is a function of y alone, will satisfy (12.91) if and only if

(12.921) $$AX''Y + BX'Y + CXY'' + DXY' + EXY = 0$$

where primes on X and Y mean, respectively, ordinary x and y derivatives. When neither X nor Y vanishes in the range of values of x and y considered, (12.921) holds if and only if

(12.922) $$A \frac{X''}{X} + B \frac{X'}{X} = -\left(C \frac{Y''}{Y} + D \frac{Y'}{Y} + E \right).$$

Since the first member is independent of y and the second member is independent of x, it can be shown that (12.922) holds if and only if its members are constant, say $-\lambda$, so that

(12.923) $$AX'' + BX' = -\lambda X$$
(12.924) $$CY'' + DY' + EY = \lambda Y.$$

In case X or Y has zeros, these equations may be obtained by another and more tedious method. The two equations (12.923) and (12.924) have the forms $L_1 X = -\lambda X$ and $L_2 Y = \lambda Y$ where L_1 and L_2 are second-order operators of the familiar type,* and accordingly we now have equations of the form considered in Section 12.3. If they are not self-adjoint, we can introduce factors as in Section 12.33 to make them self-adjoint. In many important applications of the Fourier method, the function $u_0(x, y) = X(x)Y(y)$ will satisfy some (but not all) of the boundary conditions which $u(x, y)$ must satisfy if $X(x)$ satisfies a set of linear boundary conditions which, together with the

---

* Many of the important ordinary differential equations, including those of Bessel and Legendre, arise from partial differential equations in this way.

equation $L_1X = \lambda X$, constitute an eigenvalue problem of the Sturm-Liouville type of Section 12.4.   It then often happens that the Sturm-Liouville system has an infinite set of eigenvalues $\lambda_1, \lambda_2, \lambda_3, \cdots$ and an infinite set of eigenfunctions $X_1(x), X_2(x), \cdots$ such that the functions

$$(12.925) \qquad\qquad \sqrt{p(x)}\, X_n(x) \qquad\qquad n = 1, 2, 3, \cdots$$

form a complete orthonormal set over some interval $a \leq x \leq b$. Here $p(x)$ is, as in Section 12.33, the factor introduced into $L_1X = \lambda X$ to make it self-adjoint.

The next step is to get the solutions for each n of the equation $L_2Y = \lambda_n Y$, that is, of equation (12.924) when $\lambda = \lambda_n$.   In case $C \equiv C(y) \neq 0$ while C, D, E are continuous, the solutions have the form

$$(12.93) \qquad\qquad Y_n(y) = \alpha_n U_n(y) + \beta_n V_n(y)$$

where α_n and β_n are constants and $U_n(y)$ and $V_n(y)$ are two linearly independent solutions of $L_2Y = \lambda_n Y$.   The harmonics of the solution we are seeking are then of the form

$$(12.94) \qquad\qquad X_n(x)[\alpha_n U_n(y) + \beta_n V_n(y)] \qquad n = 1, 2, 3, \cdots .$$

Since the differential equation (12.91) and the boundary conditions satisfied by the harmonics are linear, it follows that the sum $S_N(x, y)$ defined by

$$(12.95) \qquad\qquad S_N(x, y) = \sum_{n=1}^{N} X_n(x)[\alpha_n U_n(y) + \beta_n V_n(y)]$$

satisfies them for each positive integer N.   In case $C \equiv C(y) = 0$ for all y while $D(y) \neq 0$, the first-order equation $L_2y = \lambda_n y$ would have solutions of the form $Y_n(y) = \alpha_n U_n(y)$ and (12.95) would take the form

$$(12.951) \qquad\qquad S_N(x, y) = \sum_{n=1}^{N} \alpha_n X_n(x) U_n(y).$$

It should now be observed that, however N and $\alpha_1, \alpha_2, \cdots$, $\beta_1, \beta_2, \cdots$, are determined, $S_N(x, y)$ satisfies the differential equation (12.91) and *some* of the boundary conditions which $u(x, y)$ must satisfy.   In a properly formulated problem to which the Fourier method applies, it turns out that $S_N(x, y)$ is a good approximation to the function $u(x, y)$ we are seeking provided that N is sufficiently great and the constants $\alpha_1, \alpha_2, \cdots$ and $\beta_1, \beta_2, \cdots$ are suitably determined.

These constants are often determined by use of such boundary conditions as we now describe. Let the points x, y for which $a \leqq x \leqq b$ and $y = y_0$ form a part of the boundary of the region R in the interior of which $u(x, y)$ is to satisfy the differential equation. Let the values of the required function $u(x, y)$ on this part of the boundary be $f(x)$. It is not necessary to assume that $f(x)$ is continuous or that it is bounded. It is enough to assume that $f(x)$ has at most a finite set of discontinuities in the interval $a \leqq x \leqq b$ and that

$$\int_a^b |f(x)|^2 \, dx$$

exists as a Cauchy integral. The condition

(12.96) $$u(x, y_0) = f(x) \qquad\qquad a \leqq x \leqq b$$

is a sensible boundary condition provided that it is coupled with an assumption which yields a suitable connection between the values of $u(x, y)$ when (x, y) is a point of the region R and the values when (x, y) is a point of the boundary. An assumption that $u(x, y)$ is continuous at all points of the boundary would make the condition sensible provided that $f(x)$ is continuous. If $f(x)$ is not continuous, more finesse must be used in formulating a satisfactory boundary condition. There are reasons why the condition

(12.961) $$\lim_{y \to y_0} \int_a^b |f(x) - u(x, y)|^2 \, dx = 0$$

is the "best" condition to impose to make sure that the function $u(x, y)$ does not make a sudden and absurd jump from its values on the boundary to its values inside the region.* Indeed the condition (12.961) is so good that, when it is combined with (12.96), it becomes the more significant of the two conditions. In many problems, one can use (12.961) as the boundary condition, leaving (12.96) out of consideration.

---

* Suppose one is required to find a function $u(x, y)$ such that

$$\frac{\partial^2 u}{\partial x^2} + \frac{\partial^2 u}{\partial y^2} = 0$$

at all points (x, y) inside the square with opposite vertices at $(0, 0)$ and $(1, 1)$, and such that $u(x, y)$ is zero at all points of the boundary except that $u(x, 0) = x^2$ when $0 \leqq x \leqq \frac{1}{2}$. Obviously the function $u_1(x, y)$ which vanishes identically, except that $u_1(x, 0) = x^2$ when $0 \leqq x \leqq \frac{1}{2}$, meets the requirement. A practical problem would be so formulated that one is required to find a function $u(x, y)$ for which the function of x, obtained by assigning a fixed small positive value to the y in $u(x, y)$, is in some sense or other a good approximation to the function $u(x, 0)$.

We are now ready to do some optimistic supposing and concluding which lead to determinations of the α's and β's. Suppose that the series

$$(12.97) \qquad \sum_{n=1}^{\infty} X_n(x)[\alpha_n U_n(y) + \beta_n V_n(y)],$$

whether convergent or divergent, represents the solution $u(x, y)$ of our problem in the sense that

$$(12.971) \quad \lim_{N \to \infty} \int_a^b \mid u(x, y) - \sum_{n=1}^{N} X_n(x)[\alpha_n U_n(y) + \beta_n V_n(y)] \mid^2 dx = 0.$$

Setting $y = y_0$ in this formula and using (12.96) give

$$(12.972) \quad \lim_{N \to \infty} \int_a^b \mid f(x) - \sum_{n=1}^{N} [\alpha_n A_n + \beta_n B_n] X_n(x) \mid^2 dx = 0$$

where, to simplify writing, we have put $A_n = U_n(y_0)$ and $B_n = V_n(y_0)$. Upon assuming that the weight function $p(x)$ is bounded as well as positive over $a \leq x \leq b$, it can be shown that (12.972) implies

$$\lim_{N \to \infty} \int_a^b \mid \sqrt{p(x)}\, f(x) - \sum_{n=1}^{N} [\alpha_n A_n + \beta_n B_n] \sqrt{p(x)}\, X_n(x) \mid^2 dx = 0.$$

Since the functions $\sqrt{p(x)}\, X_n(x)$, which we could call $\phi_n(x)$, constitute a complete orthonormal set, this formula holds if and only if the coefficients $[\alpha_n A_n + \beta_n B_n]$ are the Fourier coefficients of the function $\sqrt{p(x)}\, f(x)$. Thus the formula holds if and only if

$$\alpha_n A_n + \beta_n B_n = \int_a^b \{\sqrt{p(x)}\, f(x)\}\{\sqrt{p(x)}\, \bar{X}_n(x)\} dx$$

or

$$(12.973) \qquad \alpha_n A_n + \beta_n B_n = \int_a^b f(x)p(x)\bar{X}_n(x)dx.$$

For the simpler problem in which $C \equiv C(y) \equiv 0$ and the β's are absent the equations serve to determine the α's, provided, of course, that $A_n = U_n(y_0) \neq 0$. In case $C \neq 0$, another boundary condition would appear in the formulation of the problem and would be used to assist in the determination of the α's and β's. In some problems the extra boundary condition takes the form

$$\frac{\partial u}{\partial y}\Big|_{y=y_0} = g(x)$$

where the left-hand side denotes the value of $\partial u/\partial x$ when $y = y_0$, and this leads to equations

$$(12.974) \qquad \alpha_n A'_n + \beta_n B'_n = \int_a^b g(x)p(x)\bar{X}_n(x)dx$$

where $A'_n = U'_n(y_0)$ and $B'_n = V'_n(y_0)$; the two equations (12.973) and (12.974) then determine the α's and β's. In other types of problems, other methods are used to determine the α's and β's; but it is characteristic of the Fourier method that Fourier series enter into the solution.

Having determined the α's and β's, applied mathematicians obtain many useful results by using

$$(12.98) \qquad S_N(x, y) = \sum_{n=1}^{N} X_n(x)[\alpha_n U_n(y) + \beta_n V_n(y)]$$

as an approximation to the solution $u(x, y)$ of the problem. The problem involved in showing why this can be true involves mathematical analysis which we cannot present here; in particular, it is impossible to construct an adequate general theory without using Lebesgue integration.

Each of the following problems is not carefully formulated since there is no requirement that the values of the function $u(x, y)$ at interior points of the region where the differential equation holds must be related in some sensible way to the values of $u(x, y)$ at points of the boundary. To formulate satisfactory requirements, and to ask that students verify that their alleged solutions satisfy the requirements, would make the problems entirely too difficult for this book. Actually, many books more advanced than this one ignore these difficulties. A student in a first course in differential equations should be content if he can apply the procedure outlined in this chapter to obtain the functions $u(x, y)$ which are presented as answers to the problems.

Problem 12.981

Use the Fourier method to find a function $u(x, y)$ such that

$$\frac{\partial^2 u}{\partial x^2} = a^2 \frac{\partial u}{\partial y} \qquad\qquad 0 < x < \pi; \, y > 0$$
$$u(0, y) = u(\pi, y) = 0 \qquad\qquad y > 0$$
$$u(x, 0) = f(x) \qquad\qquad 0 < x < \pi,$$

where a is a positive constant and $f(x)$ is a given function of the type considered above. *Ans.:*

$$u(x, y) = \sum_{n=1}^{\infty} c_n e^{-(n^2/a^2)y} \sin nx, \qquad 0 \le x \le \pi; \, y > 0,$$

where

$$c_n = \frac{2}{\pi} \int_0^{\pi} f(x) \sin nx \, dx \qquad n = 1, 2, 3, \cdots.$$

Discuss completely the special case in which the function $f(x)$ has the form

$$f(x) = \sum_{k=1}^{N} E_k \sin kx.$$

Remark: If x is the distance of a point from one end of a rod with initial temperature $f(x)$, if the ends of the rod are maintained at temperature 0, and if no heat escapes from the rod except at the ends, then $u(x, y)$ is the temperature at time $y > 0$ of the point of the rod with abscissa x.

Problem 12.982

Use the Fourier method to find approximations to a function $u(x, y)$ such that

$$\frac{\partial^2 u}{\partial x^2} + \frac{\partial^2 u}{\partial y^2} = 0 \qquad\qquad 0 < x, y < \pi$$
$$u(0, y) = u(\pi, y) = 0 \qquad\qquad 0 < y < \pi$$
$$u(x, \pi) = 0 \qquad\qquad 0 < x < \pi$$
$$u(x, 0) = f(x) \qquad\qquad 0 < x < \pi,$$

where $f(x)$ is a given function of the type considered above.   *Ans.:*

$$S_N(x, y) = \sum_{n=1}^{N} c_n[e^{n(\pi-y)} - e^{-n(\pi-y)}] \sin nx$$

where

$$c_n = \frac{2}{\pi} \frac{1}{e^{n\pi} - e^{-n\pi}} \int_0^\pi f(x) \sin nx\, dx \qquad n = 1, 2, 3, \cdots.$$

Discuss completely the special case in which the function $f(x)$ has the form

$$f(x) = \sum_{k=1}^{n} E_k \sin kx.$$

Remark: This problem has several important physical meanings.

Problem 12.983

Use the Fourier method to find approximations to a function $u(x, y)$ such that

$$\frac{\partial^2 u}{\partial x^2} = a^2 \frac{\partial^2 u}{\partial y^2} \qquad\qquad 0 < x < a; y > 0$$
$$u(0, y) = u(\pi, y) = 0 \qquad\qquad y > 0$$
$$u(x, 0) = f(x) \qquad\qquad 0 < x < \pi$$
$$u_y(x, 0) = g(x) \qquad\qquad 0 < x < \pi,$$

where u_y means $\partial u/\partial y$ and $f(x)$ and $g(x)$ are given functions of the type considered above.   *Ans.:*

$$S_N(x, y) = \sum_{n=1}^{N} [\alpha_n \cos any + \beta_n \sin any] \sin nx$$

where

$$\alpha_n = \frac{2}{\pi} \int_0^\pi f(x) \sin nx\, dx, \qquad \beta_n = \frac{2}{an\pi} \int_0^\pi g(x) \sin nx\, dx \qquad n = 1, 2, \cdots$$

CHAPTER 13

EXACT EQUATIONS OF FIRST ORDER; INTEGRATING FACTORS

13.1. Introduction.—The topics considered in this and the next chapter can be studied at any time after studying Chapter 5. The material is presented later in this book because of the author's opinion that, however important it may be, it is less important than topics heretofore presented. This chapter is concerned with a special method by means of which it is sometimes possible to find functions $y(x)$ for which

$$M(x, y) + N(x, y) \frac{dy}{dx} = 0,$$

$M(x, y)$ and $N(x, y)$ being given functions of x and y. Without aiming at the greatest possible generality, we consider cases in which $M(x, y)$ and $N(x, y)$ are continuous and have continuous partial derivatives of first order in a region R of the xy plane. The region R may be the entire plane, the interior of a rectangle or circle, or any region having the following property: There is a fixed point (x_0, y_0) of the region R such that if (x, y) is a point of R then the rectangle, with sides parallel to the axes and with opposite vertices at (x_0, y_0) and (x, y), lies in the region R.

13.2. Exact Equations.—A differential equation $M\,dx + N\,dy = 0$ is said to be *exact* if there exists a function $f(x, y)$ such that

(13.21) $$\frac{\partial f}{\partial x} = M; \qquad \frac{\partial f}{\partial y} = N.$$

Although the definition makes the assertion superfluous, we wish to emphasize the fact that, if no such function $f(x, y)$ exists then the equation is not exact. A *differential expression* $M\,dx + N\,dy$ is called *exact* when there is a function f such that (13.21) holds and hence such that

$$df = \frac{\partial f}{\partial x}\,dx + \frac{\partial f}{\partial y}\,dy = M\,dx + N\,dy.$$

If an equation $M\,dx + N\,dy = 0$ is known to be exact and if a function f for which (13.21) holds has been found, then it is easy to obtain at least formal solutions.   If $y = y(x)$ is a solution of

$$M \, dx + N \, dy = 0$$

then

$$M + N \frac{dy}{dx} = 0$$

and using (13.21) we obtain

$$\frac{\partial f}{\partial x} + \frac{\partial f}{\partial y} \frac{dy}{dx} = 0.$$

Since y is a differentiable function of x, we can use the familiar formula

$$\frac{d}{dx} f(x, \, y) = \frac{\partial f}{\partial x} + \frac{\partial f}{\partial y} \frac{dy}{dx}$$

to obtain

$$\frac{d}{dx} f(x, \, y) = 0$$

and hence $f(x, \, y) = c$.   Conversely, if c is a constant, $f(x, \, y)$ has continuous partial derivatives, and $y(x)$ is a differentiable function of x for which $f(x, \, y) = c$, then the work can be reversed to show that $y(x)$ is a solution of $M \, dx + N \, dy = 0$.   Hence $f(x, \, y) = c$ furnishes an answer to the problem.   To sum up, we may say that *if*

$$M \, dx + N \, dy = 0$$

is exact, then $f(x, \, y)$ *exists such that*

$$df(x, \, y) = \frac{\partial f}{\partial x} \, dx + \frac{\partial f}{\partial y} \, dy = M \, dx + N \, dy = 0$$

and that

(13.22) $$f(x, \, y) = c$$

represents a formal solution of the problem.

Having learned that exact equations are easily solved when f has been found, we naturally ask three questions: How do you tell whether or not $M \, dx + N \, dy$ is exact?   How do you find f when $M \, dx + N \, dy$ is exact?   Is there any way in which the problem of solving an equation which is not exact can be reduced to the problem of solving an exact equation?   We proceed to answer the first two questions; the third will be considered later in this chapter.

THEOREM 13.23.—*If M and N are continuous and have continuous first partial derivatives, a necessary and sufficient condition that*

(13.24) $$M \, dx + N \, dy$$

be exact is that

$$(13.25) \qquad \frac{\partial M}{\partial y} = \frac{\partial N}{\partial x};$$

moreover, if (13.24) *is exact, then the functions f for which* $\partial f/\partial x = M$
and $\partial f/\partial y = N$ *are those and only those representable in the form*

$$(13.26) \qquad f(x, y) = \int_{x_0}^{x} M(t, y)dt + \int_{y_0}^{y} N(x_0, u)du + k$$

where k is a constant.

To prove necessity, we assume that $M\,dx + N\,dy$ is exact. Then $f(x, y)$ exists such that

$$(13.27) \qquad \frac{\partial f}{\partial x} = M, \qquad \frac{\partial f}{\partial y} = N.$$

Since M and N are continuous and have continuous first partial derivatives, it follows from (13.27) that f has continuous partial derivatives of first and second orders; this implies (as is stated in some elementary-calculus books and is proved in advanced-calculus books) that

$$(13.28) \qquad \frac{\partial}{\partial y}\left(\frac{\partial f}{\partial x}\right) = \frac{\partial}{\partial x}\left(\frac{\partial f}{\partial y}\right), \qquad \text{or} \qquad \frac{\partial^2 f}{\partial y\,\partial x} = \frac{\partial^2 f}{\partial x\,\partial y}.$$

Using (13.27) and (13.28) we see that

$$\frac{\partial M}{\partial y} = \frac{\partial^2 f}{\partial y\,\partial x} = \frac{\partial^2 f}{\partial x\,\partial y} = \frac{\partial N}{\partial y};$$

thus (13.25) holds, and necessity is established.

13.3. Examples.—Before undertaking to complete the proof of Theorem 13.23, we indicate the nature of the problem before us by considering an example. The expression

$$(13.31) \qquad (x^2 + y)dx + (x + y^2)dy,$$

in which

$$(13.32) \qquad M = x^2 + y, \qquad N = x + y^2,$$

satisfies the criterion for exactness since $\partial M/\partial y = \partial N/\partial x = 1$. We want to find $f(x, y)$ such that $\partial f/\partial x = M$ and $\partial f/\partial y = N$. The equation $\partial f/\partial x = M$ will be true if and only if

$$(13.33) \qquad f = \tfrac{1}{3}x^3 + xy + \phi(y)$$

where $\phi(y)$ is a function of y. If $\partial f/\partial y$ exists, then (since $\tfrac{1}{3}x^3 + xy$ has a derivative with respect to y) $\phi(y)$ must be differentiable and

$$(13.34) \qquad \frac{\partial f}{\partial y} = x + \phi'(y).$$

Comparing (13.32) and (13.34) we see that $\partial f/\partial y$ will be equal to N if and only if $\phi'(y) = y^2$ or

$$(13.35) \qquad\qquad \phi(y) = \tfrac{1}{3}y^3 + k$$

where k is a constant.   Thus we see that the equations $\partial f/\partial x = M$ and $\partial f/\partial y = N$ will both hold if and only if (13.33) and (13.34) both hold, that is, if and only if

$$f = \tfrac{1}{3}x^3 + xy + \tfrac{1}{3}y^3 + k.$$

The solutions of the equation

$$(x^2 + y)dx + (x + y^2)dy = 0$$

are accordingly $\tfrac{1}{3}x^3 + xy + \tfrac{1}{3}y^3 = c_1$ or

$$x^3 + 3xy + y^3 = c.$$

Problem 13.36

Carry through the process described above to find f for the exact expression

$$(3x^2y^2 + 2xy + 1)dx + (2x^3y + x^2 + 1)dy. \quad Ans.: f = x^3y^2 + x^2y + x + y + C.$$

Problem 13.37

Find the difficulty in attempting to use the process described above to find f for the inexact expression

$$(x^2 - y)dx + (x - y^2)dy.$$

Problem 13.38

Solve the equation

$$\frac{dy}{dx} = \frac{a - xy^2}{x^2y}. \qquad\qquad Ans.: x^2y^2 - 2ax = c.$$

13.4. Proof of Sufficiency for Theorem 13.23.—We now assume that M and N have continuous partial derivatives and

$$\partial M/\partial y = \partial N/\partial x;$$

we are required to show existence of a function $f(x, y)$ such that $\partial f/\partial x = M$ and $\partial f/\partial y = N$.   The first of the two conditions will be satisfied if and only if

$$(13.41) \qquad\qquad f(x, y) = \int_{x_0}^{x} M(t, y)dt + \phi(y),$$

and the second will also be satisfied if and only if

$$(13.42) \qquad\qquad \frac{\partial}{\partial y} \int_{x_0}^{x} M(t, y)dt + \phi'(y) = N(x, y).$$

Hence the function $f(x, y)$ in (13.41) will satisfy both conditions if $\phi(y)$ is determined so that (13.42) holds. The hypotheses on M and N imply that

$$\frac{\partial}{\partial y} \int_{x_0}^{x} M(t, y)dt = \int_{x_0}^{x} \frac{\partial}{\partial y} M(t, y)dt$$

$$= \int_{x_0}^{x} \frac{\partial}{\partial t} N(t, y)dt = N(x, y) - N(x_0, y)$$

so that (13.42) holds if and only if $\phi'(y) = N(x_0, y)$ or

$$\phi(y) = \int_{y_0}^{y} N(x_0, u)du + k.$$

Thus the functions $f(x, y)$ in (13.26) are those having the required properties, and Theorem 13.23 is proved.

Problem 13.43

Show that the equation

$$(x^m + 2xy^2)dx + (y^n + 2x^2y)dy = 0$$

is exact, and find its solutions both by the method of Section 13.3 and by use of (13.26). *Ans. (partial):*

$$\frac{x^{m+1}}{m+1} + x^2y^2 + \frac{x^{n+1}}{n+1} = c,$$

provided that $m, n \neq -1$.

Problem 13.44

Show that, if $M(x, y)$ and $N(x, y)$ are the real functions determined by the formula

(13.45) $$(x + iy)^3 = M(x, y) - iN(x, y),$$

then the equation $M\,dx + N\,dy = 0$ is exact. Solve the equation.

Ans. $x^4 - 6x^2y^2 + y^4 = c.$

Show that, if $M_1(x, y)$ and $N_1(x, y)$ are the real functions determined by the formula

(13.46) $$(x + iy)^3 = N_1(x, y) + iM_1(x, y),$$

then $M_1\,dx + N_1\,dy = 0$ is exact. Solve the equation. *Ans.:* $x^3y - xy^3 = c.$

See what happens when the exponents 3 in (13.45) and (13.46) are replaced by 1; by 2; by -1. Sketch graphs of the curves at least for the case in which the exponent is 1.

13.5. Integrating Factors.—A function $\mu = \mu(x, y)$ such that

$$\mu[M\,dx + N\,dy]$$

is exact is called an *integrating factor* of $M\,dx + N\,dy$.

The expression

(13.51) $x\,dx + y\,dy$

is exact since

$$d\tfrac{1}{2}(x^2 + y^2) = x\,dx + y\,dy;$$

but (13.51) has integrating factors other than constants.   For example, $(x^2 + y^2)^{-1}$ is an integrating factor of (13.51) since

$$d\frac{1}{2}\log\,(x^2 + y^2) = \frac{x\,dx + y\,dy}{x^2 + y^2}.$$

Moreover, $(x^2 + y^2)^{\frac{1}{2}}$ and all other continuous functions of $x^2 + y^2$ are integrating factors of (13.51) in accordance with the fact that, if $\phi(u)$ is a continuous function of u and $\Phi(u)$ is a function whose derivative is $\phi(u)$, then

$$d\tfrac{1}{2}\Phi(x^2 + y^2) = \phi(x^2 + y^2)(x\,dx + y\,dy).$$

The expression

(13.52) $y\,dx - x\,dy$

is not exact.   The functions $1/y^2$ and $1/x^2$ are integrating factors of (13.52) since

$$d\left(\frac{x}{y}\right) = \frac{y\,dx - x\,dy}{y^2}, \qquad d\left(\frac{-y}{x}\right) = \frac{y\,dx - x\,dy}{x^2}.$$

That there are many integrating factors of (13.52) is shown by the fact that, if $\phi(u)$ is a continuous function of u, then $\phi(y/x)/x^2$ is an integrating factor of (13.52); for if $\Phi(u)$ is a function whose derivative is $\phi(u)$, then

$$d\left[-\Phi\left(\frac{y}{x}\right)\right] = \frac{1}{x^2}\,\phi\left(\frac{y}{x}\right)[y\,dx - x\,dy].$$

Inspection of the two above examples may lead one to suspect that the following theorem is true:

THEOREM 13.53.—*If* $\mu = \mu(x,\ y)$ *is an integrating factor of* $M\,dx + N\,dy$, $f(x,\ y)$ *is such that*

$$df = \mu M\,dx + \mu N\,dy,$$

and $\phi(u)$ *is a continuous function of* u, *then* $\phi(f(x,\ y))\mu(x,\ y)$ *is an integrating factor of* $M\,dx + N\,dy$.

Proof of this theorem is very simple.   Let $\Phi(u)$ be a function whose derivative is $\phi(u)$; then

$$d\Phi(f(x,\ y)) = \phi(f(x,\ y))df(x,\ y) = \phi(f(x,\ y))\mu(x,\ y)[M\,dx + N\,dy],$$

and our result is established.

When one is making a choice of integrating factors for the purpose of solving

(13.54) $M \, dx + N \, dy = 0,$

it is natural to try to select one which minimizes the work involved in the process of finding $f(x, y)$ such that

(13.55) $df = \mu(M \, dx + N \, dy) = 0.$

Another consideration is of importance; for from (13.55) one concludes that $f(x, y) = c$ is a solution (formal) of

(13.56) $\mu[M \, dx + N \, dy] = 0,$

and this implies only that $f(x, y) = c$ is a solution (formal) of (13.54) for values of x and y for which $\mu(x, y) \neq 0$. Hence, it is desirable to have integrating factors without zeros or with as few zeros as possible. In an extreme and ridiculous case, the function $\mu(x, y)$ which is always 0 is always an integrating factor of (13.54); but it is always useless since in this case it is impossible to conclude that a solution of (13.56) is also a solution of 13.54.

A standard method of attacking differential equations of the form $M \, dx + N \, dy = 0$ consists in grouping the terms in a promising manner and trying to find a common integrating factor of the separate groups. For example, writing

(13.57) $(x + x \sqrt{x^2 + y^2})dx + y \, dy = 0$

in the form

$$[x \, dx + y \, dy] + x \sqrt{x^2 + y^2} \, dx = 0,$$

we see that $(x^2 + y^2)^{-\frac{1}{2}}$ is an integrating factor of each of the two groups. On introducing this factor we obtain

$$\frac{d}{dx} \left[\sqrt{x^2 + y^2} + \frac{1}{2} x^2 \right] = 0$$

and the solution of (13.57) is therefore $2 \sqrt{x^2 + y^2} + x^2 = c$.

Problems

(13.581) $y \, dx - x \, dy + x^2 y^2 \, dx = 0$ Ans.: $3x + x^3 y = cy$
(13.582) $(x^2 y + y^2)dx - x^3 \, dy = 0$ Ans.: $(1 + cx)y = x^2$
(13.583) $(x \, dx + y \, dx) + (x^2 + y^2)(x \, dx - y \, dy) = 0$
                                      Ans.: $\log (x^2 + y^2) + (x^2 - y^2) = c$
(13.584) $(x^2 + y^2 + 2x)dx + (x^2 + y^2 + 2y)dy = 0$ Ans.: $x^2 + y^2 = ce^{-x-y}$

Problem 13.584

Show that the equation

$$\frac{dy}{dx} = \frac{y(1 - x^2)}{x(1 + x^2)}$$

can be written in the form

$$[y \, dx - x \, dy] - x^2[x \, dy + y \, dx] = 0,$$

and solve the equation.   *Ans.: $y = cx/(1 + x^2)$.*

Problem 13.585

Equations such as

$$\sqrt{x^2 + y^2} \, (x \, dx + y \, dy) - (x \, dy - y \, dx) = 0$$

sometimes arise when one uses rectangular coordinates in problems for which polar coordinates are convenient.   One who fails to see that $(x^2 + y^2)^{-1}$ is an integrating factor may simplify the equation by the change of variables $r = \sqrt{x^2 + y^2}$, $\theta = \tan^{-1}(y/x)$ so that

$$dr = \frac{x \, dx + y \, dy}{\sqrt{x^2 + y^2}}, \qquad d\theta = \frac{x \, dy - y \, dx}{x^2 + y^2}.$$

$$\text{\textit{Ans.: } } r = \theta + c \qquad \text{or} \qquad \sqrt{x^2 + y^2} = \tan^{-1}\frac{y}{x} + c.$$

Problem 13.59

Show that, if $\phi_1(x)$ and $\phi_2(y)$ are continuous, then

$$\phi_1(x)dx + \phi_2(y)dy = 0$$

is exact and that, if the variables in

$$M(x, y)dx + N(x, y)dy = 0$$

are separated on multiplying by $\mu(x, y)$, then $\mu(x, y)$ is an integrating factor.

13.6. Integrating Factors of the Form $x^a y^b$.—There is a straight-forward process for obtaining formal solutions of equations when these solutions can be written in the form

$$(13.61) \qquad \sum_{k=1}^{r} a_k x^{m_k} y^{n_k} = c$$

where the coefficients a_k and the exponents m_k and n_k are constants independent of c.   The exponents need not be positive integers; they be any real numbers.   For example, the equation $2x^2 + y^2 + 1 = cxy$ can be written in the form $2xy^{-1} + x^{-1}y + x^{-1}y^{-1} = c$, which has the form (13.61).   Differentiating (13.61) gives the exact differential equation

$$(13.62) \qquad \left[\sum_{k=1}^{r} a_k m_k x^{m_k-1} y^{n_k}\right] dx + \left[\sum_{k=1}^{r} a_k n_k x^{m_k} y^{n_k-1}\right] dy = 0.$$

If one were given the differential equation (13.62), one could see immediately that it is exact and could obtain the solutions (13.61).

When an equation equivalent to (13.62) arises not as we obtained it but in the course of solution of some problem, it may be and often is true that one must introduce a factor $x^a y^b$ to obtain (13.62). For example, the exact equation

$$(13.63) \quad (2y^{-1} - x^{-2}y + x^{-2}y^{-1})dx + (-2xy^{-2} + x^{-1} - x^{-1}y^{-2})dy = 0,$$

which one can obtain from $2xy^{-1} + x^{-1}y + x^{-1}y^{-1} = c$, would probably appear in the form

$$(13.64) \qquad (2x^2 y - y^3 - y)dx + (xy^2 - 2x^3 - x)dy = 0$$

obtained by multiplying (13.63) by $x^2 y^2$. To obtain the exact equation (13.63) from the given inexact equation (13.64), one must multiply (13.64) by the integrating factor $x^{-2}y^{-2}$.

Since many equations of the form

$$(13.65) \qquad\qquad M\,dx + N\,dy = 0$$

(especially those which are easy to solve by various special methods) have solutions representable in the form (13.61), it follows that *many equations of the form* (13.65) *have an integrating factor of the form* $x^a y^b$. When one wishes to know whether (13.65) has an integrating factor of the form $x^a y^b$ and wishes to determine the exponents if the factor exists, one merely seeks to determine exponents a and b such that

$$x^a y^b M\,dx + x^a y^b N\,dy = 0$$

is exact; thus one merely seeks to determine exponents such that

$$(13.66) \qquad\qquad \frac{\partial}{\partial y}\, x^a y^b M = \frac{\partial}{\partial x}\, x^a y^b N.$$

When M and N are given functions, it is usually very easy to find the exponents when they exist. When the integrating factor has been found, the solutions are easily obtained.

Problem 13.67

Show that, for the special equation (13.64), the relation (13.66) becomes $2(a + b + 4)x^{a+2}y^b - (a + b + 4)x^a y^{b+2} + (a - b)x^a y^b = 0$ and that this holds if and only if $a = b = -2$. Solve (13.64) by use of the integrating factor thus determined.

Problems

Each of the following equations has an integrating factor of the form $x^a y^b$. Find the integrating factors and use them to solve the equations.

(13.681)	$y\,dx + (x^2 - x)dy = 0$	*Ans.:* $y = cx/(x - 1)$
(13.682)	$(x^2 - y^2)dx + 2xy\,dy = 0$	*Ans.:* $(x - c)^2 + y^2 = c^2$
(13.683)	$(x^2 y^2 + y)dx + (2x^3 y - x)dy = 0$	*Ans.:* $x^2 y^2 - y = cx$
(13.684)	$(y - xy^2)dx + x\,dy = 0$	*Ans.:* $\mu = \dfrac{1}{x(c - \log x)}$

13.7. Finding of Integrating Factors.—It is often true that integrating factors of $M\,dx + N\,dy$ are found simply by inspection based on knowing formulas for differentials of certain functions of x and y such as $d(x/y) = (y\,dx - x\,dy)/y^2$ and $d(xy) = y\,dx + x\,dy$.

When inspection fails to disclose an integrating factor of $M\,dx + N\,dy = 0$, there arises the question whether a nontrivial one (*i.e.*, one which is different from 0 over significant regions of the plane) exists and whether it can be found. The question of existence of nontrivial integrating factors is closely bound up with the question of existence of solutions of the differential equation which is taken up in Chapter 15. We proceed to give a discussion of integrating factors which reveals some special types of differential equations for which integrating factors can be found.

If $M(x, y)$, $N(x, y)$, and $\mu(x, y)$ are continuous and have continuous partial derivatives, then a necessary and sufficient condition that μ be an integrating factor of $M\,dx + N\,dy$ is that $(\mu M)dx + (\mu N)dy$ be exact, *i.e.*, that

$$(13.71) \qquad \frac{\partial(\mu M)}{\partial y} = \frac{\partial(\mu N)}{\partial x}.$$

This is a partial differential equation which may be written, for values of x and y for which $\mu(x, y) \neq 0$,

$$(13.72) \qquad \frac{1}{\mu}\left(N\frac{\partial \mu}{\partial x} - M\frac{\partial \mu}{\partial y} \right) = \frac{\partial M}{\partial y} - \frac{\partial N}{\partial x}.$$

If

$$(13.73) \qquad \frac{\partial M/\partial y - \partial N/\partial x}{N} \equiv \phi_1(x)$$

is independent of y, then (13.72) will hold if μ is a function of x alone (*i.e.*, if μ is independent of y so that $\partial \mu/\partial y = 0$) and

$$(13.74) \qquad \frac{1}{\mu}\frac{d\mu}{dx} = \phi_1(x)$$

or

$$(13.75) \qquad \mu = k e^{\int \phi_1(x)\,dx}.$$

Thus, if (13.73) holds, then (13.75) is an integrating factor of $M\,dx + N\,dy$ for ranges in which $\phi_1(x)$ is continuous. Similarly, if

$$(13.76) \qquad \frac{\partial M/\partial y - \partial N/\partial x}{M} \equiv \phi_2(y),$$

then

$$\mu = k e^{\int \phi_2(y)\,dy}$$

is an integrating factor of $M\,dx + N\,dy$ for ranges in which $\phi_2(y)$ is continuous.

One case in which (13.73) is obviously satisfied is that in which

$$M = y + g(x), \qquad N = f(x) \neq 0$$

and accordingly

$$\frac{\partial M/\partial y - \partial N/\partial x}{N} = \frac{1 - f'(x)}{f(x)} \equiv \phi_1(x).$$

Hence the differential equation

$$(13.77) \qquad [y + g(x)]dx + f(x)dy = 0$$

can be solved by use of the integrating factor

$$(13.78) \qquad \mu = e^{\int \phi_1(x)\,dx} = \frac{1}{f(x)} e^{\int [1\,//f(x)]\,dx}.$$

This result looks familiar when we write (13.77) in the form

$$(13.79) \qquad f(x)\frac{dy}{dx} + y = -g(x).$$

To solve the linear equation (13.79) by the method we have used repeatedly, we should divide (13.79) by $f(x)$ and then apply the integrating factor $\exp\int [1/f(x)]\,dx$ to the resulting equation; this amounts to applying the integrating factor (13.78) to (13.77).

13.8. Homogeneous Equations; Euler's Theorem.—The function

$$f = x + \sqrt{x^2 + y^2} + y \tan^{-1}\frac{y}{x}$$

is homogeneous of degree $n = 1$; differentiation gives

$$\frac{\partial f}{\partial x} = 1 + \frac{x}{\sqrt{x^2 + y^2}} - \frac{y^2}{x^2 + y^2}$$

and

$$\frac{\partial f}{\partial y} = \frac{y}{\sqrt{x^2 + y^2}} + \tan^{-1}\frac{y}{x} + \frac{xy}{x^2 + y^2},$$

and it is seen that

$$(13.81) \qquad x\frac{\partial f}{\partial x} + y\frac{\partial f}{\partial y} = nf.$$

That (13.81) holds, whenever $f(x, y)$ is a homogeneous function of x and y of degree n having continuous partial derivatives, is asserted by *Euler's theorem on homogeneous functions.* To prove the assertion, we start with (see Section 5.6)

$$f(tx, ty) = t^n f(x, y).$$

With x and y fixed, we can differentiate with respect to t by use of the formula

$$\frac{df(u, v)}{dt} = \frac{\partial f}{\partial u}\frac{du}{dt} + \frac{\partial f}{\partial y}\frac{dy}{dt}$$

to obtain

$$(13.82) \qquad x\frac{\partial f(tx, ty)}{\partial(tx)} + y\frac{\partial f(tx, ty)}{\partial(ty)} = nt^{n-1}f(x, y).$$

Setting $t = 1$ in (13.82) gives (13.81) and completes the proof of Euler's theorem.

One use of Euler's theorem is in proof of the fact that, if M and N are homogeneous functions of x and y of degree n having continuous partial derivatives and $xM + yN \neq 0$, then $1/(xM + yN)$ is an integrating factor of $M\,dx + N\,dy$. To prove this, we must prove that

$$(13.83) \qquad \frac{M}{xM + yN}\,dx + \frac{N}{xM + yN}\,dy$$

is exact, and this amounts to proving that

$$(13.84) \qquad \frac{\partial}{\partial y}\frac{M}{xM + yN} - \frac{\partial}{\partial x}\frac{N}{xM + yN} = 0.$$

When the left-hand member of (13.84) is evaluated by the ordinary rules for differentiation of quotients and products, it is seen that several terms cancel and that the left-hand member of (13.84) is equal to

$$(13.85) \qquad \frac{1}{(xM + yN)^2} \left[N \left(x \frac{\partial M}{\partial x} + y \frac{\partial M}{\partial y} \right) - M \left(x \frac{\partial N}{\partial x} + y \frac{\partial N}{\partial y} \right) \right].$$

But, by Euler's theorem,

$$x \frac{\partial M}{\partial x} + y \frac{\partial M}{\partial y} = nM, \qquad x \frac{\partial N}{\partial x} + y \frac{\partial N}{\partial y} = nN;$$

and accordingly (13.85) is identically zero, (13.84) holds, and (13.83) is exact.

Problem 13.86

Solve the equation

$$xy \frac{dy}{dx} = x^2 + y^2$$

by the method of this section and by that of Section 5.6.

Problem 13.87

Which of the two methods used in the previous problem furnishes the better (or worse) method of attacking the equation

$$\sqrt{x^2 + y^2} \frac{dy}{dx} = x + y?$$

CHAPTER 14

SPECIAL METHODS OF SOLVING f(x, y, y′) = 0; SINGULAR SOLUTIONS

14.0. Introduction.—This chapter is concerned in the main with equations of the form

$$(14.01) \qquad \phi(x, y, y') = 0$$

in which y' enters with an exponent greater than 1. Three different methods of attempting to solve (14.01) start, respectively, with solving for y', solving for y, and solving for x.

14.1. Equations Solvable for y′.—One method of solving (14.01) may be described briefly as that of solving (14.01) for y' to obtain $y' = f(x, y)$ and applying methods previously discussed.

We illustrate this method by considering the equation

$$(14.11) \qquad y'^2 = x^2.$$

A careless attempt to solve (14.11) consists in asserting that the equation holds if and only if $y' = x$ or $y' = -x$ and hence that the solutions are given by

$$(14.12) \qquad y = \tfrac{1}{2}x^2 + c \qquad\qquad -\infty < x < \infty$$

and

$$(14.13) \qquad y = -\tfrac{1}{2}x^2 + c \qquad\qquad -\infty < x < \infty.$$

The curves represented by (14.12) form a family of parabolas which open upward, and the curves represented by (14.13) form a family of parabolas which open downward. Through each point (a, b) of the plane there passes exactly one parabola of each family. The reader should sketch, on graph paper, several curves of each family.

Let us now solve equation (14.11), paying careful attention to what we are doing. Assuming that $y(x)$ is a solution of (14.11) we can transpose and factor to obtain

$$(14.14) \qquad [y'(x) - x][y'(x) + x] = 0.$$

It is a fundamental fact of arithmetic that, if the product of two numbers A and B is 0, then at least one of A and B must be 0. Hence it is true that, for each x, at least one of the two factors in (14.14) must be 0; but (14.14) definitely does not imply that either the first factor is 0 for all values of x or the second factor is 0 for all values* of x.   All one can conclude from (14.14) is that the first factor must be 0 for some set of values of x and the second must be 0 for all other values of x. Let E (the initial letter of the French word *ensemble* which means *set*) denote the set of x for which the first factor is 0.   The nature of the set E is determined by the function $y(x)$; so far as we know at present it may contain no values of x, it may contain all values of x, or it may be any set containing some but not all values of x.   Then

$$y'(x) = x \qquad\qquad x \text{ in } E$$
$$= -x \qquad\qquad x \text{ not in } E.$$

The character of the set E can be determined by use of Rolle's theorem as follows: If $0 < a < b$ and $y(a) = y(b)$, then Rolle's theorem would imply existence of a point c between a and b such that $y'(c) = 0$; but this is impossible since

$$| \, y'(x) \, | = | \, x \, | \neq 0$$

when $a < x < b$.   Therefore $y(a) \neq y(b)$ when $0 < a < b$.   Since $y(x)$ is continuous, this implies that $y(x)$ must be an increasing function of x for $x > 0$ or $y(x)$ must be a decreasing function of x for $x > 0$.   In the first case, $y'(x) \geq 0$ so that $y'(x) = x$ for $x > 0$; and in the second case $y'(x) \leq 0$ so that $y'(x) = -x$ for $x > 0$.   It can be shown in the same way that $y'(x) = x$ for $x < 0$ or $y'(x) = -x$ for $x < 0$.   Moreover, (14.11) implies that $y'(0) = 0$.   Therefore there are just four possible cases: (i) $y'(x) = x$ for all x; (ii) $y'(x) = -x$ for all x; (iii) $y'(x) = x$ for $x \geq 0$ and $y'(x) = -x$ for $x \leq 0$; and (iv) $y'(x) = -x$ for $x \leq 0$ and $y'(x) = x$ for $x \geq 0$.   In case (i) we have $y(x) = \frac{1}{2}x^2 + c$ as in (14.12); in case (ii) we have $y(x) = -\frac{1}{2}x^2 + c$ as in (14.13); in case (iii) we have

(14.151) $$\qquad\qquad y(x) = \tfrac{1}{2}x^2 + c \qquad\qquad x \geq 0$$
$$= -\tfrac{1}{2}x^2 + c \qquad\qquad x \leq 0;$$

and in case (iv) we have

(14.152) $$\qquad\qquad y(x) = -\tfrac{1}{2}x^2 + c \qquad\qquad x \geq 0$$
$$= \tfrac{1}{2}x^2 + c \qquad\qquad x \leq 0.$$

Thus each solution of $y'^2 = x^2$ must have one of the forms (14.12), (14.13), (14.151), and (14.152).   It is easy to show that each such function satisfies $y'^2 = x^2$, and the problem is solved.   A rough sketch of graphs of the family of curves determined by (14.12), (14.13), (14.151), and (14.152) presents a vivid picture which a student of differential equations should draw and study.

In retrospect, we may remark that the careless solution of $y'^2 = x^2$ was very simple but gave incomplete results.   The careful solution was a little more difficult, but it gave complete results.

Problem 14.16

By showing that the functions $y(x)$ given by (14.151) and (14.152) do not have second derivatives at $x = 0$, or by some other method, prove that the only solutions of $y'^2 = x^2$ which have second derivatives are the functions given in (14.12) and (14.13).

* An assumption to the contrary is as silly as the assumption that, if two men A and B keep a pump going continuously, then either A pumps all the time or B pumps all the time.   All that can be concluded is that B must be pumping at least when A is not pumping.

Problem 14.17

Solve the equation

$$\left(\frac{dy}{dx}\right)^2 = y.$$

Be sure that you find *all* solutions.   Sketch graphs of typical solutions.

Problem 14.18

Show that, if

(14.181)
$$\left(y\,\frac{dy}{dx}\right)^2 + y^2 = 1$$

and

$$0 < y(x) < 1$$

over an interval $x_1 < x < x_2$, then there is a constant c such that

$$(x - c)^2 + y^2 = 1 \qquad\qquad x_1 < x < x_2.$$

Show that if (14.181) holds then $|\,y(x)\,| \leq 1$; and that if $y(x) = +1$ or $y(x) = -1$ over an interval $x_3 < x < x_4$ then (14.181) holds.

Problem 14.182

Find all solutions of the equation [see (4.222)]

$$\left(y\,\frac{dy}{dx}\right)^2 + y^2 = 1.$$

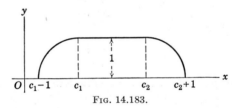

Fig. 14.183.

The graph of one of the solutions which you should obtain is shown in Fig. 14.183, the range of definition of the function being $c_1 - 1 < x < c_2 + 1$.

Problem 14.184

A family F of curves in the xy plane has the following property: If C is a curve of the family and P is a point on C, then the curve C has a normal (and hence also a tangent since a normal is, by definition, a perpendicular to a tangent) at P and at least one of the two points on the normal at a distance 1 from P lies on the x axis.   Show that, if $y = y(x)$ is an equation of a part of a curve C for which $y'(x)$ exists, then

(14.185)
$$\left(y\,\frac{dy}{dx}\right)^2 + y^2 = 1.$$

Show that the circle with equation

(14.186)
$$(x - c)^2 + y^2 = 1$$

belongs to the family F even though, at the two points where the circle meets the x axis, the tangent is vertical, dy/dx does not exist, and equation (14.185) therefore fails to hold.   Show that the family F contains each curve C which is composed of arcs of circles of the form (14.186) and segments of the lines $y = 1$ and $y = -1$. Sketch an assortment of curves belonging to the family F.

14.2. Equations Solvable for y.—In case the equation $\phi(x, y, y') = 0$ can be solved for y to obtain

$$(14.21) \qquad\qquad y = f(x, y')$$

where f has continuous partial derivatives, there is a special method which sometimes enables one to determine solutions $y(x)$ for which $y''(x)$ exists.

Assuming that $y(x)$ is a solution of (14.21) for which $y''(x)$ exists, we can use the formula

$$(14.22) \qquad\qquad \frac{d}{dt} f(u, v) = \frac{\partial f}{\partial u} \frac{du}{dt} + \frac{\partial f}{\partial v} \frac{dv}{dt}$$

to obtain

$$(14.23) \qquad\qquad y'(x) = \frac{\partial f}{\partial x} + \frac{\partial f}{\partial y'} y''(x).$$

Equation (14.23) can be made to *look* simpler by setting

$$(14.24) \qquad p = y'(x), \qquad f_1(x, p) = \frac{\partial f}{\partial x}, \qquad f_2(x, p) = \frac{\partial f}{\partial y'}$$

to obtain

$$(14.25) \qquad\qquad p = f_1(x, p) + f_2(x, p) \frac{dp}{dx}.$$

This is an equation in x and p; perhaps known methods can be used to solve it to obtain $g(x, p, c) = 0$.   If so, we obtain two equations

$$(14.26) \qquad\qquad y = f(x, y'), \qquad g(x, y', c) = 0$$

satisfied* by the function $y(x)$.   Finally, it may be possible to eliminate y' from the two equations to obtain $h(x, y, c) = 0$ or perhaps $y = F(x, c)$.   In some cases it is true that each differentiable function $y(x)$ which satisfies $h(x, y, c) = 0$ or $y = F(x, c)$ for some constant c is a solution of (14.21); in other cases this is not true.

Example 14.27

The equation

$$(14.271) \qquad\qquad \left(\frac{dy}{dx}\right)^2 + 2x^3 \frac{dy}{dx} - 4x^2 y = 0$$

---

* *Satisfied simultaneously*, if we employ terminology used to impress elementary-algebra students.

can be solved for dy/dx, but the result does not look promising. Setting $p = y'$ and solving for y give, when $x \neq 0$,

$$(14.272) \qquad\qquad y = \tfrac{1}{4}x^{-2}p^2 + \tfrac{1}{2}xp.$$

Differentiating with respect to x gives, when $p' = y''$ exists,

$$(14.273) \qquad\qquad p = \tfrac{1}{2}x^{-2}pp' - \tfrac{1}{4}x^{-3}p^2 + \tfrac{1}{2}xp' + \tfrac{1}{2}p.$$

This may look unpromising, but prospects brighten when it is written in the form

$$(14.274) \qquad\qquad (xp' - p)(p + x^3) = 0.$$

If $y(x)$ happens to be such that the first factor vanishes for all x, then $p = 2cx$ and we can use (14.272) to obtain

$$(14.275) \qquad\qquad y = c^2 + cx^2.$$

If $y(x)$ happens to be such that the second factor vanishes for all x, then $p = -x^3$ and use of (14.272) give

$$(14.276) \qquad\qquad y = -\tfrac{1}{4}x^4.$$

That the functions in (14.275) and (14.276) really satisfy (14.271), not only when $x \neq 0$ but for all x, is easily verified, by direct substitution.   We have made no pretense of finding all solutions of (14.271).   One who wants to know what happens if $y(x)$ is such that the first factor in (14.274) vanishes for some but not all x while the second factor vanishes for the remaining x may try to find out or may find some answers later in this chapter.

Problem 14.281

Solve the equation $xy' + y' - y = 0$ by the method of this section.

Ans.: $y = c(x + 1)$.

Problem 14.282

By examining the differential equation

$$y = xy' + y'$$

find what (if anything) is wrong with the idea that solving the second of equations (14.26) may give $y(x)$ without use of the first of equation (14.26).

Problem 14.283

Solve the equation $y = y'$ by the method of this section, and make pertinent remarks.

The Clairaut equation, which is presented in Section 14.4, is solved by the methods of this section; consideration of more complicated examples should follow study of Section 14.4.

This may be a proper time to point out that it is easy to manufacture complicated differential equations having simple solutions.   For example, an equation, having among its solutions the functions

$$(14.284) \qquad\qquad y = c^2x + cx^2,$$

can be obtained as follows: Differentiating (14.284) with respect to x and solving the result for c give

$$c = -x \pm \sqrt{x^2 + y'},$$

and putting this value of c in (14.284) gives

$$y - x^3 - xy' = \mp \, x^2 \sqrt{x^2 + y'}.$$

Squaring both sides gives, when all products are multiplied out and all terms are transposed to the left side, an equation having among its solutions the functions (14.284). Overindulgence in the sport of obtaining differential equations in this way is not recommended. Incidentally equation (14.271) is one of the very few equations in this book obtained in this inglorious fashion. However, it must be said that complicated differential equations with simple solutions often arise in thoroughly honorable ways.

14.3. Equations Solvable for x.—In case the equation $\phi(x, y, y') = 0$ can be solved for x to obtain

$$(14.31) \qquad\qquad x = f(y, y')$$

where f has continuous partial derivatives, there is a method analogous to that of Section 14.2 which may furnish solutions of $\phi(x, y, y') = 0$. If $y(x)$ is a solution of (14.31) over a range $x_1 < x < x_2$ in which $y''(x)$ exists and $y'(x) \neq 0$ so that the function $y = y(x)$ has an inverse $x = x(y)$ and the formula

$$(14.32) \qquad\qquad \frac{dx}{dy} = \frac{1}{dy/dx}$$

holds, then we can differentiate (14.31) with respect to y by use of formula (14.22) to obtain

$$(14.33) \qquad\qquad \frac{dx}{dy} = \frac{\partial f}{\partial y} + \frac{\partial f}{\partial y'} \frac{dy'}{dy}.$$

Making the abbreviations

$$(14.34) \qquad p(y) = \frac{dy}{dx}, \qquad f_1(y, p) = \frac{\partial f}{\partial y}, \qquad f_2(y, p) = \frac{\partial f}{\partial y'}$$

we can make (14.33) look simpler by writing it in the form

$$(14.35) \qquad\qquad \frac{1}{p} = f_1(y, p) + f_2(y, p) \frac{dp}{dy}.$$

This is an equation in y and p; perhaps known methods can be used to solve it to obtain $g(y, p, c) = 0$. We then have two equations

$$\phi(x, y, p) = 0, \qquad g(y, p, c) = 0$$

satisfied by $y(x)$. Finally, it may be possible to eliminate p' from the two equations to obtain $h(x, y, c) = 0$ or perhaps $y = F(x, c)$. In some cases it is true that each differentiable function $y(x)$ which satisfies $h(x, y, c) = 0$ or $y = F(x, c)$ is a solution of $\phi(x, y, y') = 0$; in other cases this is not true.

Problem 14.36

Solve the equation $x + y + y' = 0$ by each of the following three methods: (i) the method ordinarily used for linear equations; (ii) the method of Section 14.2; (iii) the method of this section.

$$\frac{d}{dx}\left[f(y')\right] = \left[y'' + 3xy'' + 3y'\right]y''$$

14.4. The Clairaut Equation.—The differential equation

$$(14.41) \qquad\qquad y = y'x + f(y')$$

is known as a *Clairaut equation*. We consider only cases in which $f(y')$ has a continuous derivative.

If $y(x)$ is a solution of (14.41) for which $y''(x)$ exists, then we can, as in Section 14.2, differentiate with respect to x to obtain

$$y'(x) = y'(x) + xy''(x) + f'(y'(x))y''(x)$$

or

$$(14.42) \qquad\qquad y''(x)[x + f'(y'(x))] = 0.$$

From (14.42) we can conclude only that for each x at least one of the two factors must vanish. To cover all cases one must consider the possibility that (i) the first factor may vanish for all x, (ii) the second factor may vanish for all x, and (iii) the first factor may vanish for some but not all values of x while the second factor vanishes for the remaining values of x.

If the solution $y(x)$ happens to be such that the first factor in (14.42) vanishes for all x, then $y''(x) = 0$ so that $y'(x) = c$ and we can use (14.41) to obtain

$$(14.43) \qquad\qquad y = cx + f(c).$$

That (14.43) is, for each c, a solution of (14.41) is easily shown; for if (14.43) holds, then $y' = c$ and (14.41) holds since substituting $y' = c$ in (14.41) gives the true equation (14.43). Thus (14.43) furnishes a one-parameter family of solutions of (14.41) and is accordingly commonly called "the general solution" of (14.41). It is worth remembering that the so-called "general solution" of a Clairaut equation is the family of linear functions obtained by replacing y' by c in the Clairaut equation. The graph of each of the functions in (14.43) is a line; hence the family of curves represented by (14.43) is a family of lines. Any solution of the Clairaut equation which is not in the family (14.43) is called a *singular solution* of the equation (see Section 4.3).

The problem of finding *all* solutions of the Clairaut equation (14.41) is too involved to discuss here. In particular, it must be observed that, if $y(x)$ is a solution for which $y''(x)$ does not exist, then the above method of determining $y(x)$ cannot be used. Moreover the possibilities (ii) and (iii) mentioned in the paragraph following (14.42) sometimes lead to vast numbers of solutions and sometimes to none. Consideration of an example should preceed a general discussion of the subject.

14.5. Singular Solutions.—In this and the next section we shall find some (but we shall not consider the question whether we succeed in finding all) singular solutions of the Clairaut equation*

(14.51) $y = y'x - \frac{1}{4}y'^2.$

If $y(x)$ is a solution for which $y''(x)$ exists, then

(14.52) $y''(x - \frac{1}{2}y') = 0.$

The possibility that the first factor is 0 for all x leads to the so-called general solution

(14.53) $y = cx - \frac{1}{4}c^2.$

The possibility that the second factor is 0 for all x leads to $y'(x) = 2x$ and hence, by substitution of $2x$ for $y'(x)$ in (14.51), the possibility that

(14.54) $y = x^2$

is a solution of (14.51). Substitution shows that (14.54) is indeed a solution of (14.51). Since (14.54) is not a particular solution of

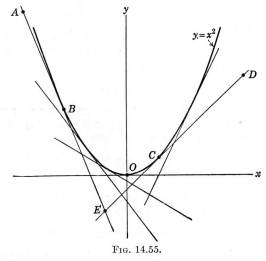

Fig. 14.55.

(14.51) obtainable by assigning a value to c in (14.53), (14.54) is a singular solution of (14.51).

Figure 14.55 shows graphs of the lines (14.53) and the parabola (14.54). The lines in the graph appear to be tangent to the parabola. In fact, it is easy to show that the line $y = cx - \frac{1}{4}c^2$ and the parabola $y = x^2$ are tangent at the point $(\frac{1}{2}c, \frac{1}{4}c^2)$. The parabola is the envelope of the family of lines in accordance with the following definition:

---

* The coefficient $-\frac{1}{4}$ is used because it leads to a neat graph.

14.6. Envelopes.—A curve which is, at each of its points, tangent to at least one curve of a family of curves is the *envelope* (or at least a part of the envelope) of the family of curves.

It is apparent that, if the graph of $y = \phi(x)$ is the envelope (or a part of the envelope) of a family $g(x, y, c) = 0$ of solutions of a first-order differential equation $f(x, y, y') = 0$ and if $\phi'(x)$ exists, then $y = \phi(x)$ must be a solution of the differential equation. To prove this, we note that for each x_0 there is a value c_0 of c such that the curve $g(x, y, c_0) = 0$ passes through the point $(x_0, \phi(x_0))$ with slope $y_0' = \phi'(x_0)$ and therefore $f(x_0, \phi(x_0), \phi'(x_0)) = 0$.

The same method of proof serves to show that portions of graphs of known solutions may be combined to furnish still more solutions of differential equations. For example, in Fig. 14.55 the part of the line AB to the left of B, the part of the parabola from A to C, and the part of the line CD to the right of D combine to furnish the graph of a solution $h_1(x)$ of $y = y'x - \frac{1}{4}y'^2$. Another solution $h_2(x)$ is given by

$$h_2(x) = x^2 \qquad\qquad x \leq 0$$
$$= 0 \qquad\qquad x \geq 0.$$

The solutions discussed in this paragraph are those for which the first factor in (14.42) vanishes for some values of x and the second factor vanishes for all remaining values of x.

Problem 14.61

Let $h_3(x)$ be the function whose graph (Fig. 14.55) consists of the part of the line ABE to the left of E, the point E itself, and the part of the line ECD to the right of E. Is $h_3(x)$ a solution of $y = y'x - \frac{1}{4}y'^2$?

Problem 14.62

The differential equation

(14.63) $$y'^2 + y^2 = 1$$

has solutions

$$y = \sin(x + c),$$

and the envelope consists of the two lines $y = 1$ and $y = -1$. Plot the function

$$y_1(x) = -1 \qquad\qquad x \leq -\pi/2$$
$$= \sin x \qquad\qquad -\pi/2 \leq x \leq \pi/2$$
$$= 1 \qquad\qquad x \geq \pi/2,$$

and show that it is a solution of (14.63). Sketch graphs of several more solutions of (14.63).

Problem 14.64

Prove that for each c the curve

(14.65) $$y = (x - c)^3$$

is tangent to the line $y = 0$ at the point $(0,\ c)$ and hence that $y = 0$ is an envelope of the family (14.65).   Sketch a few curves of the family.   Prove that each point in the plane lies on one and only one curve of the family.

14.7. Finding of Envelopes.—Since a family of solutions of a differential equation may have an envelope which is also a solution, it is clear that a method of finding envelopes is a method of finding solutions of differential equations.

We are going to show that, under certain conditions involving derivatives, the coordinates of each point $(x,\ y)$ of the envelope E of a family $f(x,\ y,\ c) = 0$ satisfy the two equations

(14.71) $$f(x,\ y,\ c) = 0, \qquad \frac{\partial}{\partial c} f(x,\ y,\ c) = 0.$$

An equation $D(x,\ y) = 0$ resulting from elimination of c from the two equations (14.71) is called a *c-discriminant equation* of the equation $f(x,\ y,\ c) = 0$.   Therefore, under certain conditions, the coordinates of each point $(x,\ y)$ of the envelope of a family $f(x,\ y,\ c) = 0$ satisfy each c-discriminant equation of $f(x,\ y,\ c) = 0$. The function $D(x,\ y)$ in the left-hand member of a c-discriminant equation is called a *c-discriminant.*

Before proving these assertions, let us see how the result is used.   Eliminating c from the two equations

$$y - cx + \tfrac{1}{4}c^2 = 0, \qquad -x + \tfrac{1}{2}c = 0$$

we obtain the c-discriminant equation

$$y = x^2,$$

and the result is in agreement with that of Section 14.5.   Eliminating c from the two equations (see Problem 14.62)

$$y - \sin\,(x + c) = 0, \qquad -\cos\,(x + c) = 0$$

gives $y^2 = 1$; hence, if the "certain conditions" are satisfied, each point of the envelope must lie on the line $y = 1$ or the line $y = -1$.

Let a curve E be the envelope (or a part of the envelope) of a family

(14.721) $$f(x,\ y,\ c) = 0$$

of curves, let the partial derivatives f_x, f_y, and f_c exist and be continuous, let $x(c)$ and $y(c)$ be differentiable functions such that for each c the curve (14.721) is tangent to E at the point $(x(c),\ y(c))$, and let each point $(x,\ y)$ of E be representable in the form $(x(c),\ y(c))$ for at least one c.   For each c, let $y = y_c(x)$ be a differentiable function of x such that

(14.722) $$f(x,\ y_c(x),\ c) = 0$$

and $y_c(x(c)) = y(c)$.   Then, for each c, the fact that the curve (14.721) *intersects* the envelope E at the point $(x(c),\ y(c))$ implies that

(14.723) $$f(x(c),\ y(c),\ c) = 0.$$

Our hypothesis justifies differentiation of (14.723) to obtain

(14.724) $$\frac{\partial f}{\partial x}\,x'(c) + \frac{\partial f}{\partial y}\,y'(c) + \frac{\partial f}{\partial c} = 0.$$

For each fixed c, differentiation of (14.722) with respect to x gives

$$(14.725) \qquad\qquad \frac{\partial f}{\partial x} + \frac{\partial f}{\partial y} y_c'(x) = 0,$$

and setting $x = x(c)$ gives

$$(14.726) \qquad\qquad \frac{\partial f}{\partial x} + \frac{\partial f}{\partial y} y_c'(x(c)) = 0.$$

The number $y_c'(x(c))$ is the slope of the graph of $y = y_c(x)$ at the point $(x(c), y(c))$, and this is the slope of the envelope at that point. Since $x = x(c)$, $y = y(c)$ are parametric equations of E, the slope of E at the point $(x(c), y(c))$ is equal to $y'(c)/x'(c)$ in case $x'(c) \neq 0$; in this case we have

$$(14.727) \qquad\qquad y_c'(x(c)) = \frac{y'(c)}{x'(c)},$$

and we can multiply (14.726) by $x'(c)$ and use (14.727) to obtain

$$(14.728) \qquad\qquad \frac{\partial f}{\partial x} x'(c) + \frac{\partial f}{\partial y} y'(c) = 0.$$

In case $x'(c) = 0$ we must have also $y'(c) = 0$; and in this case (14.728) obviously holds. From (14.723), (14.724), and (14.728) we see that, when the conditions involving derivatives are satisfied, the points (x, y) on the envelope satisfy the two equations

$$(14.729) \qquad\qquad f(x, y, c) = 0, \qquad \frac{\partial f(x, y, c)}{\partial c} = 0$$

and our result is attained.

Anyone who is irked by the fact that it is only "under certain conditions" that the coordinates of points (x, y) on the envelope satisfy the two equations (14.729) may profit by considering the following example: For each c, the curve

$$(14.73) \qquad\qquad y^{\frac{1}{3}} = x - c$$

is tangent to the line $y = 0$ at the point $(0, c)$; hence the line $y = 0$ is an envelope of the family (14.73). But for the family (14.73) the two equations (14.729) become

$$(14.74) \qquad\qquad y^{\frac{1}{3}} - x + c = 0, \qquad 1 = 0;$$

and it must be reluctantly admitted that the coordinates of points of the envelope do not satisfy the two equations (14.74). The trouble is that, when

$$f(x, y, c) = y^{\frac{1}{3}} - x + c,$$

the partial derivative f_y does not exist when $y = 0$ and the "certain conditions" are not satisfied. It is amusing to see, however, that the family (14.73) is the same as the family

$$(14.75) \qquad\qquad y = (x - c)^3$$

and that the points of the envelope do satisfy each c-discriminant equation of (14.75).

Problem 14.76

Use the definition of c-discriminant given in this section to prove that, if A, B, and C are functions of x and y, then $B^2 - 4AC$ is a c-discriminant of the quadratic equation $Ac^2 + Bc + C = 0$. One who has a flair for algebra may show that

(14.761) $$27A^2D^2 + 4(AC^3 + B^3D) - B^2C^2 - 18ABCD$$

is a c-discriminant of the cubic equation

(14.762) $$Ac^3 + Bc^2 + Cc + D = 0.$$

Problems

Find the envelopes of the following families of curves:

(14.771)	$y = (x + c)^2$	*Ans.:* $y = 0$
(14.772)	$(x - c)^2 + y^2 = 49$	*Ans.:* $y = \pm 7$
(14.773)	$y = cx - \frac{1}{4}c^2$	*Ans.:* $y = x^2$
(14.774)	$y = \sin (x + c)^2$	*Ans.:* $y = 0, \pm 1$
(14.775)	$y = c(x + 1)$	*Ans.:* None

14.8. Parabolic Reflectors.—A well-known problem is that of determining a plane curve such that light or sound striking it from a point source in the same plane is reflected in a given direction. Let the point source be the origin, and let the given direction be that of the positive x axis. Let us assume that $y = y(x)$, defined for some range of values of x, is a differentiable function whose graph is a part or all of the desired curve.

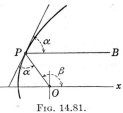

Fig. 14.81.

At a point $P \equiv P(x, y)$ on the curve the incident ray OP and the reflected ray BP make equal angles α with the tangent at P, and the identity $\tan \alpha = \tan (\beta - \alpha)$ gives, when $x \neq 0$,

$$y' = \frac{(y/x) - y'}{1 + (y/x)y'}$$

or

(14.82) $$y = 2y'x + yy'^2.$$

A neat way of solving this equation is to multiply by y and to set $v = y^2$ and $v'(x) = 2y(x)y'(x)$ to obtain

(14.83) $$v = v'x + \frac{1}{4}v'^2.$$

This is a Clairaut equation with so-called "general solution" $v = cx + \frac{1}{4}c^2$ and singular solution $v = -\frac{1}{4}x^2$. The "general solution" gives

(14.84) $$y^2 = c(x + \frac{1}{4}c).$$

For each $c > 0$, (14.84) is the equation of a parabola with vertex at the point $(-\frac{1}{4}c, 0)$ and focus at the origin; and it can be shown that this is a solution of our problem. Do $c = 0$ and $c < 0$ furnish solutions of the problem? Does the singular solution $v = -x^2/4$ furnish a solution of the problem?

Problem 14.85

Show that equation (14.82) can be written in the form

$$y\, dy + x\, dx = \pm\sqrt{x^2 + y^2}\, dx,$$

and proceed to solve the equation by use of an integrating factor.

14.9. Elliptic Reflectors.—Another well-known problem is that of determining a plane curve such that light or sound striking it from a fixed point source is reflected to a second fixed point. Let the two fixed points be taken as the points $(a, 0)$ and $(-a, 0)$ of a rectangular coordinate system (see Fig. 14.91).

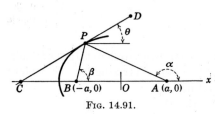

Fig. 14.91.

Let $y(x)$ be a differentiable function whose graph is at least a part of the required curve, and let CPD be the tangent to the graph at $P(x, y)$. The angles APD and BPC at which rays of light from A and B meet the tangent must be equal. This implies that

$$\alpha + \beta = 2\theta + \pi$$

where $\tan\theta = y'$ and hence that

$$(14.92)\qquad xyy'^2 + (x^2 - y^2 - a^2)y' - xy = 0.$$

This is (see Problem 4.29 and Section 4.5) the differential equation of the family of conics with foci $(\pm a, 0)$. The following is a method by which we can solve (14.92) when solutions are not known in advance: Multiplying (14.92) by $4y$ and setting $u(x) = [y(x)]^2$, $u' = 2yy'$, we obtain the simpler equation

$$(14.93)\qquad xv'^2 + 2(x^2 - v - a^2)v' - 4xv = 0$$

to solve for $v(x)$. Since the substitution $u = y^2$ simplified (14.92), we may hope that the substitution $t = x^2$ will simplify (14.93). To set $t = x^2$ is to change the independent variable in a differential equation, and this operation requires more thought than change of dependent variable. If $t = x^2$ and $x > 0$, then $v(x) = v(t^{\frac{1}{2}})$ and we may set

$$V(t) = v(t^{\frac{1}{2}}) = v(x).$$

Then $v'(x) = V'(t)(dt/dx) = 2xV'(t) = 2\sqrt{t}\,V'(t)$, and substitution in (14.93) gives

(14.94) $$tV'^2 + (t - V - a^2)V' - V = 0$$

where the prime on V means differentiation with respect to t. Solutions of (14.94) for which $V''(t)$ exists must satisfy the equation obtained by differentiating with respect to t, that is,

(14.95) $$V''(2tV' + t - V - a^2) = 0.$$

The possibility that $V''(t) = 0$ for all t leads to $V' = c_1$ and hence to the possibility that $tc_1^2 + (t - V - a^2)c_1 - V = 0$ or

(14.96) $$(c_1^2 + c_1)t - (c_1 + 1)V = a^2 c_1$$

is a solution of (14.94) and hence to the possibility that

(14.97) $$(c_1^2 + c_1)x^2 - (c_1 + 1)y^2 = a^2 c_1$$

is a solution of (14.92). If we set $c^2 = a^2/(c_1 + 1)$, then (14.97) takes the more familiar form

(14.98) $$(c^2 - a^2)x^2 + c^2 y^2 = c^2(c^2 - a^2).$$

That (14.98) does in fact furnish solutions of (14.92) was shown in Problem 4.29. If $c > a$, then (14.98) furnishes an ellipse which is a curve with the required light-reflection property. If $0 < c < a$, then (14.98) furnishes a hyperbola which does not have the required light-reflection property.

Problem 14.99

Does the result of eliminating V' from (14.94) and the equation obtained by setting the second factor in (14.94) equal to 0 give a solution of (14.94) which in turn leads to a solution of (14.92)?

Problem 14.991

An enemy ship was seen at nightfall ($t = 0$ hours) at a point O on the ocean. For present purposes, the ocean is a plane and O is the origin of a polar coordinate system with polar coordinates ρ and θ. Suppose the enemy ship attempts to escape by sailing in a straight line from O with its maximum velocity v, and that v is known to you. If, at daybreak ($t = h$ hours) the next day, you could fly around the circle $\rho = vh$ with center at O and radius vh fast enough, you should spot the ship. Show that if you start at daybreak from the point $\theta = 0$, $\rho = vh$ with velocity kv, where $k > 1$, and fly counterclockwise in a suitable spiral, you will pass over the ship at some time in your first revolution.

Hint: The length of the part of the graph of $\rho = \rho(\theta)$ from the point $\theta = 0$, $\rho = \rho(0)$ to $\theta = \phi$, $\rho = \rho(\phi)$ is

$$\int_0^\phi \sqrt{[\rho(\theta)]^2 + [\rho'(\theta)]^2}\, d\theta.$$

The function $\rho(\theta)$ should be such that you fly this distance while the ship sails the distance $\rho(\phi) - vh$. The equation of the spiral is $\rho = vh\, e^{a\theta}$ where $a = 1/\sqrt{k^2 - 1}$.

CHAPTER 15

PICARD'S METHOD OF APPROXIMATING SOLUTIONS OF $y' = f(x, y)$; EXISTENCE THEOREMS

15.1. Introduction.—Earlier parts of this book have presented special methods by which the differential equation

$$(15.11) \qquad \frac{dy}{dx} = f(x, y)$$

can be solved when $f(x, y)$ has certain special forms.

In this chapter we prove Picard's theorem on existence of solutions of differential equations of the form (15.11). The method of proof is the *Picard method of successive approximations*. This method furnishes an excellent practical method of obtaining approximations to functions which satisfy equations of the form (15.11).

In Sections 15.2 and 15.3 we give the fundamental ideas of the Picard method; and in Sections 15.4, 15.5, and 15.6 we give and discuss applications. In Section 15.7 we give Picard's theorem with some comments. In Section 15.8 we prove Picard's theorem and thereby show that the Picard method will always furnish solutions of $y' = f(x, y)$ when $f(x, y)$ belongs to a certain class of functions.

15.2. The Picard Method.—Postponing discussion of the vital question whether or not the method really produces results, we outline the Picard method of finding a function $y = y(x)$ such that $y(a) = b$ and

$$(15.21) \qquad \frac{dy}{dx} = f(x, y)$$

for all values of x in an interval containing the point $x = a$. Thus we propose to outline the Picard method of finding a solution of (15.21) whose graph passes through the point (a, b) of an xy plane.

The first step is to select a function $y_1(x)$. We shall discuss later the effect of choosing different functions $y_1(x)$. There is a reason why it may be desirable to choose $y_1(x)$ such that $y_1(a) = b$, but even this is not essential. An easy way to solve the problem of selecting a function $y_1(x)$ is to set $y_1(x) = b$ for all x; but in any case choice of $y_1(x)$ must be made by the solver.

Having selected $y_1(x)$, we next determine $y_2(x)$ such that $y_2(a) = b$ and

$$(15.22) \qquad \frac{d}{dx} y_2(x) = f(x, y_1(x)).$$

Having determined $y_2(x)$, we next determine $y_3(x)$ such that $y_3(a) = b$ and

$$(15.23) \qquad \frac{d}{dx} y_3(x) = f(x, y_2(x)).$$

Proceeding in this manner, we obtain a sequence of functions

$$y_1(x), \; y_2(x), \; y_3(x), \; \cdots$$

such that $y_n(a) = b$ and

$$(15.24) \qquad \frac{d}{dx} y_n(x) = f(x, y_{n-1}(x)) \qquad n = 2, 3, 4, \cdots.$$

A person with foresight and optimism can now recognize the possibility of being able to obtain a solution of the problem in the form $y(x) = \lim y_n(x)$. If it can be shown that a function $y(x)$ exists such that

$$\lim_{n \to \infty} y_n(x) = y(x), \qquad \lim_{n \to \infty} \frac{d}{dx} y_n(x) = \frac{d}{dx} y(x),$$

$$\lim_{n \to \infty} f(x, y_n(x)) = f(x, y(x)),$$

then we can let $n \to \infty$ in (15.24) to obtain

$$\frac{d}{dx} y(x) = f(x, y(x));$$

and since $y_n(a) = b$ when $n > 1$, $y(a) = b$. It thus appears that, if all goes well, we come out with a function $y(x)$ having the desired properties. Everyone should see the fundamental idea involved in Picard's method and should admire the idea; it is a good idea.

15.3. Introduction of Integrals.—Our first step in developing the good idea is to show that, in important cases, the functions $y_2(x)$, $y_3(x)$, $\cdots$ about which we have talked so glibly really exist. In fact, by use of theorems of Chapter 2, we are able to obtain formulas for these functions.

In case $f(x, y_1(x))$ is a continuous function of x, the unique function $y_2(x)$ for which $y_2(a) = b$ and (15.22) holds is

$$y_2(x) = b + \int_a^x f(t, y_1(t)) dt.$$

In case $f(x, y_2(x))$ is a continuous function of x, the unique function $y_3(x)$ for which $y_3(a) = b$ and (15.23) holds is

$$y_3(x) = b + \int_a^x f(t, y_2(t))dt.$$

This process can be continued to show that, if the functions $f(x, y_n(x))$ are all continuous functions of x, then the function $y_n(x)$ is given in terms of $y_{n-1}(x)$ by the *recursion formulas*

(15.31) $$y_n(x) = b + \int_a^x f(t, y_{n-1}(t))dt \qquad n = 2, 3, 4, \cdots.$$

This formula for $y_n(x)$ suggests another way of handling the question whether or not the sequence $y_1(x)$, $y_2(x)$, $\cdots$ converges to a solution of the differential equation. *If a function $y(x)$ exists such that*

(15.32) $$\lim_{n \to \infty} y_n(x) = y(x),$$

if we can let $n \to \infty$ in (15.31) to obtain

(15.33) $$y(x) = b + \int_a^x f(t, y(t))dt,$$

and *if* $f(x, y(x))$ is continuous, then, by the fundamental theorem of the calculus, $y'(x) = f(x, y(x))$; and (15.33) implies $y(a) = b$. Thus, if all goes well, we find that the function $y(x)$ in (15.32) has the desired properties.*

15.4. An Application of Picard's Method.—In this section we apply Picard's method to find a function $y(x)$ satisfying the boundary condition $y(0) = 0$ and the differential equation

(15.41) $$\frac{dy}{dx} = x + y.$$

This equation is linear and can be quickly solved by elementary methods. To solve the problem by Picard's method, let $y_1(x) = 0$. For each $n = 2, 3, \cdots$ the function $y_n(x)$ is the unique function for which

$$y_n(0) = 0, \qquad y_n'(x) = x + y_{n-1}(x)$$

or

(15.42) $$y_n(x) = \int_0^x [t + y_{n-1}(t)]dt.$$

---

* It may interest the reader to know that equation (15.33) is called an *integral equation*. The method of successive approximations which we are using is a standard method of solving integral equations.

Using this *recursion formula*, we obtain

$$y_2(x) = \int_0^x [t + 0]dt = \frac{x^2}{2}$$

$$y_3(x) = \int_0^x \left[t + \frac{t^2}{2}\right] dt = \frac{x^2}{2} + \frac{x^3}{3!}$$

$$y_4(x) = \int_0^x \left[t + \frac{t^2}{2!} + \frac{t^3}{3!}\right] dt = \frac{x^2}{2!} + \frac{x^3}{3!} + \frac{x^4}{4!}.$$

It is very easy to prove by mathematical induction that

$$(15.43) \qquad y_n(x) = \frac{x^2}{2!} + \frac{x^3}{3!} + \cdots + \frac{x^n}{n!} \qquad n = 2, 3, 4, \cdots.$$

In this application of Picard's method, it was very easy to get simple formulas for the *approximating functions* $y_1(x)$, $y_2(x)$, $y_3(x)$, $\cdots$. It happens that it is easy to do more. Using the fundamental formula

$$e^x = 1 + x + \frac{x^2}{2!} + \frac{x^3}{3!} + \frac{x^4}{4!} + \cdots$$

we find that

$$(15.44) \qquad e^x - 1 - x = \frac{x^2}{2!} + \frac{x^3}{3!} + \frac{x^4}{4!} + \cdots.$$

Since the sequence $y_2(x)$, $y_3(x)$, $\cdots$ is the sequence of partial sums of the series in (15.44), the sequence does converge and $\lim y_n(x) = y(x)$ where

$$y(x) = e^x - 1 - x.$$

That $y(x)$ is indeed a function for which $y(0) = 0$ and (15.41) holds is easily verified.

It is now time to consider the manner in which the functions $y_2(x)$, $y_3(x)$, $\cdots$ represent approximations to $y(x)$. The facts can be obtained either by drawing graphs or by such inequalities as the following: If $|x| \le 1$, then

$$|y(x) - y_5(x)|$$

$$= \left|\frac{x^6}{6!} + \frac{x^7}{7!} + \frac{x^8}{8!} + \cdots\right| \le \frac{1}{6!} + \frac{1}{7!} + \frac{1}{8!} + \cdots = \frac{1}{6!}\left[1 + \frac{1}{7}\right.$$

$$+ \frac{1}{7 \cdot 8} + \frac{1}{7 \cdot 8 \cdot 9} + \cdots\left.\right] < \frac{1}{720}\left[1 + \frac{1}{7} + \frac{1}{7^2} + \frac{1}{7^3} + \cdots\right] = \frac{7}{4,320}.$$

The function $y_2(x)$ is, for many purposes, a good approximation to $y(x)$ in a small interval containing $x = 0$; the function $y_3(x)$ is a better approximation to $y(x)$ in the small interval and is a good approximation over a larger interval; the function $y_4(x)$ is a still better approximation over small intervals and is a good approximation over still larger intervals; and so on. The function $y_5(x)$ is a very good approximation to $y(x)$ when $|\ x\ | \leq \frac{1}{2}$; is a good approximation when $|\ x\ | \leq 1$; is a fair approximation when $|\ x\ | \leq 3$; and is a very bad approximation when $x = 10$. It happens in the present case that the approximating functions $y_n(x)$ are exceptionally near the solution $y(x)$ when x is near 0 but that for each n the approximations are exceptionally bad when x is larger than n. In many applications, one fixes his attention on an interval in which he is interested and then chooses an approximating function $y_n(x)$ suitable for that interval. When the length of the interval is increased, it is often necessary to increase n.

Problems

15.45. Solve the above problem by the Picard method, starting with the function $y_1(x) = 1$.

15.46. Find the solution of $y' = y$ for which $y(1) = 1$.

15.5. More Complicated Applications.—The real test of Picard's method comes when one must solve an equation to which no elementary method can possibly apply. Whether such an equation as

$$(15.51) \qquad \frac{dy}{dx} = \frac{1 + xy^4}{1 + x^2y^2} \sin xy^2$$

is ridiculous or not depends on whether it arises in the course of solution of a sensible problem. By Theorem 15.71, which follows in Section 15.7, there is a function $y(x)$, defined over an interval containing the point $x = 1$, for which $y(1) = 2$ and (15.11) holds; and moreover one can apply the Picard method to find approximations to $y(x)$. It is true that the approximating functions must be obtained by some method of finding approximate values of integrals, such as the methods described in Chapter 2; but the essential point is that one can get them.

15.6. A Significant Application of Picard's Method.—In this section, we apply the Picard method to find a function $y(x)$ satisfying the condition $y(0) = 0$ and the nonlinear differential equation

$$(15.61) \qquad \frac{dy}{dx} = 1 + y^2.$$

Letting $y_1(x) = 0$ and defining $y_2(x)$, $y_3(x)$, $\cdots$ by the formulas

$$(15.62) \qquad y_n(x) = \int_0^x [1 + \{y_{n-1}(t)\}^2]dt \qquad n = 2, 3, \cdots$$

we find that

$$y_2(x) = \int_0^x 1\, dt = x$$

$$y_3(x) = \int_0^x (1 + t^2)dt = x + \frac{1}{3}x^3$$

$$y_4(x) = x + \frac{1}{3}x^3 + \frac{2}{15}x^5 + \frac{1}{63}x^7$$

$$y_5(x) = x + \frac{1}{3}x^3 + \frac{2}{15}x^5 + \frac{17}{315}x^7 + \frac{38}{2,835}x^9 + \frac{134}{51,927}x^{11}$$
$$+ \frac{4}{12,285}x^{13} + \frac{1}{59,535}x^{15}$$

$$y_6(x) = x + \frac{1}{3}x^3 + \frac{2}{15}x^5 + \frac{17}{315}x^7 + \frac{62}{2,835}x^9 + \frac{1,142}{115,925}x^{11} + \cdots$$
$$+ \frac{1}{59,535 \cdot 59,535 \cdot 31}x^{31}.$$

The parts of the graphs of the functions $y_3(x)$, $\cdots$, $y_6(x)$ which lie near the origin are nearly coincident. For values of x more remote from 0, the graphs are widely separated. Taking $x = 10$ to make computation easy, we see by use of the last terms in the formulas for $y_2(x)$, $y_3(x)$, $\cdots$ that $y_2(10) = 10$, $y_3(10) > 10^2$, $y_4(10) > 10^5$, $y_5(10) > 10^{10}$, $y_6(10) > 10^{19}$. These considerations may lead one to guess that for values of x in some interval about $x = 0$ the sequence $y_1(x)$, $y_2(x)$, $\cdots$ converges to a function $y(x)$ satisfying the required conditions and that, for values of x remote from 0, the sequence does not converge.

We may now consider what would happen to a person who uses $y_5(x)$, over an interval such as $-1.5 \leqq x \leqq 1.5$, as an approximation to the function he is seeking.

In Section 5.9 we solved the problem of this section and found that a function $y(x)$ for which $y(0) = 0$ and $y' = 1 + y^2$ must be $\tan x$ in the interval $-\pi/2 < x < \pi/2$ and that the function does not extend beyond this interval. The first four terms of $y_5(x)$ are the first four terms of the power-series expansion [see (7.55)]

$$(15.63) \qquad x + \frac{1}{3}x^3 + \frac{2}{15}x^5 + \frac{17}{315}x^7 + \frac{62}{2,835}x^9 + \cdots$$

of $\tan x$, and accordingly $y_5(x)$ is for many purposes a very good approximation to $y(x)$ over intervals extending well beyond the interval $-1 \leqq x \leqq 1$ but with end points not too close to $-\pi/2$ and $\pi/2$.

The refusal of the sequence $y_n(x)$ to converge for larger values of x (in fact when $|x| \geqq \pi/2$) is quite appropriate. The sequence

$y_n(x)$ cannot converge over $-10 \leq x \leq 10$ to a function $y(x)$ satisfying the equation $y' = 1 + y^2$ over that interval because (see Section 5.9) no such function exists.

Problem 15.64

Find a few of the Picard approximations to the function $y(x)$ satisfying the condition $y(0) = 0$ and the differential equation

$$\frac{dy}{dx} = 1 + x^2 + y^2.$$

Problem 15.65

Show without solving the differential equations that, if $y_1(x)$ and $y_2(x)$ are, respectively, solutions of

$$\frac{dy}{dx} = 1 + y^2, \qquad \frac{dy}{dx} = 1 + x^2 + y^2$$

over an interval $0 \leq x < a$ and if $y_1(0) = y_2(0) = 0$, then

$$0 \leq y_1(x) \leq y_2(x) \qquad\qquad 0 \leq x < a.$$

What can you do with your answer?

15.7. Picard's Theorem.—The following theorem gives conditions under which the Picard method necessarily furnishes a solution of $y' = f(x, y)$ such that $y(a) = b$. The theorem is an *existence theorem* since it gives conditions under which solutions of $y' = f(x, y)$ must exist; and it is a *uniqueness theorem* since it gives conditions under which there is exactly one solution of $y' = f(x, y)$ for which $y(a) = b$.

When a sequence $y_1(x)$, $y_2(x)$, $\cdots$ has been constructed by the Picard method, it may be very difficult to find, by examination of the sequence, the range of values of x for which the sequence converges. Hence the information about the interval $x_1 \leq x \leq x_2$ is an important part of the conclusion of Picard's theorem.

PICARD'S THEOREM 15.71.—*If $f(x, y)$ is a continuous function of x and y in a region R containing the point (a, b) in its interior; if M is a constant such that*

(15.72) $$|f(x, y)| < M$$

for all points (x, y) of R; if $x_1 \leq x \leq x_2$ is an interval of the x axis such that R includes the region T consisting of the two triangles (shaded in Fig. 15.76) bounded by the lines $x = x_1$, $x = x_2$, and the two lines through (a, b) with slopes $-M$ and M, respectively; if A is a constant such that

(15.73) $$|f(x, y) - f(x, \eta)| \leq A|y - \eta|$$

when (x, y) and (x, η) are two points of T; if $y_1(x)$ is a continuous func-

*tion of x such that the points $(x, y_1(x))$ for which $x_1 \leqq x \leqq x_2$ all lie
in the region R; and if*

$$(15.74) \qquad y_n(x) = b + \int_a^x f(t, y_{n-1}(t))dt \qquad n = 2, 3, 4, \cdots ,$$

*then the sequence $y_1(x)$, $y_2(x)$, $\cdots$ converges over the interval $x_1 \leqq x \leqq x_2$
to a function $y(x)$ satisfying the conditions $y(a) = b$ and*

$$(15.75) \qquad \frac{dy}{dx} = f(x, y) \qquad\qquad x_1 \leqq x \leqq x_2.$$

*The graph over the interval $x_1 \leqq x \leqq x_2$ of this solution lies in the region
T.   Moreover, the solution $y(x)$ thus obtained by the Picard method is,
insofar as the interval $x_1 \leqq x \leqq x_2$ is concerned, the only function $y(x)$*

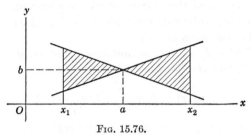

Fig. 15.76.

*for which $y' = f(x, y)$ and $y(a) = b$; and all the different functions $y_1(x)$
which may be used at the start of the Picard method yield this unique
solution.*

The hypotheses of this theorem are satisfied in many important
cases.   If $f(x, y)$ is continuous at (a, b), then there necessarily exist a
constant M and a region R (for example, a rectangle) containing the
point (a, b) in its interior such that (15.72) holds for all points (x, y)
of R.   It is then possible to draw through (a, b) two lines of slopes
$-M$ and M and then to determine x_1 and x_2 such that the shaded
region T described in the theorem is a subset of R.

The condition (15.73) has a very simple interpretation: it means
simply that when x is fixed the resulting function of y has bounded
difference quotients and that the bound A is independent of x.   It is
known as a *Hölder condition* or a *Lipschitz condition*.   In case $f(x, y)$
has a partial derivative $f_y(x, y)$ which is continuous over T, then
(15.73) necessarily holds.   For when (x, y) and (x, η) are points of T,
we can apply the law of the mean (Theorem 2.21) to obtain

$$(15.77) \qquad f(x, y) - f(x, \eta) = f_y(x, \eta_1)(y - \eta) \qquad\text{MW Satz}$$

where η_1 is properly chosen between y and η; and choosing A such that
$|f_y(x, y)| \leqq A$ when (x, y) is a point of T we can use (15.77) to obtain

(15.73). However, (15.73) can hold when $f(x, y)$ does not have a partial derivative with respect to y; the function

$$f(x, y) = 1 + |\sin x| + |\sin y|$$

is an example.

The phrase "insofar as the interval $x_1 \leqq x \leqq x_2$ is concerned" in the conclusion of Picard's theorem must be taken seriously. Figure 5.121 and Section 5.1 show clearly that there is a difference between the statement "there is a unique solution $y(x)$ for which $y(a) = b$" and the statement "insofar as an interval $x_1 \leqq x \leqq x_2$ containing a is concerned, there is a unique solution for which $y(a) = b$." There are situations in which the first statement is false and the second is true.

15.8. Proof of Picard's Theorem.—In proving Picard's theorem, we use the notation of the statement of the theorem. Moreover, we shall consider only values of x for which $x_1 \leqq x \leqq x_2$. Our first step is to prove the following lemma:

LEMMA 15.81.—*If $y_{n-1}(x)$ is continuous and $(x, y_{n-1}(x))$ is a point of the region R, then the function $y_n(x)$ defined by*

$$(15.82) \qquad y_n(x) = b + \int_a^x f(t, y_{n-1}(t))dt$$

is continuous and $(x, y_n(x))$ is a point of the region T.

Our hypotheses imply that the integrand in (15.82) is continuous and hence that the right-hand member of (15.82) defines a continuous function $y_n(x)$ such that $y_n'(x) = f(x, y_{n-1}(x))$. From (15.82) we obtain

$$|y_n(x) - b| = \left| \int_a^x f(t, y_{n-1}(t))dt \right|$$

$$\leqq \left| \int_a^x |f(t, y_{n-1}(t))| \, dt \right| \leqq M \left| \int_a^x dt \right| = M|x - a|.$$

This implies that $y_n(a) = b$ and that if $x \neq a$ then the slope of the line joining (a, b) to $(x, y_n(x))$ is neither greater than M nor less than $-M$. Hence, the graph of $y_n(x)$ lies in the region T, and Lemma 15.81 is proved.

Since the graph of $y_1(x)$ lies in the region R and T is a subset of R, it follows from repeated application of Lemma 15.81 that the graphs of $y_2(x)$, $y_3(x)$, $\cdots$ over the interval $x_1 \leqq x \leqq x_2$ all lie in the region T.

We now show that the sequence $y_n(x)$ converges by showing that the series

$$(15.83) \qquad y_1(x) + [y_2(x) - y_1(x)] + [y_3(x) - y_2(x)] + \cdots$$

converges. For this it is sufficient to show that the series

$$(15.831) \qquad [y_3(x) - y_2(x)] + [y_4(x) - y_3(x)] + [y_5(x) - y_4(x)] + \cdots$$

converges. Subtracting (15.74) from the equation obtained by replacing n by $n + 1$ in it, we get

$$(15.84) \qquad y_{n+1}(x) - y_n(x) = \int_a^x [f(t, y_n(t)) - f(t, y_{n-1}(t))]dt.$$

If $n \geq 3$ and t lies within the range of integration in (15.84), then the points $(t, y_n(t))$ and $(t, y_{n-1}(t))$ lie in the region T and we can apply (15.73) to obtain

$$(15.841) \qquad |f(t, y_n(t)) - f(t, y_{n-1}(t))| \leq A|y_n(t) - y_{n-1}(t)|.$$

Using (15.84) and (15.841) we obtain

$$(15.85) \qquad |y_{n+1}(x) - y_n(x)| \leq A \left| \int_a^x |y_n(t) - y_{n-1}(t)| \, dt \right| \qquad n > 2.$$

Choose a constant B such that

$$(15.86) \qquad |y_3(x) - y_2(x)| \leq B \qquad x_1 \leq x \leq x_2.$$

Setting $n = 3$ in (15.85) and using (15.86), we obtain

$$(15.87) \qquad |y_4(x) - y_3(x)| \leq BA \left| \int_a^x dt \right| = BA|x - a|.$$

Setting $n = 4$ in (15.85) and using (15.87) we obtain

$$(15.88) \qquad |y_5(x) - y_4(x)| \leq BA^2 \left| \int_a^x (t - a)dt \right| = \frac{BA^2|x - a|^2}{2!}.$$

This process gives, as may be proved by induction,

$$(15.89) \qquad |y_{n+3}(x) - y_{n+2}(x)| \leq \frac{BA^n|x - a|^n}{n!} \qquad n = 0, 1, 2, \cdots$$

Let C be equal to the greater of the numbers $x_2 - a$ and $a - x_1$ so that $|x - a| \leq C$ when $x_1 \leq x \leq x_2$. Then (15.89) gives

$$(15.90) \qquad |y_{n+3}(x) - y_{n+2}(x)| \leq \frac{B(AC)^n}{n!}.$$

Using (15.90) we see that the series (15.831) is dominated by the series of constants

$$(15.901) \qquad B + B\frac{AC}{1!} + B\frac{(AC)^2}{2!} + B\frac{(AC)^3}{3!} + \cdots.$$

$$x = AC$$
$$B \sum \frac{x^m}{m!} = Be^x$$
$$= Be^{AC}$$

This series is convergent; in fact, it converges to Be^{AC}. Therefore, by the comparison test, the series (15.831) is convergent. Thus we have proved that there is a function $y(x)$ such that

$$(15.91) \qquad y(x) = \lim_{n \to \infty} y_n(x)$$

and

$$(15.92) \quad y(x) = y_1(x) + [y_2(x) - y_1(x)] + [y_3(x) - y_2(x)] + \cdots .$$

Since the point $(x, y_n(x))$ lies in the region T when $n \geq 2$ and $x_1 \leq x \leq x_2$, it follows that the point $(x, y(x))$ lies in the region T when $x_1 \leq x \leq x_2$; thus the graph over the interval $x_1 \leq x \leq x_2$ of $y(x)$ lies in the region T. In particular, $y(a) = b$.

To show that $y(x)$ satisfies the differential equation, it will be sufficient to show that $y(x)$ is continuous and

$$(15.93) \qquad\qquad y(x) = b + \int_a^x f(t, y(t))dt;$$

for in this case (by the fundamental theorem of the calculus) the right-hand member has a derivative which is $f(x, y(x))$, and the same must therefore be true of the left-hand member.

From (15.92) we obtain for each $n > 2$ and each x in the interval $x_1 \leq x \leq x_2$

$$y(x) = \{y_1(x) + [y_2(x) - y_1(x)] + \cdots + [y_n(x) - y_{n-1}(x)]\} \\ + \{[y_{n+1}(x) - y_n(x)] + [y_{n+2}(x) - y_{n+1}(x)] + \cdots \}$$

so that, because of (15.90),

$$| y(x) - y_n(x) | \leq | y_{n+1}(x) - y_n(x) | + | y_{n+2}(x) - y_{n+1}(x) | + \cdots \\ \leq B \left[\frac{(AC)^{n-2}}{(n-2)!} + \frac{(AC)^{n-1}}{(n-1)!} + \frac{(AC)^n}{n!} + \cdots \right].$$

Since the series (15.901) converges, it follows that to each $\epsilon > 0$ corresponds an index N such that

$$B \left[\frac{(AC)^{n-2}}{(n-2)!} + \frac{(AC)^{n-1}}{(n-1)!} + \frac{(AC)^n}{n!} + \cdots \right] < \epsilon \qquad n > N$$

and therefore

$$| y(x) - y_n(x) | < \epsilon \qquad\qquad x_1 \leq x \leq x_2; n > N.$$

This means that $y_n(x)$ converges *uniformly* over $x_1 \leq x \leq x_2$ to $y(x)$; and since $y_n(x)$ is continuous for each n, this implies (as is shown in advanced calculus) that $y(x)$ must be continuous.

To prove (15.93), we observe that, if $n > N \geq 1$, then

$$(15.94) \quad \left| y(x) - b - \int_a^x f(t, y(t))dt \right| \\ = \left| y(x) - y_{n+1}(x) + \int_a^x [f(t, y_n(t)) - f(t, y(t))]dt \right| \\ \leq | y(x) - y_{n+1}(x) | + \left| \int_a^x A| y_n(t) - y(t) | dt \right| \\ \leq \epsilon + \epsilon A| x - a | \leq \epsilon(1 + AC)$$

where A and C are fixed constants previously defined. If the first member of (15.94) were a number $P \neq 0$, we could obtain a contradiction of (15.94) by choosing ϵ to be a positive number less than $P/(1 + AC)$; hence, the left-hand member of (15.94) must be zero, and (15.93) is proved. This completes the "existence" part of the proof of Picard's theorem.

We prove that, insofar as the interval $x_1 \leqq x \leqq x_2$ is concerned, there is only one function $Y(x)$ such that $Y(a) = b$ and

$$(15.95) \qquad Y'(x) = f(x, Y(x)) \qquad\qquad x_1 \leqq x \leqq x_2$$

by proving that each such function must be equal, when $x_1 \leqq x \leqq x_2$, to the functoin $y(x)$ just obtained by the Picard method.

Our first step is to prove that the graph of $Y(x)$ must lie in the region T. Using (15.95) and the facts that $Y(a) = b$ and

$$| f(a, b) | < M,$$

we obtain

$$(15.951) \qquad | Y'(a) | = | f(a, b) | < M.$$

This implies existence of a positive number δ such that

$$(15.952) \qquad | Y(x) - Y(a) | < M| x - a | \qquad 0 < | x - a | \leqq \delta.$$

We can now show that

$$(15.953) \qquad | Y(x) - Y(a) | < M(x - a) \qquad a < x \leqq x_2.$$

If (15.953) fails to hold, then (15.952) and continuity of $Y(x)$ imply that there must be a least value of x greater than $a + \delta$, say ξ, such that

$$(15.954) \qquad | Y(\xi) - Y(a) | \geqq M(\xi - a).$$

But by the law of the mean there must be a point ξ_1 between a and ξ such that

$$(15.955) \qquad Y(\xi) - Y(a) = Y'(\xi_1)(\xi - a).$$

Hence,

$$(15.956) \qquad | f(\xi_1, Y(\xi_1)) | = | Y'(\xi_1) | \geqq M,$$

and this is a contradiction of (15.72) since $(\xi_1, Y(\xi_1))$ is a point of the region T. Thus (15.953) holds, and a similar proof shows that

$$(15.957) \qquad | Y(a) - Y(x) | < M(a - x) \qquad x_1 \leqq x < a.$$

But (15.953), (15.957), and the fact that $Y(a) = b$ together imply that

$$| Y(x) - b | \leqq M | x - a | \qquad x_1 \leqq x \leqq x_2;$$

and this in turn implies that the graph of $Y(x)$ over the interval $x_1 \leq x \leq x_2$ must lie in the region T.

We can now use (15.93) and the equation resulting from replacing $y(x)$ by $Y(x)$ in it to obtain

$$(15.96) \quad | y(x) - Y(x) | = \left| \int_a^x [f(t, y(t)) - f(t, Y(t))]dt \right|$$

$$\leq A \left| \int_a^x | y(t) - Y(t) | dt \right|.$$

Let D be the maximum value for $x_1 \leq t \leq x_2$ of $| y(t) - Y(t) |$. Then use of (15.96) gives

$$(15.961) \qquad | y(x) - Y(x) | \leq AD | x - a |.$$

Using (15.961) in the last member of (15.96) gives

$$| y(x) - Y(x) | \leq \frac{DA^2| x - a |^2}{2!};$$

and iteration of this process gives

$$| y(x) - Y(x) | \leq \frac{DA^n| x - a |^n}{n!} \qquad n = 1, 2, 3, \cdots .$$

Thus, if $x_1 \leq x \leq x_2$ and C is, as before, the greater of the numbers $x_2 - a$ and $a - x_1$, then

$$(15.962) \qquad | y(x) - Y(x) | \leq \frac{D(AC)^n}{n!}.$$

Since the right-hand member of (15.962) can be made arbitrarily small by taking n sufficiently great (observe that the right-hand member is the general term of the convergent series for De^{AC}), it follows that the left-hand member of (15.962) must be 0 and that

$$Y(x) = y(x) \qquad\qquad x_1 \leq x \leq x_2.$$

This completes proof of the "uniqueness" part of Picard's theorem.

That all different functions $y_1(x)$ which may be used at the start of Picard's method must yield the same solution is a consequence of the fact that each yields a solution and that there is just one solution over $x_1 \leq x \leq x_2$. This completes the proof of Picard's theorem (Theorem 15.71).

CHAPTER 16

APPROXIMATIONS TO SOLUTIONS AND EXISTENCE THEOREMS FOR EQUATIONS OF HIGHER ORDER AND FOR SYSTEMS OF EQUATIONS

16.0. Introduction.—In this chapter, we apply the Picard method of successive approximations to obtain approximations to solutions of and existence theorems for differential equations and systems of differential equations. In particular, we shall obtain proofs of the fundamental theorems (Theorems 6.03 and 6.04) on linear equations.

It may seem strange to the reader that the problem of solving a single equation of order greater than 1 is "reduced" to the problem of solving a system of equations; perhaps the reader has always regarded a single equation as being essentially easier to handle than a system containing more than one equation.

It is hoped that the reader will see, in the complications which follow, a practical method for obtaining approximations to solutions of difficult problems. In many cases, application of the method involves much tedious work; but the essential point is that the method produces results.

16.1. Linear Equations.—In this section, we show that the problem of finding an approximation to a function $y(x)$ satisfying equations (16.12) and (16.13) below can be reduced to the problem of finding one of a set of functions which satisfies a system of equations, and that proof of Theorem 16.11 can be reduced to proof of a theorem involving a system of equations. Theorem 16.11 is essentially a restatement of Theorem 6.03 since (6.032) can, when $a_0(x) \neq 0$, be thrown into the form (16.12) by division by $a_0(x)$.

THEOREM 16.11.—*If $a_1(x)$, $a_2(x)$, $\cdots$, $a_n(x)$, and $f(x)$ are continuous over an interval I, then corresponding to each point x_0 of I and each set of constants k_1, k_2, $\cdots$, k_n there is one and only one function $y(x)$, satisfying the differential equation*

$$(16.12) \quad \frac{d^n y}{dx^n} + a_1(x) \frac{d^{n-1} y}{dx^{n-1}} + \cdots + a_{n-1}(x) \frac{dy}{dx} + a_n(x)y = f(x)$$

over the interval I, for which

$$(16.13) \quad y(x_0) = k_1, \qquad y'(x_0) = k_2, \cdots, \qquad y^{(n-1)}(x_0) = k_n.$$

Our first step is to define n functions $y_1(x)$, $y_2(x)$, $\cdots$, $y_n(x)$ in terms of $y(x)$ by the formulas

$$(16.14)\quad y_1(x) = y(x), \qquad y_2(x) = y'(x), \qquad y_3(x) = y''(x), \cdots,$$
$$y_n(x) = y^{(n-1)}(x).$$

It is easy to see that (16.12) can then be written in the form

$$y_n'(x) + a_1 y_n(x) + a_2 y_{n-1}(x) + \cdots + a_{n-1} y_2(x) + a_n y_1(x) = f(x).$$

Hence, if $y(x)$ satisfies (16.12) and (16.13) and y_1, y_2, $\cdots$ y_n are defined by (16.14), then

$$(16.15)\quad \begin{cases} y_1'(x) = y_2(x) \\ y_2'(x) = y_3(x) \\ \cdots \cdots \cdots \\ y_{n-1}'(x) = y_n(x) \\ y_n'(x) = -a_n y_1(x) - a_{n-1} y_2(x) - \cdots - a_1 y_n(x) + f(x) \end{cases}$$

and

$$(16.16)\quad y_1(x_0) = k_1, \qquad y_2(x_0) = k_2, \cdots, \qquad y_n(x_0) = k_n.$$

Conversely, if $y_1(x)$, $y_2(x)$, $\cdots$, $y_n(x)$ is a set of n functions satisfying the system of differential equations (16.15) and the boundary conditions (16.16), then the function $y(x)$ defined by $y(x) = y_1(x)$ satisfies (16.12) and (16.13).

Thus we have transformed the problem of finding a function satisfying the linear nth-order differential equation (16.12) and the n boundary conditions (16.13) into the problem of finding the first of a set of n functions y_1, y_2, $\cdots$, y_n satisfying the system (16.15) of n linear first-order equations and the n boundary conditions (16.16). Therefore, since special choices of the functions in the right-hand member of (16.22) reduce the system (16.22) to the system (16.15), we can (and shall) prove Theorem 16.11 by proving Theorem 16.21.

16.2. Systems of Linear Equations.—In this section we show that the system of equations (16.22) of the following theorem has a property which turns out to be very useful when we apply the Picard method of successive approximations to the system.

Theorem 16.21.—*If the coefficients $a_{m,k}(x)$ and the functions $\phi_k(x)$ in the system of equations*

$$(16.22)\quad \begin{cases} y_1' = a_{1,1} y_1 + a_{1,2} y_2 + \cdots + a_{1,n} y_n + \phi_1 \\ y_2' = a_{2,1} y_1 + a_{2,2} y_2 + \cdots + a_{2,n} y_n + \phi_2 \\ \cdots \cdots \cdots \cdots \cdots \cdots \cdots \cdots \\ y_n' = a_{n,1} y_1 + a_{n,2} y_2 + \cdots + a_{n,n} y_n + \phi_n \end{cases}$$

are continuous when x is in an interval I, if x_0 is a point of I, and if $k_1, k_2, \cdots, k_n$ are constants, then there is one and only one set of n functions

$$y_1(x), y_2(x), \cdots, y_n(x)$$

satisfying the system of equations (16.22) over the interval I, for which

(16.23) $y_1(x_0) = k_1, \qquad y_2(x_0) = k_2, \cdots, \qquad y_n(x_0) = k_n.$

If we set, for each $m = 1, 2, \cdots, n,$

(16.24) $f_m(x, y_1, y_2, \cdots, y_n) = a_{m,1}(x)y_1 + \cdots$
$$+ a_{m,n}(x)y_n + \phi_m(x),$$

then it can be shown easily that the function $f_m(s, y_1, \cdots, y_n)$ satisfies the Hölder condition (16.25) which is analogous to that in Picard's theorem (Theorem 15.71). In case the interval I is not a finite closed interval, let I_1 be a finite closed subinterval of I; otherwise, let $I_1 = I$. Let A_{mk} denote the maximum value of $|a_{m,k}(x)|$ for x in the interval I_1, and let A denote the greatest of the numbers A_{mk} so that $|a_{m,k}(x)| \leq A$ when x is in I_1. When x is in I_1 and $y_1, \cdots, y_n$ and $\eta_1, \cdots, \eta_n$ are any two sets of n numbers,

(16.25) $|f_m(x, y_1, \cdots, y_n) - f_m(x, \eta_1, \cdots, \eta_n)|$
$$= |a_{m,1}(x)(y_1 - \eta_1) + a_{m,2}(x)(y_2 - \eta_2) + \cdots$$
$$+ a_{m,n}(x)(y_n - \eta_n)|$$
$$\leq |a_{m,1}(x)||y_1 - \eta_1| + |a_{m,2}(x)||y_2 - \eta_2| + \cdots$$
$$+ |a_{m,n}(x)||y_n - \eta_n|$$
$$\leq A(|y_1 - \eta_1| + |y_2 - \eta_2| + \cdots + |y_n - \eta_n|).$$

Because of the estimate (16.25) we can (and shall) prove Theorem 16.21 by proving a still more general theorem (Theorem 16.31 of the next section).

16.3. Systems of Equations Which Are Not Necessarily Linear; A General Theorem on Approximation, Existence, and Uniqueness.— In this section we state and comment briefly upon the following theorem; in the next section we point out important applications; and in Section 16.5 we prove the theorem.

THEOREM 16.31.—*If the functions $f_1, \cdots, f_n$ in the system of equations*

(16.32)
$$\begin{cases} y_1' = f_1(x, y_1, y_2, \cdots, y_n) \\ y_2' = f_2(x, y_1, y_2, \cdots, y_n) \\ \quad \cdots \cdots \cdots \cdots \cdots \cdots \\ y_n' = f_n(x_1, y_1, y_2, \cdots, y_n) \end{cases}$$

are continuous in a region R defined by

(16.33) $|x - x_0| \leq r_0, \qquad |y_1 - k_1| \leq r_1, \cdots, \qquad |y_n - k_n| \leq r_n$

and for each $m = 1, 2, \cdots , n$ *the function* f_m *satisfies the Hölder condition*

(16.34) $| f_m(x, y_1, \cdots , y_n) - f_m(x, \eta_1, \cdots , \eta_n) |$
$$\leq A(| y_1 - \eta_1 | + | y_2 - \eta_2 | + \cdots + | y_n - \eta_n |)$$

when $x, y_1, \cdots , y_n$ *and* $x, \eta_1, \cdots , \eta_n$ *are in* R, *then there is an interval* I *containing* x_0 *such that there is one and only one set of* n *functions*

(16.35) $y_1(x), y_2(x), \cdots , y_n(x),$

satisfying the system (16.32) *over the interval* I, *for which*

(16.36) $y_1(x_0) = k_1, \qquad y_2(x_0) = k_2, \cdots , \qquad y_n(k_0) = k_n.$

For the case of the system (16.22) *in which the f's are defined by* (16.24), *the interval* I *may be taken to be the interval over which the functions* $a_{m,k}(x)$ *and* $\phi_m(x)$ *are continuous.*

This theorem does not, except for the case (16.22), tell anything about the extent of the interval I containing x_0 over which there exists one and only one set of functions (16.35) satisfying (16.32) and (16.36). In some cases the interval I is relatively short; in other cases it is the entire interval $-\infty < x < \infty$. It is the duty of one who applies the method of successive approximations to a particular problem to find the extent of the interval I for that problem.

16.4. Equations of Order Greater than 1.—The previous chapter dealt with equations of the form $y' = f(x, y)$. By use of Theorem 16.31 we obtain existence theorems for equations of the types

$$\frac{d^2y}{dx^2} = f\left(x, y, \frac{dy}{dx}\right), \frac{d^3y}{dx^3} = f\left(x, y, \frac{dy}{dx}, \frac{d^2y}{dx^2}\right).$$

To show this, let n be an integer greater than 1 and consider the differential equation

(16.41) $\dfrac{d^n y}{dx^n} = f\left(x, y, \dfrac{dy}{dx}, \dfrac{d^2y}{dx^2}, \cdots , \dfrac{d^{n-1}y}{dx^{n-1}}\right)$

and the boundary conditions

(16.42) $y(x_0) = k_1, \qquad y'(x_0) = k_2, \cdots , \qquad y^{(n-1)}(x_0) = k_n.$

It is easy to see that, if $y(x)$ satisfies (16.41) and (16.42) and we set $y_1 = y, y_2 = y', \cdots , y_n = y^{(n-1)}$, then the functions $y_1, y_2, \cdots , y_n$ satisfy the system of differential equations

(16.43) $y_1' = y_2, y_2' = y_3, \cdots , y_{n-1}' = y_n, y_n' = f(x, y_1, \cdots , y_n)$

and the boundary conditions

(16.44) $y_1(x_0) = k_1, \qquad y_2(x_0) = k_2, \cdots , \qquad y_n(x_0) = k_n;$

and, conversely, that, if y_1, y_2, $\cdots$, y_n satisfy (16.43) and (16.44), then the function $y(x)$ defined by $y(x) = y_1(x)$ satisfies (16.41) and (16.42). The system composed of (16.43) and (16.44) is a special form of the system composed of (16.32) and (16.36).

For example, one seeks a function $y(x)$ satisfying the equation

$$(16.45) \qquad \frac{d^2y}{dx^2} + a_1(x, y)\frac{dy}{dx} + a_2(x, y) = 0$$

and the boundary conditions

$$(16.46) \qquad y(x_0) = k_1, \qquad y'(x_0) = k_2$$

by seeking a pair of functions $y_1(x)$ and $y_2(x)$ which satisfy the system of equations

$$(16.47) \qquad \frac{dy_1}{dx} = y_2$$

$$\frac{dy_2}{dx} = -a_1(x, y_1)y_2 - a_2(x, y_1)$$

and the conditions

$$(16.48) \qquad y_1(x_0) = k_1, \qquad y_2(x_0) = k_2.$$

Problem 16.49

Show that if we set

$$x = t, \qquad y_1 = \theta(t), \qquad y_2 = \theta'(t), \qquad y_3 = r(t), \qquad y_4 = r'(t)$$

then the system composed of the two equations (11.52) and (11.53) takes the form

$$y_1' = y_2$$

$$y_2' = -\frac{g \sin x}{y_3}$$

$$y_3' = y_4$$

$$y_4' = g \cos x - \frac{E}{ml}(x - l) + y_3 y_2^2$$

and that this system has the form (16.32).

16.5. Proof of Theorem 16.31.—In spite of the fact that Theorem 16.31 involves a system of n equations whereas Theorem 15.71 involves a single equation, the proof of Theorem 16.31 is somewhat simpler than that of Theorem 15.71; this situation is possible because Theorem 15.71 gives precise information about a special region T whereas no such special region is involved in Theorem 16.31.

The proof of Theorem 16.31 uses the method of successive approximations used in proof of Theorem 15.71. We start with the set of n functions $y_{1,0}$, $y_{2,0}$, $\cdots$, $y_{n,0}$ defined by the formulas

$$(16.51) \quad y_{1,0}(x) = k_1, \qquad y_{2,0}(x) = k_2, \cdots, \qquad y_{n,0}(x) = k_n;$$

we could start with other functions, but we make the simple choice (16.51). Further sets of n functions

$$(16.52) \quad y_{1,q}(x), \quad y_{2,q}(x), \quad \cdots, \quad y_{n,q}(x) \quad\quad q = 1, 2, 3, \cdots$$

are defined, for x in a certain range $|x - x_0| \leq r$ to be determined below, by induction by the *recursion formulas*

$$(16.53) \quad \begin{cases} y_{1,q}(x) = k_1 + \int_{x_0}^x f_1(t,\, y_{1,q-1}(t),\, \cdots,\, y_{n,q-1}(t))dt \\ \cdots\cdots\cdots\cdots\cdots\cdots\cdots\cdots\cdots\cdots\cdots \\ y_{n,q}(x) = k_n + \int_{x_0}^x f_n(t,\, y_{1,q-1}(t),\, \cdots,\, y_{n,q-1}(t))dt. \end{cases}$$

Let M be a constant such that

$$(16.531) \quad\quad |f_m(x, y_1, y_2, \cdots, y_n)| \leq M \quad\quad m = 1, 2, \cdots, n$$

when (16.33) holds, and let r be the least of the numbers r_0, r_1/M, r_2/M, $\cdots$, r_n/M. Let x be confined to the interval I of points for which $|x - x_0| \leq r$. The formulas

$$(16.54) \quad\quad |y_{m,q}(x) - k_q| \leq r_m \quad\quad m = 1, 2, \cdots, n$$

hold when $q = 0$. Assuming that the formulas (16.54) hold when q is replaced by $(q - 1)$, we find by use of (16.53) that

$$|y_{m,q}(x) - k_q| = \left| \int_{x_0}^x f_m(t,\, y_{1,q-1}(t),\, \cdots,\, y_{n,q-1}(t))dt \right|$$
$$\leq \left| \int_{x_0}^x M\,dt \right| = M|x - x_0| \leq Mr \leq r_m.$$

This proves by induction that (16.54) holds for each $q = 0, 1, 2, \cdots$. Therefore we can use the recursion formulas (16.53) and the Hölder condition (16.34) to obtain for each $m = 1, 2, \cdots, n$ and $q = 1, 2, 3, \cdots$

$$(16.55) \quad |y_{m,q+1}(x) - y_{m,q}(x)|$$
$$\leq \left| \int_{x_0}^x |f_m(t,\, y_{1,q}(t),\, \cdots,\, y_{n,q}(t)) - f_m(t,\, y_{1,q-1}(t),\, \cdots, \right.$$
$$\left. y_{n,q-1}(t))|\, dt \right|$$
$$\leq \left| \int_{x_0}^x A[|\, y_{1,q}(t) - y_{1,q-1}(t)\,| + \cdots + |\, y_{n,q}(t) - y_{n,q-1}(t)\,|]\, dt \right|.$$

Let B be a constant such that

$$(16.56) \quad\quad |y_{m,1}(x) - y_{m,0}(x)| \leq B \quad\quad m = 1, 2, \cdots, n.$$

Using (16.56) and (16.55) with $q = 1$, we find that

$$(16.57) \quad |y_{m,2}(x) - y_{m,1}(x)| \leq BAn|x - x_0| \quad\quad m = 1, 2, \cdots, n.$$

Using (16.57) and (16.55) with $q = 2$, we find that the formula

$$(16.571) \qquad |\, y_{m,q}(x) - y_{m,q-1}(x) \,| \leqq \frac{B(An\,|\, x - x_0\,|)^q}{q!}$$

$$m = 1, 2, \cdots, n.$$

holds when $q = 2$. It being assumed that (16.571) holds for a fixed q, the same procedure proves it for $q + 1$. Therefore, the inequality

$$(16.572) \qquad |\, y_{m,q}(x) - y_{m,q-1}(x) \,| \leqq \frac{B(Anr)^q}{q!} \qquad q = 2, 3, \cdots$$

holds for each $m = 1, 2, \cdots, n$.

For each fixed m the inequalities (16.572) are, except for differences in notation, the same as the inequalities (15.90); accordingly it follows exactly as in Section 15.8 that for each m the sequence

$$y_{m,0}(x),\ y_{m,1}(x),\ y_{m,2}(x),\ \cdots$$

converges uniformly to the function $y_m(x)$ defined by the series

$$y_m(x) = y_{m,0}(x) + [y_{m,1}(x) - y_{m,0}(x)] + [y_{m,2}(x) - y_{m,1}(x)] + \cdots$$

when $|\, x - x_0\,| \leqq r$. It follows by arguments used in Section 15.8 that y_m is continuous for each m, that x, y_1, y_2, $\cdots$, y_m satisfy (16.33), and that

$$(16.58) \qquad y_m(x) = k_m + \int_{x_0}^{x} f_m(t, y_1(t), \cdots, y_n(t)) dt$$

when $|\, x - x_0\,| \leqq r$. From (16.58) we see that $y_m(x_0) = k_m$ so that the boundary conditions (16.36) are satisfied; and using the fundamental theorem of the calculus we see that the system (16.32) of differential equations is satisfied. Proof of uniqueness of the solution proceeds as in Section 15.8; we shall not repeat the arguments.

For the case of the system (16.22) in which the f's are defined by (16.24), the foregoing proof can be simplified and the conclusion strengthened. If I_1 is a bounded closed interval over which the functions $a_{m,k}(x)$ and $g_m(x)$ are continuous, then the approximations $y_{m,q}(x)$ as defined by (16.53) exist for each x in the whole interval I_1. The inequality $|\, x - x_0\,| \leqq r$ and the inequalities (16.54) are not required. The Hölder condition (16.34) having been established in (16.25), we can use (16.34) with (16.53) to obtain (16.55) for each x in I_1 and proof proceeds without further change for the whole interval I_1. This completes the proof of Theorem 16.31.

16.6. Use of Linear Spaces.—By introducing appropriate definitions and notation, the statement and proof of Theorem 16.31 can be made to appear much simpler. Let a set of n ordered numbers $w_1, w_2, \cdots, w_n$ be called a *vector* (or *point*) W and write

$$W = \{w_1, w_2, \cdots, w_n\}.$$

Let two vectors W and

$$V = \{v_1, v_2, \cdots, v_n\}$$

be called equal if and only if $w_1 = v_1, \cdots, w_n = v_n$. Let

$$kW = \{kw_1, kw_2, \cdots, kw_n\}$$

when k is a constant, and let

$$W + V = \{w_1 + v_1, w_2 + v_2, \cdots, w_n + v_n\}.$$

With these definitions the vectors (or points) W form a *linear space*. Let the *metric* $\| W \|$ be defined by

$$\| W \| = | w_1 | + | w_2 | + \cdots + | w_n |.$$

With this metric, the vectors (or points) form a non-Euclidean * vector metric space in which the *distance* between two vectors (or points) W and V is defined by $\| W - V \|$. If $w_1, w_2, \cdots, w_n$ are differentiable functions of x, let

$$W' = \{w_1', w_2', \cdots, w_n'\}$$

where primes represent differentiation with respect to x; and let

$$\int_{x_0}^{x} W(t)dt = \left\{ \int_{x_0}^{x} w_1(t)dt, \cdots, \int_{x_0}^{x} w_n(t)dt \right\}$$

when the integrals on the right exist. If $f_1(x, y_1, \cdots, y_n), \cdots, f_n(x, y_1, \cdots, y_n)$ are n given functions, let

$$F(x, Y) = \{f_1(x, y_1, \cdots, y_n), \cdots, f_n(x, y_1, \cdots, y_n)\}.$$

The system (16.32) of differential equations can now be written

$$Y' = F(x, Y),$$

the boundary conditions (16.36) become

$$Y(x_0) = K,$$

the Hölder conditions (16.34) become (where H is the Greek capital letter eta)

$$\| F(x, Y) - F(x, H) \| \leq A \| Y - H \|,$$

and the recursion formulas (16.53) defining the successive approximations become

$$Y_q(x) = K + \int_{x_0}^{x} F(t, Y_{q-1}(t))dt.$$

Thus one who is accustomed to working with linear spaces sees close connections between the system $Y' = F(x, Y)$ of equations involved in Theorem 16.31 and the single equation $y' = f(x, y)$ involved in Theorem 15.71.

* For Euclidean space, distance is defined by use of the metric

$$\| W \| = [| w_1 |^2 + | w_2 |^2 + \cdots + | w_n |^2]^{\frac{1}{2}}.$$

16.7. Linear Equations.—We now develop some properties of solutions of the linear differential equation

$$(16.71) \qquad a_0 \frac{d^n y}{dx^n} + a_1 \frac{d^{n-1} y}{dx^{n-1}} + \cdots + a_{n-1} \frac{dy}{dx} + a_n y = f,$$

x being restricted to an interval I in which the functions $a_0(x), \cdots,$ $a_n(x)$ and $f(x)$ are continuous and $a_0(x) \neq 0$. In particular, we shall obtain a proof of Theorem 6.04.

Let (16.71) be abbreviated in the form $Ly = f$, and let the corresponding homogeneous equation be written $Ly = 0$. Since the equations $Ly = 0$ and $Ly = f$ can be thrown into the form (16.12) by division by $a_0(x)$ and a slight change of notation, we can apply Theorem 16.11 to $Ly = 0$ and $Ly = f$. Let x_0 be a point of I.

Let $Y_1(x)$, $Y_2(x)$, $\cdots$, $Y_n(x)$ be the special solutions of $Ly = 0$ which satisfy, respectively, the boundary conditions

$$(16.72) \quad \begin{cases} Y_1(x_0) = 1,\ Y_1'(x_0) = 0,\ Y_1''(x_0) = 0,\ \cdots,\ Y_1^{(n-1)}(x_0) = 0 \\ Y_2(x_0) = 0,\ Y_2'(x_0) = 1,\ Y_2''(x_0) = 0,\ \cdots,\ Y_2^{(n-1)}(x_0) = 0 \\ Y_3(x_0) = 0,\ Y_3'(x_0) = 0,\ Y_3''(x_0) = 1,\ \cdots,\ Y_3^{(n-1)}(x_0) = 0 \\ \cdots \cdots \cdots \cdots \cdots \cdots \cdots \cdots \cdots \cdots \cdots \\ Y_n(x_0) = 0,\ Y_n'(x_0) = 0,\ Y_n''(x_0) = 0,\ \cdots,\ Y_n^{(n-1)}(x_0) = 1. \end{cases}$$

This system of solutions of $Ly = 0$ is called a *fundamental system of solutions*. These solutions are linearly independent over the interval I; to prove this, let c_1, c_2, $\cdots$, c_n be constants such that

$$(16.73) \qquad c_1 Y_1(x) + c_2 Y_2(x) + \cdots + c_n Y_n(x) = 0$$

when x is in I. Then we can set $x = x_0$ in (16.73) to obtain $c_1 = 0$; differentiate (16.73) once and set $x = x_0$ to obtain $c_2 = 0$; differentiate again and set $x = x_0$ to obtain $c_3 = 0$; and continue the process to obtain $c_1 = c_2 = \cdots = c_n = 0$ and thus establish linear independence. It is also easy to show that each solution of $Ly = 0$ must be a linear combination of Y_1, Y_2, $\cdots$, Y_n. If $y(x)$ is a solution of $Ly = 0$ and we define d_1, d_2, $\cdots$, d_n by the formulas

$$d_1 = y(x_0), \qquad d_2 = y'(x_0), \qquad d_3 = y''(x_0), \cdots, \qquad d_n = y^{(n-1)}(x_0)$$

and set

$$(16.731) \qquad \tilde{y}(x) = d_1 Y_1(x) + d_2 Y_2(x) + \cdots + d_n Y_n(x),$$

then $y(x)$ and $\tilde{y}(x)$ are two solutions of $Ly = 0$ which are, together with their first $n - 1$ derivatives, equal when $x = x_0$; accordingly, by

Theorem 16.11, $y(x) = \tilde{y}(x)$ and it follows that *each solution $y(x)$ of $Ly = 0$ can be represented in the form*

$$(16.74) \quad y(x) = y(x_0)Y_1(x) + y'(x_0)Y_2(x) + \cdots + y^{(n-1)}(x_0)Y_n(x).$$

Thus we have shown that each solution of $Ly = 0$ is a linear combination of functions in the fundamental set.

Now let $y_1(x)$, $y_2(x)$, $\cdots$, $y_n(x)$ denote any set, linearly independent or not, of n solutions of $Ly = 0$. Making use of (16.74), we obtain

$$(16.75) \quad \begin{cases} y_1(x) = y_1(x_0)Y_1(x) + y_1'(x_0)Y_2(x) + \cdots + y_1^{(n-1)}(x_0)Y_n(x) \\ y_2(x) = y_2(x_0)Y_1(x) + y_2'(x_0)Y_2(x) + \cdots + y_2^{(n-1)}(x_0)Y_n(x) \\ \cdots\cdots\cdots\cdots\cdots\cdots\cdots\cdots\cdots\cdots\cdots\cdots\cdots\cdots \\ y_n(x) = y_n(x_0)Y_1(x) + y_n'(x_0)Y_2(x) + \cdots + y_n^{(n-1)}(x_0)Y_n(x). \end{cases}$$

The solutions y_1, $\cdots$, y_n are linearly independent if and only if the identity $c_1 y_1 + \cdots + c_n y_n = 0$ implies $c_1 = c_2 = \cdots = c_n = 0$. But

$$\sum_{m=1}^{n} c_m y_m(x) = \sum_{m=1}^{n} c_m \sum_{k=1}^{n} y_m^{(k-1)}(x_0)Y_k(x)$$
$$= \sum_{k=1}^{n} \left[\sum_{m=1}^{n} c_m y_m^{(k-1)}(x_0) \right] Y_k(x);$$

and since Y_1, $\cdots$, Y_k are linearly independent, it follows that $\Sigma c_m y_m(x) = 0$ over I if and only if the sums in brackets all vanish. Thus y_1, y_2, $\cdots$, y_n are linearly independent over I if and only if the system of algebraic equations

$$(16.751) \quad \begin{cases} c_1 y_1(x_0) + c_2 y_2(x_0) + \cdots + c_n y_n(x_0) = 0 \\ c_1 y_1'(x_0) + c_2 y_2'(x_0) + \cdots + c_n y_n'(x_0) = 0 \\ \cdots\cdots\cdots\cdots\cdots\cdots\cdots\cdots\cdots\cdots\cdots\cdots \\ c_1 y_1^{(n-1)}(x_0) + c_2 y_2^{(n-1)}(x_0) + \cdots + c_n y_n^{(n-1)}(x_0) = 0 \end{cases}$$

is satisfied only when $c_1 = c_2 = \cdots = c_n = 0$, and therefore if and only if the determinant of the coefficients of the c's is different from 0. Thus we obtain the following:

THEOREM 16.76.—*A set of n solutions $y_1(x)$, $\cdots$, $y_n(x)$ of $Ly = 0$ is linearly independent over I if and only if*

$$\begin{vmatrix} y_1(x_0) & y_2(x_0) & \cdots & y_n(x_0) \\ y_1'(x_0) & y_2'(x_0) & \cdots & y_n'(x_0) \\ \cdots\cdots & \cdots\cdots & \cdots & \cdots\cdots \\ y_1^{(n-1)}(x_0) & y_2^{(n-1)}(x_0) & \cdots & y_n^{(n-1)}(x_0) \end{vmatrix} \neq 0.$$

This determinant is called the Wronskian of $y_1, y_2, \cdots, y_n$ and is denoted by $W(y_1, y_2, \cdots, y_n; x_0)$. Since the point x_0 could be taken to be any point of the interval I over which $a_0(x), \cdots, a_n(x)$ are continuous and $a_0(x) \neq 0$, it follows that *if* $y_1, \cdots, y_n$ *are linearly dependent over I their Wronskian* $W(y_1, y_2, \cdots, y_n; x)$ *vanishes for all x in I and if $y_1, \cdots, y_n$ are linearly independent over I their Wronskian* $W(y_1, y_2, \cdots, y_n; x)$ *is different from 0 for all x in I.*

We can now prove that, if $y_1, y_2, \cdots, y_n$ are linearly independent solutions of $Ly = 0$, then each solution $y(x)$ of $Ly = 0$ can be written in the form

$$(16.77) \qquad y(x) = c_1 y_1(x) + c_2 y_2(x) + \cdots + c_n y_n(x).$$

We have seen in (16.74) that $y(x)$ is a linear combination of $Y_1(x)$, $\cdots, Y_n(x)$. But the hypothesis that $y_1, \cdots, y_n$ are linearly independent implies that $W(y_1, y_2, \cdots, y_n; x) \neq 0$, and hence using (16.75) we see that $Y_1, \cdots, Y_n$ are linear combinations of $y_1, \cdots, y_n$; our result follows.

This proves all the results of Theorem 6.04 which pertain to the homogeneous equation $Ly = 0$. The results pertaining to the equation $Ly = f$ follow from (i) Theorem 6.03 which shows that $Ly = f$ must have at least one solution, (ii) linearity of L which implies that if Y_1 and Y_2 are two solutions of $Ly = f$ then $L(Y_2 - Y_1) = 0$, and (iii) the known character of solutions of $Ly = 0$.

Problem 16.78

If $y_1 = e^{m_1 x}, y_2 = e^{m_2 x}, \cdots, y_n = e^{m_n x}$ where $m_1, m_2, \cdots, m_n$ are complex constants, prove that

$$W(y_1, \cdots, y_n; x) = e^{(m_1 + m_2 + \cdots + m_n)x} \Delta$$

where Δ is the determinant (called *Vandermonde's determinant*),

$$\Delta = \begin{vmatrix} 1 & 1 & \cdots & 1 \\ m_1 & m_2 & \cdots & m_n \\ m_1^2 & m_2^2 & \cdots & m_n^2 \\ \cdot & \cdot & \cdots & \cdot \\ m_1^{n-1} & m_2^{n-1} & \cdots & m_n^{n-1} \end{vmatrix},$$

and that

$$\Delta = (m_2 - m_1)(m_3 - m_1) \cdots (m_n - m_1)(m_3 - m_2) \cdots (m_n - m_2) \cdots (m_n - m_{n-1}),$$

the right-hand member containing all factors of the form $m_p - m_q$ where $p > q$. What conditions must $m_1, \cdots, m_n$ satisfy to ensure linear independence of $y_1, \cdots, y_n$?

Problem 16.781

Show that the derivative with respect to x of the Wronskian $W(y_1, \cdots, y_n; x)$ of n functions each having n derivatives is given by the formula

$$W'(y_1, \cdots, y_n; x) = \begin{vmatrix} y_1 & y_2 & y_3 & \cdots & y_n \\ y_1' & y_2' & y_3' & \cdots & y_n' \\ \cdots & \cdots & \cdots & \cdots & \cdots \\ y_1^{(n-2)} & y_2^{(n-2)} & y_3^{(n-2)} & \cdots & y_n^{(n-2)} \\ y_1^{(n)} & y_2^{(n)} & y_3^{(n)} & \cdots & y_n^{(n)} \end{vmatrix}.$$

Problem 16.782

Prove that, if

$$Ly = a_0 y^{(n)} + a_1 y^{(n-1)} + \cdots a_{n-1} y' + a_n y$$

where $a_0(x), a_1(x), \cdots, a_n(x)$ are continuous and $a_0(x) \neq 0$ over an interval I and $y_1(x), y_2(x), \cdots y_n(x)$ are n solutions of $Ly = 0$, then for each x in I

(16.783) $W(y_1, \cdots, y_n; x)Ly = (-1)^n a_0(x)\Delta$
(16.784) $W'(y_1, \cdots, y_n; x)Ly = (-1)^{n+1} a_1(x)\Delta$

where Δ is the determinant

$$\Delta = \begin{vmatrix} y & y_1 & y_2 & \cdots & y_n \\ y' & y_1' & y_2' & \cdots & y_n' \\ y'' & y_1'' & y_2'' & \cdots & y_n'' \\ \cdots & \cdots & \cdots & \cdots \\ y^{(n)} & y_1^{(n)} & y_2^{(n)} & \cdots & y_n^{(n)} \end{vmatrix}$$

with $(n+1)$ functions of x in each row and column. Show that, if t is a point in the interval I and we put $y(x) = (x - t)^n/n!$ in (16.784) and set $x = t$ in the result, we obtain

$$W'(y_1, \cdots, y_n; t)a_0(t) = -a_1(t)W(y_1, \cdots, y_n; t).$$

Use this result to show that

(16.79) $$W(y_1, \cdots, y_n; x) = C \exp\left[-\int_{x_0}^x \frac{a_1(t)}{a_0(t)} dt\right].$$

This is *Abel's formula for the Wronskian* of n solutions of $Ly = 0$; the case $n = 2$ was treated in Section 6.67 by a different method. Can you obtain (16.79) by a less (or more) elaborate method?

APPENDIX 17

BENDING OF BEAMS

In order to design beams to support specified loads, it is necessary to have appropriate formulas. These formulas are obtained by means of differential equations. The simplest problems lead to complicated differential equations which cannot be solved by simple methods. One either finds approximations to solutions of the equations or replaces the equations by simpler approximate equations which can be more easily solved. In the following discussion, the complicated differential equations are replaced by approximate equations having the form $y''(x) = f(x)$. When the values of $y(x_0)$ and $y'(x_0)$ are known for some value x_0 of x, determination of $y'(x)$ and then $y(x)$ is accomplished by methods of the calculus set forth in Chapter 2. The problems may be described as problems in *elastic stability*.

A beam of uniform cross section (which may, for example, be an I beam or a beam having a rectangular cross section) may be regarded as being composed of many small fibers running the length of the beam. When the beam is bent, the fibers in one part of the beam are stretched and those in the other part of the beam are compressed. Between these parts there is a *neutral surface* of fibers which are neither stretched nor compressed. Let I be the moment of inertia of the area of a given cross section of the beam, computed with reference to the line (say AB) in which this cross section intersects the neutral surface. Let E denote Young's modulus (see Section 9.02) for the material constituting the beam.

In ordinary circumstances, the beam remains relatively straight after bending. It may then be assumed that two near-by cross sections of the straight beam are, when the beam is bent, deformed into two plane sections of the bent beam and that the extensions of these sections intersect at the center of curvature of the fibers lying between the sections. It is then possible to use fundamental principles of geometry, physics, and calculus to show that the tensile and compressive forces acting on a given cross section of the beam have a moment about AB equal to EI/R where R is the radius of curvature of the fibers at the cross section. This moment EI/R tends to straighten the beam. When the beam is bent in static equilibrium, this moment EI/R must be balanced by the total moment M (about AB) of all other forces acting upon one of the two segments into which the cross section separates the beam. Thus $EI/R = M$. When one of the fibers of the bent beam lies in an xy plane we can use the standard formula for $1/R$ to put the equation of the fiber in the form

(17.1)
$$EI \frac{\dfrac{d^2y}{dx^2}}{\left[1 + \left(\dfrac{dy}{dx}\right)^2\right]^{\frac{3}{2}}} = M.$$

When the beam is, at all of its points, nearly parallel to the x axis, so that dy/dx is near 0 and the denominator in (17.1) is near 1, it is standard practice to replace (17.1) by the approximate equation

(17.2)
$$EI \frac{d^2y}{dx^2} = M.$$

The quantity EI is a measure of the ability of the beam to resist bending; it is called the *flexural rigidity* of the beam. Many textbooks in physics and engineering, in particular, books on strength of materials, present these matters in greater detail and provide many problems, of which the following are typical:*

Problem 17.3

A *cantilever beam* of length l is placed on the interval $0 \leq x \leq l$ of a horizontal x axis. The end at $x = 0$ is clamped so that it remains horizontal, and the beam is allowed to sag under the load of:

  (i) a single weight W at the free end
  (ii) a uniform weight w per unit length
  (iii) both (i) and (ii).

Find in each case an approximation to the equation of the beam, and find how much the free end sags below the clamped end. *Ans.:*

(i) $y = -\dfrac{W[3lx^2 - x^3]}{6EI}$; $\text{Sag} = \dfrac{Wl^3}{3EI}$

(ii) $y = -\dfrac{w[6l^2x^2 - 4lx^3 + x^4]}{24EI}$; $\text{Sag} = \dfrac{wl^4}{8EI}$

(iii) $y = $ sum of y's in (i) and (ii); $\text{Sag} = \dfrac{l^3[8W + 3wl]}{24EI}$

Problem 17.4

A beam of length $2l$ has its ends resting on supports at the same horizontal level and is loaded with

  (i) a single weight W at the center
  (ii) a uniform weight w per unit length
  (iii) both (i) and (ii).

* For the theory of oscillation of vibrating beams, see *Mathematical Methods in Engineering*, T. v. Kármán and M. A. Biot, McGraw-Hill Book Company, Inc., New York, 1940.

Taking the x axis horizontal and the origin at the center of the bent beam, find in each case an approximation to the equation of the beam, and find how much the center sags below the ends. *Ans.:*

(i) $y = \dfrac{W[3lx^2 - |x|^3]}{12EI}$; Sag $= \dfrac{Wl^3}{6EI}$

(ii) $y = \dfrac{w[6l^2x^2 - x^4]}{24EI}$; Sag $= \dfrac{5wl^4}{24EI}$

(iii) $y =$ sum of y's in (i) and (ii); Sag $= \dfrac{l^3[4W + 5wl]}{24EI}$.

Problem 17.5

A horizontal beam of length $2l$ has its ends supported at the points $(-l, 0)$ and $(l, 0)$ of an xy plane. Let a be a number for which $0 < a < l$, and let the beam be allowed to sag under the load of a single weight W placed on the beam at the point $(a, 0)$. Find an approximation to the equation of the beam and to the coordinates of the lowest point on the beam. At what point on the beam should the weight be placed in order to obtain a maximum value for the slope of the beam at the point upon which the weight rests? *Ans.:* It is found that (17.2) becomes the first of the formulas

(17.51) $\dfrac{2lEI}{W}\dfrac{d^2y}{dx^2} = (l - a)(l + x)$, $\dfrac{2lEI}{W}\dfrac{d^2y}{dx^2} = (l + a)(l - x)$

when $-l \leq x \leq a$ and the second when $a \leq x \leq l$. It follows that the formula

(17.52) $\dfrac{2lEI}{W}\dfrac{d^2y}{dx^2} = l^2 - ax - l|a - x|$

holds over the whole interval $-l \leq x \leq l$. Hence constants c_1 and c_2 exist such that

(17.53) $\dfrac{12lEI}{W}y = 3l^2x^2 - ax^3 - l|a - x|^3 + c_1x + c_2$.

The fact that $y = 0$ when $x = l$ and when $x = -l$ gives two equations to solve for c_1 and c_2. The results are

(17.54) $c_1 = -2al^2 - a^3$, $c_2 = 3a^2l^2 - 2l^4$.

Considering separately the cases in which $-l \leq x \leq a$ and $a \leq x \leq l$, we substitute in (17.53) to find that the equation of the beam is

(17.55) $y = \dfrac{W(l - a)}{12lEI}[(l + x)^3 - (3l^2 + 2al - a^2)(l + x)]$ $-l \leq x \leq a$

$= \dfrac{W(l + a)}{12lEI}[(l - x)^3 - (3l^2 - 2al - a^2)(l - x)]$ $a \leq x \leq l$.

It is possible to obtain the equation (17.55) of the beam in a different way. From (17.51), it is seen that four constants c_1, c_2, c_3, and c_4 exist such that

$$\frac{12lEI}{W} y = (l - a)[(l + x)^3 + c_1(l + x) + c_2] \qquad -l \leq x \leq a$$

and

$$\frac{12lEI}{W} y = (l + a)[(l - x)^3 + c_3(l - x) + c_4] \qquad a \leq x \leq l.$$

Upon determining the four constants so that $y(-l) = y(l) = 0$ and so that $y(x)$ and $y'(x)$ are continuous at $x = a$, we obtain (17.55).

Differentiation of (17.55) gives

$$(17.56) \qquad \frac{dy}{dx} = \frac{W(l - a)}{12lEI} [\ 3(l + x)^2 - (3l^2 + 2al - a^2)] \qquad -l \leq x \leq a$$

$$= \frac{W(l + a)}{12lEI} [-3(l - x)^2 + (3l^2 - 2al - a^2)] \qquad a \leq x \leq l.$$

As (17.51) shows, $y''(x) > 0$ over $-l < x < l$, and it follows that the x coordinate of the lowest point of the beam is the unique value of x in the interval $-l \leq x \leq l$ for which $y'(x) = 0$. This coordinate, say x_0, is found to be

$$(17.57) \qquad x_0 = \sqrt{l^2 + \tfrac{1}{3}a(2l - a)} - l.$$

Since $0 < x_0 < a$, substitution in the first part of (17.55) shows that the y coordinate of the lowest point of the beam is

$$(17.58) \qquad y_0 = -\frac{W(l - a)(l + a)(3l - a)}{18lEI} \sqrt{l^2 + \tfrac{1}{3}a(2l - a)}.$$

The sag and slope of the beam at the point on which the weight rests are given by the simpler formulas

$$(17.59) \qquad -y(a) = \frac{W}{6lEI} (l^2 - a^2)^2, \qquad y'(a) = \frac{Wa}{3lEI} (l^2 - a^2).$$

The slope of the beam at the point upon which the weight rests depends upon a. Use of ordinary rules for obtaining the maximum value of a function shows that this slope is a maximum when $a = \sqrt{3}\,l/3 = .577l$, that is, when the weight is a little more than halfway from the center to the end of the beam.

Remark: Even those unaccustomed to making connections between equations and physical phenomena should find it easy to place a weight upon a flexible bar of wood or metal and to see that (17.57) seems to give the distance from the center to the lowest point of the bar. It is especially interesting to see what happens when the weight is placed near an end of the bar.

INDEX